BIG CATS

ZIFF DAVIS
PUBLISHING COMPANY
Chicago · New York · Los Angeles

★

ZIFF-DAVIS LIMITED
London

BIG CATS

Kings of the Jungle in Fact and Fiction

edited by
FRANCES BRENTANO

with an introduction by
W. ADOLPHE ROBERTS

ZIFF-DAVIS PUBLISHING COMPANY
CHICAGO · NEW YORK

ALAN DEVOE   265
LYNX from *The American Mercury,* March, 1944. Reprinted by permission of the author and publisher.

J. FRANK DOBIE   246
BUT WAS IT AN ONZA? from *Tongues of the Monte.* Copyright 1935 by Doubleday, Doran & Co. Republished (under the title *The Mexico I Like*) by the University Press, Dallas, Texas. Republished 1947 by Little, Brown & Company. Copyright 1936, 1947 by J. Frank Dobie. Reprinted by permission of the author and Little, Brown & Company.

JULIAN DUGUID
(Sacha Siemel)   221
THE HARDEST CHASE OF ALL from *Tiger-Man.* Copyright 1932 by the Century Company. Reprinted by permission of the author through Raymond Savage, agent.

JOHN EYTON   94
THE HOLY TIGER from *Mainly Horses,* edited by Ernest Rhys and C. A. Dawson-Scott. Copyright 1929 by D. Appleton-Century Company. Reprinted by permission of the author through Christy & Moore, Ltd., Gerards Cross, Bucks, agents.

LEWIS R. FREEMAN   67
HUNTING WITH CHEETAHS IN INDIA from *Travel,* August, 1915. Copyright 1915 by Travel. Reprinted by their permission.

JOHN GALSWORTHY   108
NEVER GET OUT from *The Collected Poems of John Galsworthy.* Copyright 1934 by Charles Scribner's Sons. Reprinted by their permission.

JACQUES LE CLERCQ,
translator   1
A PASSION IN THE DESERT by Honoré de Balzac. Copyright 1949 by Frances Brentano. Published by permission of Jacques Le Clercq.

RUTH MANNING-SANDERS   76
THE CAGE from *New English Poems,* collected by Lascelles Abercrombie. Published 1931 by Victor Gollancz. Reprinted by permission of Ruth Manning-Sanders.

EDWIN MARKHAM   245
THE PANTHER from *The Captive Lion and Other Poems,* edited by William Henry Davies. Published 1931 by Yale University Press. Reprinted by permission of Virgil Markham.

DON MARQUIS   160
THE SPOTS OF THE LEOPARD from *When the Turtles Sing and Other Unusual Tales.* Copyright 1928 by Doubleday, Doran & Co. Reprinted by permission of Bernice M. Marquis.

W. Adolphe Roberts

INTRODUCTION

IF YOU HAVE A sympathetic understanding of domestic cats, which the Greeks called "little lions," you already know a good deal about their cousins of the wilderness. Size and incidental ferocity apart, the members of the genus are integrated. Evolution has practically ceased for them because they have perfected their type. They are better adapted to life, in the terms of their own necessities, than is any other mortal breed. Their grace and beauty result from this, and so does their extreme individualism. They do not depend for happiness upon any external circumstance, not even upon the companionship of their kind. Their needs are simple. Under the right conditions, they pass suavely through existence, dreaming some inner dream of profound sensuous pleasure in the mere fact of living. They have playful moods, and where the primordial instincts are involved they will fight with limitless courage. They endure misery with stoicism.

I recall watching a magnificent male lion that drowsed on a platform in one of those modern zoos that assuage captivity by providing space for roving. At a distance of perhaps thirty feet I uttered the sibilant *"Pss-pss-pss!"* with which one attracts the attention of a house cat, keeping the sound quite low. Immediately the lion's eyes came open. He blinked at me, sheathed and unsheathed his claws with an indolence that showed the gesture was amiable, and dropped off to sleep again. It was astonishing that he should have been able to hear me. The really curious point, however, was the form his reaction took. He probably would have glared at some persons. I am persuaded that he knew I loved cats.

That that same lion would have leapt upon and made a meal of me if he had been hungry does not disprove my contention that wild big cats and tame little ones are very similar. Nor does the fact that he would have been a lethally dangerous playmate, even if I had reared him from cubhood. It takes generations of wooing before a species of this proud lineage will accept friendship with man. *Felis domestica* is descended from a strain that was first gentled by the Egyptians five thousand years ago, and later was crossed with the European wild cat. The Siamese is of parallel remote ancestry in southeastern Asia. And in proof that small size is not the prerequisite for tameness we have the cheetah, standing as high as a wolfhound, which has been used as a hunting animal for so many centuries in India and Africa that individuals can now be trained as reliable household pets.

The big cats, being purely carniverous, kill to obtain food, or to rid themselves of enemies, active or presumed. They inflict suffering callously, toying with their mutilated prey before they devour it, in the manner that a tabby toys with a mouse, and purring most genially the while. But unlike some animals, the weasel for instance, they do not kill for the sake of killing. They are not really cruel. For the refinements of sadism you have to look to their mental superiors. A monkey will seize a bird that it does not intend to eat and slowly tear it to pieces, grinning diabolically and dropping the fragments one by one. Gustave Flaubert, in *Salammbô,* one of the greatest of historical novels and based upon unimpeachable research, tells of lions crucified along the Carthaginian roadsides to punish them for their offenses against man.

It is as egoists intolerant of compromise in the pursuit of their way of life that we must appraise the feral cats. They do not operate in groups. The closest they come to partnership of any description is the mating of certain varieties over periods longer than is required for the begetting of offspring; but despite legends to the contrary, such associations are broken up by caprice and, assuredly, whenever a male is defeated in combat by a stronger opponent bent on taking his spouse from him.

The feral cat regards the wilderness as a domain in which

each one roams at will, not clashing with its own kind except in rare instances, and then usually over sex; in which it seizes whatever victims appeal to it and eliminates direct rivals of its sway. It has nothing against the herbiverous elephant, rhinoceros, and hippopotamus, and knowing these giants to be impracticable as food, it wisely ignores them unless first attacked. There is no other beast, not even the savage water buffalo, that a lion or tiger will hesitate to subdue if famished or enraged. The same holds good down the line, proportionately, to the lynx and wild cat. Pound for pound, the feline is superior to antagonists of many times its weight. This is due to its superb muscular power and litheness, the deadly weapons it possesses in fang and claw, and—by no means least—the looseness of its skin that in a fight slips here and there over the body, often causing wounds that would have been fatal otherwise, to be deflected from vital spots.

As for the unarmed human being, he is a puerile opponent indeed for any big cat. The latter considers him the easiest kind of soft-bodied prey, particularly if he is naked and encountered in the wilderness. But clothing has the effect of making him seem bizarre, and his dwellings produce a still more positive effect of strangeness. That is why a big cat will ordinarily not go out of its way to stalk a civilized human being. The "man-killer" is simply an individual that has overcome its hesitations, through having once tasted human flesh or for some other reason.

Within the framework of their essential oneness, there are differences to be noted among the great cats. The lion has been accorded the title of "king of beasts" because the ancients encountered it early in North Africa and acquired a respect for it. But the term persisted, one surmises, largely on account of the male lion's noble countenance and his mane. From the standpoint of aggressiveness and strength in combat, however, the tiger is the true king among the blazoned despots of its race.

But the smaller leopard is relatively fiercer than either of them. It has wider versatility in stalking and assault, being able to climb trees and pounce from the low branches, which the lion and tiger are not. Its agility passes belief, and in battle the creature is incarnate fury. Significantly, an intertribal secret society of magicians and assassins in Africa names itself after the leopard. No organization is more dreaded by the blacks. It is of hoary antiquity.

At the other end of the scale in the Old World we find the mild cheetah, predominantly a hunter with food as the object and very seldom stung into fighting to defend its prestige. Swiftness of foot is its major asset. It runs down game in the open, and for short bursts can outdistance a horse. That is why man has enlisted the cheetah as an ally in the chase. This great cat has certain advantages over any dog.

Entirely different breeds of felines are found in the New World. There are none that match the bulk of lion or tiger. The two largest, the jaguar and the cougar or puma, correspond more to the leopard type. European explorers saw in the gorgeously spotted jaguar an approximation of the tiger and in the dun-colored cougar a sort of lion. Though the aboriginal names have prevailed for formal usage, the jaguar is still *el tigre* in the everyday talk of Latin Americans, while United States westerners commonly refer to the cougar as the mountain lion.

The jaguar is a dangerous customer, bold and pugnacious. The cougar, on the other hand, has the reputation of being fainthearted. Some naturalists deny this. My sole encounter with an uncaged big cat was with a cougar. I cite it for what it is worth. Wandering a short distance outside of a camp on the border between Arizona and Mexico, I ventured into a hollow and turned a corner to find one of the beasts stretched on a rock about twenty-five feet from me. I had an unpleasant moment, for my only weapon was a revolver. If the cougar felt timid, its fixed stare belied that state of mind. But it did not budge and allowed me to retreat ignominiously.

Inevitably man has created a literature around the whole resplendent brotherhood. This falls into three categories: myth, fiction, and observed facts. The first goes back beyond the age of the written word. The big cats were popular figures in oral fable, and by some peoples were held to be semidivine. Tiger-faced gods grimace amidst the stupendous ruins of eastern Asia. A particularly fierce-looking jaguar god recurs over and over in the sculptures of the Maya and other pre-Columbian civilizations in America. The living beast was feared as the symbol of the deity and credited with superhuman intelligence. From this stories grew.

Straight fiction on the subject, whether romantic or realistic, has often been a retelling of the old myths. But there is a more important school based on natural history, which began to develop as a modern science in the latter part of the eighteenth century. Thenceforward, both fiction and non-fiction portrayed the big cats with increasing fidelity to their true behaviorism.

We have tales, or actual experiences, by the naturalists themselves, by hunters, circus people, and plain nature lovers. A comparatively recent variation is the narrative in which man does not appear at all, or at the most plays a subordinate role. The author takes an animal as his hero, enters its mind so to speak, shows how it gratifies its impulses and outwits its foes, and weaves the whole into a drama. The method enjoyed a vogue forty or fifty years ago. Theodore Roosevelt indignantly called some of its practitioners "nature fakers." But it has its good points, and it is still being used. If the author really knows his theme he gets a vivid effect by dispensing lore through the acts of a free being of the wilderness.

BIG CATS offers a wide selection of the best things that have been written on the subject. All approaches are represented, from the exploits of zestful sportsmen to subtle observations by the essayists; from Balzac's *A Passion in the Desert,* which set a fashion in animal stories, to fiction by several brilliant writers of today.

Any one who has indulged armchair visions of high adventure will applaud. In other words, you do not have to be a devotee of cats, or a hunter, or a naturalist to appreciate the book. The sum total is a compound of color and excitement— two qualities that are never absent from the deeds of the supple creatures that tread through the pages of BIG CATS.

CONTENTS

~~~~~~

Honoré de Balzac

A PASSION IN THE DESERT

(Translated by Jacques le Clercq)

"WHAT A FRIGHTENING SHOW!" she said, as we came out of
Monsieur Martin's menagerie.

We had just witnessed the daredevil performance in which,
to quote the billboards, Monsieur Martin had "worked" with
his hyena.

"How on earth can he tame his beasts so that he is certain
of their affection?"

"That is no problem," I said. "He works quite naturally."

She smiled, incredulous.

"Tell me, do you think animals are incapable of passion?"
I went on. "*I* don't. *I* believe we humans can give them all our
own vices, and more . . ."

She looked at me dubiously.

"Well, the first time I saw Monsieur Martin, I was just as
surprised as you are now. I remember I was sitting next to a
one-legged veteran. I watched him; he had a fine face, clean
and sheer, with scars on it that marked Napoleon's campaigns,
battle by battle. I liked his frank, open air (gaiety always ap-
peals to me in a man) and I spotted him at once for a true
soldier, a veteran beyond the hazards of surprise. He was the
type of fellow who can find something to laugh at in the face
of a dying comrade, whether burying or robbing him . . . the
type who stands up boldly under fire, who wastes no time in
deliberation, who chums it with the Devil himself. . . .

"After carefully watching the proprietor of the menagerie
leave his loge, my companion pursed up his lips with an air of

1

derisive contempt, with that particular and expressive pout a
superior man makes to show that he is no dupe. When I protested, extolling Monsieur Martin's courage, he smiled, wagged
his head, and:

" 'There's nothing very new in all that!' he said.

" 'How do you mean, nothing new? If you would explain,
I should be much obliged to you.'

"We spent a few minutes making each other's acquaintance.
Then we went off to dine at the first restaurant we could find.
At dessert, a bottle of champagne prompted this picturesque
veteran to reminisce. As he told me his story, I realized that he
was right in his appraisal of Monsieur Martin's heroism. There
was indeed nothing new about it all."

"Well, *I* think the Martin show extraordinary!" she repeated.

Then, as I went home with her, she teased me so much, and
held out such promises, that I agreed to write up the soldier's
confidences for her. Next day, I sent her the following episode
of an epic which might well be entitled *The French in Egypt*.

During General Desaix's expedition in Upper Egypt, a Provençal soldier fell into the hands of Arabs who took him into
the desert far beyond the cataracts of the Nile. In order to place
a safe distance between the French army and themselves, they
made forced marches, stopping to rest only by night. They
camped round a well, overshadowed by palm trees, under
which they had previously concealed some provisions. Never
supposing that their prisoner might be minded to flee, they
were content merely to bind his hands; then, after eating some
dates and foddering their horses, they went to sleep.

When the gallant Provençal saw that his enemies no longer
watched him, he picked up a scimitar with his teeth, he
propped the blade between his knees, cut the cords which
bound his hands, and so freed himself. He acquired a rifle and
dagger lying nearby; provided himself with some dried dates,
a little sack of oats, some powder and shot; buckled a scimitar
around his waist, leaped onto a horse, and galloped away towards what he fancied were French Army Headquarters. In his

impatience to regain camp, he rode his already tired mount so hard, and spurred it so viciously, that the wretched beast died, leaving him alone in the desert.

He set out over the sands with all the courage of an escaped convict. Presently, at nightfall, he was forced to stop. Despite the beauty of night skies in the desert, he could not bear to go on. Fortunately he had reached a hummock with a few palm trees topping it. He had gazed long at them as he trudged on through the afternoon, anticipating the hope and consolation their verdure would offer. Arriving there, he was so exhausted that he flung himself on a rock, curiously shaped like a camp bed, and fell asleep, without thinking of protecting himself as he slept. "After all," he mused, "I have all but sacrificed my life already."

His last thought was one of regret.

"Why did I ever leave the Arabs?" he thought. "Now I am away from them and utterly helpless. Compared with mine, theirs is a fine life."

And so he fell asleep.

He was awakened by the pitiless rays of a sun which, streaming full on his rocky bed, generated an intolerable heat. Worse, he had been foolish enough to lie down outside the shadows cast by the green, tall palms. He gazed up at these solitary trees and shuddered. It occurred to him that they were much like the graceful shafts, crowned with long leaves, that adorn the Saracen columns in the Cathedral of Arles.

He counted the palm trees, then looked around him once again. The most horrible despair fell upon his soul. Before him spread an illimitable ocean. The dark sands of the desert stretched in all directions, far as the eye could travel, glittering as steel glitters when a bright flame is flashed upon it. Was this a sea of mirrors or a group of lakes blended together to form a single mirror? A fiery vapor, rising in waves, whirled tempestuously above the quivering sands. The sky blazed in oriental splendor, unbearably pure, for it left nothing to the imagination. All heaven and earth were aflame. The silence was terrible in its wild majesty. Infinity, immensity closed in upon the soul

from every side . . . never a cloud in the sky . . . never a breath
in the air . . . never a flaw on the bosom of the sands as they
moved in light, slender waves . . . and the horizon, seen as at
sea on a clear day, ended in a single line of light, trenchant
as the blade of a sword.

The Provençal embraced the trunk of the nearest palm tree
as though it were the body of a friend. Next, he stood under
the slight thin shadow which the palm tree cast upon the rock.
Next, he wept. Next, he sat down, remaining motionless as he
contemplated with intense sadness the implacable scene at his
feet. Next, he shouted as though to defy the solitude. His voice,
lost in the hollows of the hummock, sounded very faintly in
the distance. Distance made no echo, the only echo was in his
own heart. (The Provençal was twenty-two years old. He loaded
his rifle.)

"Oh well! Time aplenty for that!" he decided, and he put
aside the weapon which could, if need were, bring him deliverance.

As he gazed now at the black expanse of the sands, now at the
blue expanse of the sky, the soldier dreamed of France. The
memory of the gutters of Paris rose so poignantly to his mind
that he could smell their tart odors . . . he recalled the towns
through which he had passed . . . he conjured up the faces of
this army comrade and that . . . he evoked the most minute de-
tails of his short life. . . . As the heat beat mercilessly down,
undulant over the flat reaches of the desert, his imagination—
the imagination of a Southerner—flashed upon his enchanted
eyes the red hues of Provençal earth and brick and stone.

A lively fear of this cruel mirage led him down the hill along
the further slope which he had not yet explored. To his immense delight, he came upon a cave of natural formation, hewn
deep in the granite blocks at the foot of the hummock. Remnants of matting disclosed that this refuge had once been inhabited. A little farther along, there were some date-bearing
palm trees.

The sight reawakened his instincts of self-preservation. Might
he not live long enough to be rescued by some passing Arabs?

Might he not even hear the welcome rumor of cannon? After all, Bonaparte was scouring Egypt!

Cheered by this thought, the Provençal shook down some dates from the palm trees groaning under their weight. As he tasted this unhoped-for manna, he felt sure that the previous resident of the cave must have given the trees his loving care. The savory fresh meat of the fruit fell gratefully upon his tongue. Suddenly he passed from the blackest despair to a joy almost insane.

Climbing up the hill again, he spent the rest of the day chopping down one of the fruitless palm trees which had served him for shelter the night before. A vague memory made him think of the beasts of the desert. Might they not come to drink at the spring lost in the sands below the rocks? If so, he must safeguard himself against their visit by setting up a barrier at the entrance to his hermitage.

Tenacious as he was and spurred by his fear of being devoured while he slept, he could not manage to chop the palm tree into pieces. But he did manage to cut it down.

Toward evening, the huge tree fell with a crash that resounded afar. It was as though the very solitude were moaning; the soldier shuddered as though he had heard a voice foretelling the dire woes that awaited him. But like an heir who does not mourn a dead relative for long, he tore off the tall wide leaves which form this tree's poetic ornament, and used them to mend the matting on which he intended to bed. Exhausted by heat and work, he fell asleep under the russet curtains of his damp cave.

Suddenly, in the middle of the night, an eerie sound disturbed his slumbers. He sat up. All was silence again. Then, across the silence, he detected an alternate inhalation and expiration, so sharp in its savage energy, that he knew it was not the breath of a human creature.

Terror, increased by the darkness, by the silence, and by his waking fancies, gripped his heart in its icy maw. He stared into the blackness of the night; he could feel his scalp ache, as his

eyes strove to pierce the darkness. Then he saw two faint yellow
lights glowing athwart the shadows.

At first he attributed these lights to the reflection of his own
eyeballs; gradually however the darkness, brightening as the
moon rose, helped him identify the various objects about him.
Clearest of these was a huge animal lying but two steps from
him.

Was it a lion, a tiger or a crocodile? The soldier was no
scholar; he could not assign his enemy to its proper zoological
sub-species. His fright, though, was no less ghastly, for his igno-
rance led him to imagine horrors that transcended reality. For
a long time, he suffered bitterly as he listened to every strain
in the breathing of the creature beside him. He did not dare
move an inch. A pungent foxlike odor, but an odor more pene-
trant and, as it were, more sheer, filled the cave. As the soldier
breathed it in, his terror reached its height. There could be no
further doubt; now he knew what kind of fierce companion lay
close to him in the royal den in which he was camping.

Presently the rays of the moon, as it raced towards the horizon, lighted up the cave. The soldier now clearly discerned the
spotted skin of a panther hard beside him. This lion of Egypt
slept, curled up like a large dog who knows himself to be the
serene tenant of a sumptuous kennel at the mansion gates. Its
eyes opened for a trice, then closed again; it was facing him
squarely. A thousand confused imaginings passed through his
mind. First, he considered shooting his captor, but he soon
realized the animal was too close for range; there was not
enough room between them to allow him to take proper aim.

What if he were to waken it? The very thought chilled the
marrow of his bones. In the silence, he listened to his own
heartbeats now, cursing the blood that thumped through his
veins. He must not disturb the panther's slumber. What chance
had he else to escape?

Twice he took up his scimitar, determined to decapitate his
enemy; but the difficulty of cutting through the short stiff hair
forced him to give up this bold plan.

Suppose he missed? That would spell inevitable death; better to wait for daylight and stand his chance of a fair fight. Daylight broke soon after, affording the soldier a clear view of the panther. Its muzzle was smeared with blood.

"Well," he thought, "the beast has dined well!"

Nor did he trouble to ponder whether its feast had been one of human flesh.

"That beast will not be hungry when it wakes up!" he thought again.

The beast was a female. The fur on her belly and flanks glistened very white: a few small velvet-like rings formed charming bracelets around her feet: her sinuous tail was white, too, but tipped with black rings. The nape of her coat was yellow as unburnished gold, very lissom and soft, with the variously shaded rose-shaped specks that distinguish panthers from all other felines.

This tranquil, fearsome hostess of his lay snoring in a pose as graceful as that of a cat stretched out on a divan. On the blood-stained, nervous, sharp-clawed paws extended in front of her, she rested her head; her sparse, razor-straight whiskers radiated from her jowls like threads of silver.

Had she lain thus in a cage, the Provençal would assuredly have admired the grace of the animal and the picturesque contrasts of vivid colors which gave her coat its imperial splendor. But in these circumstances, this sinister sight troubled him considerably. The presence of the panther, even asleep, produced the same effect upon him as the magnetic eyes of the serpent are said to produce on the nightingale.

For a moment, the soldier's courage failed him before his danger, though it would doubtless have thrilled in the face of cannons vomiting shells. However, a dauntless thought, flashing through his mind, dried up the cold sweat that had broken from his brow. As men driven to bay by misfortune finally defy death and challenge her to do her worst, so he unconsciously saw the tragedy in his plight and resolved to play his part honorably until the curtain was ushered down upon the last act.

"After all, the Arabs might well have killed me the day before yesterday!" he mused. Considering himself as good as dead already, he waited bravely and with an excited curiosity for his enemy to awake.

When the sun appeared, the panther suddenly opened her eyes, then stretched out her paws violently, as though to rid them of numbness and cramp. She yawned, then bared her frightening teeth and her forked tongue, rough as a rasp.

"Well, well, just like a young mistress waking up beside her lover!" he thought, as he watched her rolling about with the softest, most coquettish movements imaginable. She licked the blood off her paws and muzzle and scratched her head with repeated gestures of provoking charm. . . .

"Ay, wash up a little bit!" the soldier urged, his gaiety returning with his courage. "We'll have a little chat now, eh?" And he gripped the dagger he had stolen from the Arabs. At just that moment, the panther turned her head towards him, looking fixedly at him without moving.

The rigidity and the overpowering sheen of her metallic eyes froze his blood, especially when the beast walked towards him; but looking at her caressingly, ogling her as though to hypnotize her, he let her draw nearer. Then, with the gentle, amorous movement he might have used to caress the most beautiful of women, he passed his hand over her whole body, from her head to her tail, scratching the flexible vertebrae which divided her yellow back. The beast wagged her tail voluptuously; her eyes turned gentle, and when the Provençal had completed this caress for the third time, she purred as our own cats do to express their pleasure. But this murmur rose from so deep and so powerful a throat that it resounded through the cave like the last throbbing of organ notes in a church . . . .

The soldier, realizing how important his caresses were, increased them in order to daze and to stupefy the imperious courtesan. When he was assured that he had allayed the ferocity of his capricious cave mate (her hunger had luckily been well satisfied the day before) he rose and made to leave the cave. The panther suffered him to go out. But as he reached the crest of the hummock, she sprang after him with all the lightness of a sparrow hopping from branch to branch, and, joining him, rubbed up against his legs, rounding her back after the manner of all cats. Then, gazing at her guest with eyes that softened a little, she uttered that wild cry which naturalists compare to the grating of a saw.

"Hm! She *is* difficult!" he said with a smile, attempting to play with her ears, to caress her belly and to scratch her head as hard as he could. His efforts crowned with success, he made bold to tickle her skull with the point of his dagger, watching for an opportune moment to kill her; but the hardness of her bones made him tremble lest he fail.

The sultana of the desert acknowledged the talents of her slave by raising her head and craning her neck, the tranquillity of her attitude bespeaking her rapture. Suddenly it occurred to the Provençal that to kill this fierce princess at one blow he must stab her in the throat. As he raised the dagger, the panther, no doubt glutted with caresses, lay down gracefully at his feet, casting an occasional glance at him from eyes which, in spite of their natural fierceness, held a sort of confused expression of good will.

The poor Provençal leaned against a palm tree, eating his dates; but he kept an eye now on the desert in quest of a liberator, now on his terrible companion in watch of a break in her uncertain clemency. Each time he finished a date and spat out its stone, her eyes followed it as it landed, her glance fraught with utmost mistrust. As she surveyed him, her eyes were prudent in a sense that I can describe only as commercial. Her scrutiny, however, seemed favorable to him, for when he had finished his sparse meal, she crawled towards him to lick his boots. Her powerful rough tongue brushed off the dust caked in the cracks of the leather.

"All very good!" he thought. "But suppose she gets hungry?"

An unwelcome idea! Nevertheless, he scrutinized her, noting her proportions. A splendid specimen of the race: three feet high, four feet long, plus the tail, three feet long, a powerful weapon, round as a cudgel. A head broad as a lioness' head and chiseled with rare refinement. True, the tiger strain predominated, coldly cruel; but there was something in the panther's face reminiscent of a crafty and sensual woman. The gaiety depicted on the face of this solitary queen of the desert was that of Nero drunk. She had sated her thirst for blood; she was now ready to play.

The Provençal tested whether he could walk up and down with impunity; the panther did not interfere. She merely followed him with her eyes, like a faithful dog, or better, like a giant Angora cat, spying upon the slightest movements of her master.

He turned around to discover what had once been his horse close by the spring; the panther had dragged the carcass all the way from where he had left it, and devoured some two-thirds of it. The sight proved heartening since it explained the panther's absence and her respect of him while he slept.

Here was great luck; let him look to the future! All day long, he would cultivate the panther; he would neglect no means of gratifying her pleasures; he would win his way into her good graces.

He moved towards her. To his vast joy, she twinged her tail ever so slightly as he approached. He sat down, fearless, and they began to play together. He took her paws in his hands, twiddled her muzzle, pulled her ears, rolled her over on her back, and stroked her warm silken flanks. She was acquiescent to his touch. When he made bold to smooth the soft down covering her claws, she drew them in as one might close a damask curtain timidly over the night.

He kept his free hand on his dagger, still hoping for a chance to bury it deep into the over-confident panther; but he was so close to her that he feared her death-grip.

Besides, deep in his heart, he felt a disgust at violating the respect he owed a poor dumb beast of the desert. He had found a friend in her, too; and as he thought of this, he recalled his first mistress. Mignonne, he had called her by contrast, the pure and delicate, because she was so atrociously jealous. Throughout their association, he had lived in mortal fear of the knife she held poised over his head.

Youthful memories inspired him to call the panther Mignonne; as he did so, and found the young panther responsive, he marveled with less fright at her graceful, smooth, agile carriage.

Toward evening, he realized his perilous situation; but by then he had come to cherish the anguish it occasioned. Now, whenever he called "Mignonne" *falsetto*, she would look up at him. By sundown, Mignonne was heard several times to groan in deep melancholy tones.

"There's a lass that was well reared!" cried the jovial soldier. "And she says her prayers, too!" he jested, as he saw the peaceful attitude his mate had assumed. "Come, blondie, my love, I shall let you go to bed first!" he said to her, trusting in the activity of his own two legs to flee, the moment she was asleep, in search of some other shelter for the night.

Impatiently, he awaited the hour for flight. The time at last come, he made swiftly across the sands in the direction of the Nile. But he had gone less than a mile when he heard the panther bounding after him, punctuating the heavy thud of her leaps with those even more fearsome cries of hers, reminiscent of the rasping and squeaking of a saw.

"Well," he said to himself. "She's taken a fancy to me, eh? Probably this young panther never met a man before; it's very flattering to be her first love!"

As he spoke, he slipped into one of those quicksands so much feared by travelers in the desert, for it is impossible to save oneself from the suction of their whirling eddies. Feeling himself caught fast, he gave a shriek of alarm; the panther seized him by the collar with her teeth and, springing powerfully backward, drew him as though by magic from the abyss.

"Ah, Mignonne!" cried the soldier, caressing her enthusiastically. "Now we are bound together for life and death! But no tricks, mind you!"

And he retraced his steps.

From then on, the desert seemed inhabited. It contained a being to whom the Provençal could talk, a ferocious creature that had turned gentle for his sake, without his understanding the reason for their incredible friendship. Fervently though the soldier wished to remain standing and on his guard, he lay down and slept. On awakening he could not find Mignonne. He climbed the hummock and, from its crest, discerned her in the distance, advancing by leaps and bounds, as do animals who cannot run because of the extreme flexibility of their spinal column.

Mignonne arrived, her chops covered with blood; she received the necessary caresses her mate gave her, showing by her deep purring how happy they made her. Her eyes, fraught with languor, turned upon the Provençal even more gently than they had the day before. He talked to her as one would talk to a tame animal.

"Ah! Ah! Mademoiselle, you're a straight, decent girl, eh? Just look at her! So we like to be fondled and coddled, eh? Aren't you ashamed of yourself? You've been eating some Arab or other, eh? Ah, well, it's all right, even though Arabs are animals like yourself! But don't you start gobbling up any Frenchman! I wouldn't like you any more if you did that!"

She played like a puppy with its master, suffering him to roll her over and alternately to thwack and to stroke her; sometimes she teased him by stretching out one paw towards him in a gesture of solicitation.

Some days passed in this manner. This companionship enabled the Provençal to enjoy the sublime beauty of the desert. Now that he had alternate moments of fear and tranquillity, plenty to eat, and a living creature to occupy his mind, he was struck by the contrasts in the desert and in his own life.

Solitude revealed all her secrets to him and cast on him her every spell. He discovered in sunrise and sunset a wealth of sights unknown to the world. He experienced what it meant to tremble when, hearing the soft whirring of a bird's wings overhead, he watched the rare passer-by fly out of sight. He thrilled as he beheld the clouds, varying and many-colored voyagers, blend and fuse into curious patterns. At night, he studied the play of the moon over the ocean of sand, as the simoon churned up waves that undulated, sinuous and swiftly changing. He lived the life of the Orient day, marveling at its magnificent pageantry. Often, having reveled in the awesome sight of a hurricane sweeping this plain over which the whirling sands formed red, dry mists and clouds bearing death in their womb, he would joyfully greet the coming of night, drinking in the welcome coolness of the stars and listening to imaginary music in the skies.

And then solitude taught him to exploit the rich treasures of daydreaming. He would spend hours at a stretch, recalling the most trifling things, and comparing his present life with his past. In time, he grew passionately fond of the panther, for he had to have some sort of affection. Either because his will, powerfully projected, had altered the character of his mate, or because she found food aplenty in her desert hunting, she respected the Provençal's life, and he, seeing her so well tamed, ceased to mistrust her.

He spent much of his time sleeping, but he was forced to watch, like a spider in its web, so as not to miss the moment of his deliverance, if any one should happen to pass along the far horizon. He had sacrificed his shirt to make a flag; this he hung at the top of a palm tree whose foliage he had hacked off. Counseled by necessity, he found a means of keeping it spread out by fastening it with twigs, for the wind might not happen to be blowing at the moment when the awaited traveler chanced to look across the desert . . .

It was during the long hours when hope had forsaken him that he played with his panther. He had come to recognize the different inflections of her voice, the expressions of her glance; he had studied the capricious design of all the flecks which variegated the gold of her coat. Mignonne was no longer angry now, when he seized the tuft that capped her tail to count her white and black rings, so many graceful ornaments that glistened from afar in the sun like precious gems. He found it pleasurable to contemplate the slender, delicate lines of her body, the whiteness of her belly, the graceful pose of her head. But it was especially when she was frolicking that he most delighted in observing her. The agility and youthful elasticity of her movements never failed to surprise him; he marveled at her suppleness as she bounded here or crept there or slipped through the narrowest spaces or fastened upon objects or rolled over or huddled against him or darted where she would. No matter how swift her bound or how slippery the rock she frisked on, he had but to cry "Mignonne" and she stopped dead.

One day, under a dazzling sun, a huge bird of prey hovered in the sky. The Provençal left his panther's side to look at this new guest. The deserted sultana paused a moment, then uttered a low, deep growl.

"God bless me!" he cried, noticing her eyes grow hard again. "I swear the wench is jealous." Then, recalling that other wench whose nickname he had conferred upon the panther, "The soul of Virginie has passed into her body, no doubt about it!"

The eagle disappeared into the air. The soldier watched his panther, admiring the arched curve of her crupper. Savage, she was, ay; but what youth and what grace in her figure! She was beautiful as a woman. The tawny fur of her coat blent exquisitely with the delicate tints, of dead white tones, that marked her flanks . . . the dazzling light turned her body to living gold . . . and the brown flecks upon her glowed in such a way as to make them indefinably attractive . . .

Man and panther looked at each other meaningfully. The coquette quivered as she felt her mate scratch her head. Her eyes flashed like lightning. Then she shut them tight.

"She has a soul!" he decided, looking down at this motionless queen of the sands, golden like them, and white like them, and, like them, burning and solitary.

"Well," she said. "I have read your plea in favor of animals. But what finally happened to these two persons who seemed so well mated?"

"Yes, you're right to ask about *that!* They ended, as all great passions end, in a misunderstanding. Each party suspects the other of infidelity, pride prevents any explanation, obstinacy causes a break."

"And yet, at the best moments, a mere word, a look even is enough to . . . But go on with your story!"

"It's difficult to tell. But you will understand when I quote what the old soldier said when he had finished his champagne."

"What did he say?" she asked.

" 'I don't know what hurt I had done my panther,' said the old soldier, 'but she turned upon me as if she were mad. Her sharp teeth caught my leg, gently I daresay. But I thought she meant business. So I buried my dagger in her throat. She rolled over with a cry that froze the blood in my veins. I saw her writhing, still looking at me without the slightest anger. I would have given the whole world—even my Legion of Honor cross which I earned later—to bring her back to life. It was as though I had murdered a real person. The soldiers, who had sighted my flag and come to my rescue, found me in tears.'

"He paused.

" 'Well, Monsieur,' he went on, 'since then I have soldiered in Germany and Spain and Russia and France. I have trundled this carcass of mine pretty much everywhere. But I have never seen anything like the desert. How beautiful it is!'

" 'What were your impressions and feelings in the desert?' I asked.

" 'They defy all description, young man. Besides, I'm not always pining for my palm trees and my panther. I should have to be a sad dog for that, eh? You see, the desert holds at once everything and nothing.'

" 'How do you mean?'

" 'Well,' he answered with an impatient gesture, 'the desert is God without mankind.' "

THE GREATER CATS

The greater cats with golden eyes
Stare out between the bars,
Deserts are there, and different skies,
And night with different stars.
They prowl the aromatic hill,
And mate as fiercely as they kill,
And hold the freedom of their will
To roam, to live, to drink their fill;
But this beyond their wit know I;
Man loves a little, and for long shall die.

Their kind across the desert range
Where tulips spring from stones,
Not knowing they will suffer change
Or vultures pick their bones,
Their strength's eternal in their sight,
They rule the terror of the night,
They overtake the deer in flight,
And in their arrogance they smite;
But I am sage, if they are strong:
Man's love is transient as his death is long.

Yet oh what powers to deceive!
My wit is turned to faith,
And at this moment I believe
In love, and scout at death.
I came from nowhere, and shall be

Strong, steadfast, swift, eternally:
I am a lion, a stone, a tree,
And as the Polar star in me
Is fixed my constant heart on thee.
Ah, may I stay forever blind
With lions, tigers, leopards, and their kind.

J. H. Patterson

DEATH OF A MAN-EATER

As a matter of fact, it was some months before the lions attacked us again, though from time to time we heard of their depredations in other quarters. Not long after our night in the goods-wagon, two men were carried off from railhead, while another was taken from a place called Engomani, about ten miles away. Within a very short time, this latter place was again visited by the brutes, two more men being seized, one of whom was killed and eaten, and the other so badly mauled that he died within a few days. As I have said, however, we at Tsavo enjoyed complete immunity from attack, and the coolies, believing that their dreaded foes had permanently deserted the district, resumed all their usual habits and occupations, and life in the camps returned to its normal routine.

At last we were suddenly startled out of this feeling of security. One dark night the familiar terror-stricken cries and screams awoke the camps, and we knew that the "demons" had returned and had commenced a new list of victims. On this occasion a number of men had been sleeping outside their tents for the sake of coolness, thinking, of course, that the lions had gone for good, when suddenly in the middle of the night one of the brutes was discovered forcing its way through the *boma*. The alarm was at once given, and sticks, stones and firebrands were hurled in the direction of the intruder. All was of no avail, however, for the lion burst into the midst of the terrified group, seized an unfortunate wretch amid the cries and shrieks of his companions, and dragged him off through the thick thorn fence. He was joined outside by the second lion, and so

18

daring had the two brutes become that they did not trouble
to carry their victim any further away, but devoured him
within thirty yards of the tent where he had been seized. Although several shots were fired in their direction by the
jemadar of the gang to which the coolie belonged, they took no
notice of these and did not attempt to move until their horrible
meal was finished. The few scattered fragments that remained
of the body I would not allow to be buried at once, hoping
that the lions would return to the spot the following night; and
on the chance of this I took up my station at nightfall in a convenient tree. Nothing occurred to break the monotony of my
watch, however, except that I had a visit from a hyæna, and the
next morning I learned that the lions had attacked another
camp about two miles from Tsavo—for by this time the camps
were again scattered, as I had works in progress all up and
down the line. There the man-eaters had been successful in obtaining a victim, whom, as in the previous instance, they devoured quite close to the camp. How they forced their way
through the *bomas* without making a noise was, and still is, a
mystery to me; I should have thought that it was next to impossible for an animal to get through at all. Yet they continually did so, and without a sound being heard.

After this occurrence, I sat up every night for over a week
near likely camps, but all in vain. Either the lions saw me and
then went elsewhere, or else I was unlucky, for they took man
after man from different places without ever once giving me a
chance of a shot at them. This constant night watching was
most dreary and fatiguing work, but I felt that it was a duty
that had to be undertaken, as the men naturally looked to me
for protection. In the whole of my life I have never experienced
anything more nerve-shaking than to hear the deep roars of
these dreadful monsters growing gradually nearer and nearer,
and to know that some one or other of us was doomed to be
their victim before morning dawned. Once they reached the
vicinity of the camps, the roars completely ceased, and we knew
that they were stalking for their prey. Shouts would then pass
from camp to camp, *"Khabar dar, bhaieon, shaitan ata"* ("Be-

ware, brothers, the devil is coming"), but the warning cries would prove of no avail, and sooner or later agonising shrieks would break the silence and another man would be missing from roll-call next morning.

I was naturally very disheartened at being foiled in this way night after night, and was soon at my wits' end to know what to do; it seemed as if the lions were really "devils" after all and bore a charmed life. As I have said before, tracking them through the jungle was a hopeless task; but as something had to be done to keep up the men's spirits, I spent many a weary day crawling on my hands and knees through the dense undergrowth of the exasperating wilderness around us. As a matter of fact, if I had come up with the lions on any of these expeditions, it was much more likely that they would have added me to their list of victims than that I should have succeeded in killing either of them, as everything would have been in their favour. About this time, too, I had many helpers, and several officers—civil, naval and military—came to Tsavo from the coast and sat up night after night in order to get a shot at our daring foes. All of us, however, met with the same lack of success, and the lions always seemed capable of avoiding the watchers, while succeeding at the same time in obtaining a victim.

I have a very vivid recollection of one particular night when the brutes seized a man from the railway station and brought him close to my camp to devour. I could plainly hear them crunching the bones, and the sound of their dreadful purring filled the air and rang in my ears for days afterwards. The terrible thing was to feel so helpless; it was useless to attempt to go out, as of course the poor fellow was dead, and in addition it was so pitch dark as to make it impossible to see anything. Some half a dozen workmen, who lived in a small enclosure close to mine, became so terrified on hearing the lions at their meal that they shouted and implored me to allow them to come inside my *boma*. This I willingly did, but soon afterwards I remembered that one man had been lying ill in their camp, and on making enquiry I found that they had callously left him behind alone. I immediately took some men with me to bring him to my *boma,* but on entering his tent I saw by the light of the lantern that the poor fellow was beyond need of safety. He had died of shock at being deserted by his companions.

From this time matters gradually became worse and worse. Hitherto, as a rule, only one of the man-eaters had made the attack and had done the foraging, while the other waited outside in the bush; but now they began to change their tactics, entering the *bomas* together and each seizing a victim. In this way two Swahili porters were killed during the last week of November, one being immediately carried off and devoured. The other was heard moaning for a long time, and when his terrified companions at last summoned up sufficient courage to go to his assistance, they found him stuck fast in the bushes of the *boma,* through which for once the lion had apparently been unable to drag him. He was still alive when I saw him next morning, but so terribly mauled that he died before he could be got to the hospital.

Within a few days of this the two brutes made a most ferocious attack on the largest camp in the section, which for safety's sake was situated within a stone's throw of Tsavo Station and close to a Permanent Way Inspector's iron hut. Suddenly in the dead of night the two man-eaters burst in among the terrified workmen, and even from my *boma,* some distance away, I could plainly hear the panic-stricken shrieking of the coolies. Then followed cries of "They've taken him; they've taken him," as the brutes carried off their unfortunate victim and began their horrible feast close beside the camp. The Inspector, Mr. Dalgairns, fired over fifty shots in the direction in which he heard the lions, but they were not to be frightened and calmly lay there until their meal was finished. After examining the spot in the morning, we at once set out to follow the brutes, Mr. Dalgairns feeling confident that he had wounded one of them, as there was a trail on the sand like that of the toes of a broken limb. After some careful stalking, we suddenly found ourselves in the vicinity of the lions, and were greeted with ominous growlings. Cautiously advancing and pushing the bushes aside, we saw in the gloom what we at first took to be a lion cub;

closer inspection, however, showed it to be the remains of the unfortunate coolie, which the man-eaters had evidently abandoned at our approach. The legs, one arm and half the body had been eaten, and it was the stiff fingers of the other arm trailing along the sand which had left the marks we had taken to be the trail of a wounded lion. By this time the beasts had retired far into the thick jungle where it was impossible to follow them, so we had the remains of the coolie buried and once more returned home disappointed.

Now the bravest men in the world, much less the ordinary Indian coolie, will not stand constant terrors of this sort indefinitely. The whole district was by this time thoroughly panic-stricken, and I was not at all surprised, therefore, to find on my return to camp that same afternoon (December 1) that the men had all struck work and were waiting to speak to me. When I sent for them, they flocked to my *boma* in a body and stated that they would not remain at Tsavo any longer for anything or anybody; they had come from India on an agreement to work for the Government, not to supply food for either lions or "devils." No sooner had they delivered this ultimatum than a regular stampede took place. Some hundreds of them stopped the first passing train by throwing themselves on the rails in front of the engine, and then, swarming on to the trucks and throwing in their possessions anyhow, they fled from the accursed spot.

After this the railway works were completely stopped; and for the next three weeks practically nothing was done but build "lion-proof" huts for those workmen who had had sufficient courage to remain. It was a strange and amusing sight to see these shelters perched on the top of water-tanks, roofs and girders—anywhere for safety—while some even went so far as to dig pits inside their tents, into which they descended at night, covering the top over with heavy logs of wood. Every good-sized tree in the camp had as many beds lashed on to it as its branches would bear—and sometimes more. I remember that one night when the camp was attacked, so many men swarmed on to one particular tree that down it came with a crash, hurl-

ing its terror-stricken load of shrieking coolies close to the very
lions they were trying to avoid. Fortunately for them, a victim
had already been secured, and the brutes were too busy devouring him to pay attention to anything else.

*   *   *

A day or two after the departure of my allies, as I was leaving
my *boma* soon after dawn on December 9, I saw a Swahili running excitedly towards me, shouting out *"Simba! Simba!"*
("Lion! Lion!"), and every now and again looking behind him
as he ran. On questioning him I found that the lions had tried
to snatch a man from the camp by the river, but being foiled
in this had seized and killed one of the donkeys, and were at
that moment busy devouring it not far off. Now was my chance.

I rushed for the heavy rifle which Farquhar had kindly left
with me for use in case an opportunity such as this should
arise, and, led by the Swahili, I started most carefully to stalk
the lions, who, I devoutly hoped, were confining their attention
strictly to their meal. I was getting on splendidly, and could
just make out the outline of one of them through the dense
bush, when unfortunately my guide snapped a rotten branch.
The wily beast heard the noise, growled his defiance, and disappeared in a moment into a patch of even thicker jungle close
by. In desperation at the thought of his escaping me once again,
I crept hurriedly back to the camp, summoned the available
workmen and told them to bring all the tom-toms, tin cans and
other noisy instruments of any kind that could be found. As
quickly as possible I posted them in a half-circle round the
thicket, and gave the head *jemadar* instructions to start a simul-
taneous beating of the tom-toms and cans as soon as he judged
that I had had time to get round to the other side. I then crept
round by myself and soon found a good position and one which
the lion was most likely to retreat past, as it was in the middle
of a broad animal path leading straight from the place where
he was concealed. I lay down behind a small ant hill, and waited
expectantly. Very soon I heard a tremendous din being raised

by the advancing line of coolies, and almost immediately, to my intense joy, out into the open path stepped a huge maneless lion. It was the first occasion during all these trying months upon which I had had a fair chance at one of these brutes, and my satisfaction at the prospect of bagging him was unbounded.

Slowly he advanced along the path, stopping every few seconds to look round. I was only partially concealed from view, and if his attention had not been so fully occupied by the noise behind him, he must have observed me. As he was oblivious to my presence, however, I let him approach to within about fifteen yards of me, and then covered him with my rifle. The moment I moved to do this, he caught sight of me, and seemed much astonished at my sudden appearance, for he stuck his forefeet into the ground, threw himself back on his haunches and growled savagely. As I covered his brain with my rifle, I felt that at last I had him absolutely at my mercy, but . . . . never trust an untried weapon! I pulled the trigger, and to my horror heard the dull snap that tells of a misfire.

Worse was to follow. I was so taken aback and disconcerted by this untoward accident that I entirely forgot to fire the left barrel, and lowered the rifle from my shoulder with the intention of reloading—if I should be given time. Fortunately for me, the lion was so distracted by the terrific din and uproar of the coolies behind him that instead of springing on me, as might have been expected, he bounded aside into the jungle again. By this time I had collected my wits, and just as he jumped I let him have the left barrel. An answering angry growl told me that he had been hit; but nevertheless he succeeded once more in getting clear away, for although I tracked him for some little distance, I eventually lost his trail in a rocky patch of ground.

Bitterly did I anathematise the hour in which I had relied on a borrowed weapon, and in my disappointment and vexation I abused owner, maker, and rifle with fine impartiality. On extracting the unexploded cartridge, I found that the needle had not struck home, the cap being only slightly dented; so that the whole fault did indeed lie with the rifle, which I later returned to Farquhar with polite compliments. Seriously, however, my continued ill-luck was most exasperating; and the result was that the Indians were more than ever confirmed in their belief that the lions were really evil spirits, proof against mortal weapons. Certainly, they did seem to bear charmed lives.

After this dismal failure there was, of course, nothing to do but to return to camp. Before doing so, however, I proceeded to view the dead donkey, which I found to have been only slightly devoured at the quarters. It is a curious fact that lions always begin at the tail of their prey and eat upwards towards the head. As their meal had thus been interrupted evidently at the very beginning, I felt pretty sure that one or other of the brutes would return to the carcase at nightfall. Accordingly, as there was no tree of any kind close at hand, I had a staging erected some ten feet away from the body. This *machan* was about twelve feet high and was composed of four poles stuck into the ground and inclined towards each other at the top, where a plank was lashed to serve as a seat. Further, as the nights were still pitch dark, I had the donkey's carcase secured by strong wires to a neighbouring stump, so that the lions might not be able to drag it away before I could get a shot at them.

At sundown, therefore, I took up my position on my airy perch, and much to the disgust of my gun-bearer, Mahina, I decided to go alone. I would gladly have taken him with me, indeed, but he had a bad cough, and I was afraid lest he should make any involuntary noise or movement which might spoil all. Darkness fell almost immediately, and everything became extraordinarily still. The silence of an African jungle on a dark night needs to be experienced to be realised; it is most impressive, especially when one is absolutely alone and isolated from one's fellow creatures, as I was then. The solitude and stillness, and the purpose of my vigil, all had their effect on me, and from a condition of strained expectancy I gradually fell into a dreamy mood which harmonised well with my surroundings. Suddenly I was startled out of my reverie by the snapping of a twig: and, straining my ears for a further sound, I fancied I could hear the rustling of a large body forcing its way through the bush. "The man-eater," I thought to myself; "surely to-night my luck will change and I shall bag one of the brutes." Profound silence again succeeded; I sat on my eyrie like a statue, every nerve tense with excitement. Very soon, however, all doubt as to the presence of the lion was dispelled. A deep long-drawn sigh—sure sign of hunger—came up from the bushes, and the rustling commenced again as he cautiously advanced. In a moment or two a sudden stop, followed by an angry growl, told me that my presence had been noticed; and I began to fear that disappointment awaited me once more.

But no; matters quickly took an unexpected turn. The hunter became the hunted; and instead of either making off or coming for the bait prepared for him, the lion began stealthily to stalk *me!* For about two hours he horrified me by slowly creeping round and round my crazy structure, gradually edging his way nearer and nearer. Every moment I expected him to rush it; and the staging had not been constructed with an eye to such a possibility. If one of the rather flimsy poles should break, or if the lion could spring the twelve feet which separated me from the ground . . . the thought was scarcely a pleasant one. I began to feel distinctly "creepy," and heartily repented my folly in having placed myself in such a dangerous position. I kept perfectly still, however, hardly daring even to blink my eyes: but the long-continued strain was telling on my nerves, and my feelings may be better imagined than described when about midnight suddenly something came flop and struck me on the back of the head. For a moment I was so terrified that I nearly fell off the plank, as I thought that the lion had sprung on me from behind. Regaining my senses in a second or two, I realised that I had been hit by nothing more formidable than an owl, which had doubtless mistaken me for the branch of a tree—not a very alarming thing to happen in ordinary circumstances, I admit, but coming at the time it did, it almost paralysed me. The involuntary start which I could not help giving was immediately answered by a sinister growl from below.

After this I again kept as still as I could, though absolutely trembling with excitement; and in a short while I heard the lion begin to creep stealthily towards me. I could barely make out his form as he crouched among the whitish undergrowth; but I saw enough for my purpose, and before he could come any nearer, I took careful aim and pulled the trigger. The sound of the shot was at once followed by a most terrific roar, and then I could hear him leaping about in all directions. I was no longer able to see him, however, as his first bound had taken him into the thick bush; but to make assurance doubly sure, I kept blazing away in the direction in which I heard him plunging about. At length came a series of mighty groans, gradually subsiding into deep sighs, and finally ceasing altogether; and I felt convinced that one of the "devils" who had so long harried us would trouble us no more.

As soon as I ceased firing, a tumult of inquiring voices was borne across the dark jungle from the men in camp about a quarter of a mile away. I shouted back that I was safe and sound, and that one of the lions was dead: whereupon such a mighty cheer went up from all the camps as must have astonished the denizens of the jungle for miles around. Shortly I saw scores of lights twinkling through the bushes: every man in camp turned out, and with tom-toms beating and horns blowing came running to the scene. They surrounded my eyrie, and to my amazement prostrated themselves on the ground before me, saluting me with cries of *"Mabarak! Mabarak!"* which I believe means "blessed one" or "saviour." All the same, I refused to allow any search to be made that night for the body of the lion, in case his companion might be close by; besides, it was possible that he might be still alive, and capable of making a last spring. Accordingly we all returned in triumph to the camp, where great rejoicings were kept up for the remainder of the night, the Swahili and other African natives celebrating the occasion by an especially wild and savage dance.

For my part, I anxiously awaited the dawn; and even before it was thoroughly light I was on my way to the eventful spot, as I could not completely persuade myself that even yet the "devil" might not have eluded me in some uncanny and mysterious way. Happily my fears proved groundless, and I was relieved to find that my luck—after playing me so many exasperating tricks—had really turned at last. I had scarcely traced the blood for more than a few paces when, on rounding a bush, I was startled to see a huge lion right in front of me, seemingly alive and crouching for a spring. On looking closer, however, I satisfied myself that he was really and truly stone-dead, whereupon my followers crowded round, laughed and danced and shouted with joy like children, and bore me in triumph shoulder-high round the dead body. These thanksgiving ceremonies being over, I examined the body and found that two bullets had taken effect—one close behind the left shoulder, evidently penetrating the heart, and the other in the off hind leg. The prize was indeed one to be proud of; his length from tip of nose to tip of tail was nine feet eight inches, he stood three feet nine inches high, and it took eight men to carry him back to camp. The only blemish was that the skin was much scored by the *boma* thorns through which he had so often forced his way in carrying off his victims.

The news of the death of one of the notorious man-eaters soon spread far and wide over the country: telegrams of congratulation came pouring in, and scores of people flocked from up and down the railway to see the skin for themselves.

t repine, and seem, for the most part, to be sufficiently
light-hearted, and happy.

men, meanwhile, had each rolled up a quid of betel-nut,
the four ingredients carefully from the little brass boxes
wooden tray before them, and having prepared cigarettes
nese tobacco, with the dried shoots of the *nîpah* palm for
ers, had at length broken the absorbed silence, which had
em fast while the matter of the meal was occupying their
ded attention.

talk flitted lightly over many subjects; for a hearty meal,
e peace of soul which repletion brings with it, are not
ive to concentration of attention, nor yet to activity of
The Malay, too, is always superficial, and talk among
generally plays round facts, rather than round ideas.
ēman, the owner of the house, and his two sons, Âwang
ʒah, discussed the prospects of the crop then growing in
ds behind the compound. Their cousin Äbdollah, who
l to be passing the night in the house, told of a fall
his wife's aunt's brother had come by, when climbing a
ut tree. Mat, his *bîras* (for they had married two sisters,
stablished a definite form of relationship between them,
ng to Malay ideas), added a few more or less ugly de-
Äbdollah's description of the corpse after the accident.
this attracted the attention of the two remaining men,
nd Kassim, who had been discussing the price of rice,
varying chances of *gĕtah* hunting, the talk at this point
general. Pôtek and Kassim had recently returned from
1, where, as has been said, the present Sultân of Pahang
that time, collecting the force with which he afterwards
ully invaded and conquered the State. They told of all
l seen and heard, multiplying their figures with the dar-
lessness that is born of unfettered imaginations, and the
a rudimentary knowledge of arithmetic. But even this
ng topic could not hold the attention of their hearers
. Before Pôtek and Kassim had well finished the enu-
n of the heavy artillery, of the thousands of the ele-
and the tens of thousands of the followers, with which

Hugh Clifford

A NIGHT OF TERROR

The glaring eyes through the brushwood shine,
   And the striped hide shows between
The trees and bushes, 'mid trailing vine
   And masses of ever-green.
A snarling moan comes long and low,
   We may neither flee nor fight,
For well our leaping pulses know
   The Terror that stalks by Night.

IF YOU PUT YOUR finger on the map of the Malay Peninsula an
inch or two from its exact centre, you will find a river in
Pahang territory which has its rise in the watershed that divides
that State from Kĕlantan and Trĕnggânu. This river is called
the Tĕmbĕling, and it is chiefly remarkable for the number of
its rapids and the richness of its gutta-bearing forests. Its inhabitants are a ruffianly lot of Malays, who are preyed upon by
a family of *Wans*, a semi-royal set of nobles who do their best
to live up to their traditions. Below the rapids the natives are
chiefly noted for the quaint pottery that they produce from the
clay which abounds there, and the rude shapes and ruder
tracery of their vessels have probably suffered no change since
the days when Solomon's fleets sought gold and peafowl and
monkeys in the jungles of the Peninsula, as everybody knows.
Above the rapids the Malays plant enough *gambir* to supply
the wants of the whole betel-chewing population of Pahang,
and, as the sale of this commodity wins them a few dollars annually, they are too indolent to plant their own rice. This
grain, which is the staple of all Malays, without which they

29

cannot live, is therefore sold to them by down river natives, at the exorbitant price of half a dollar the bushel.

A short distance up stream, and midway between the mouth and the big rapids, there is a straggling village, called Ranggul, the houses of which, made of wattled bamboos and thatched with palm leaves, stand on piles, amid the groves of cocoa-nut and areca-nut palms, varied by clumps of smooth-leaved banana trees. The houses are not very close together, but a man can call from one to the other with ease; and thus the cocoa-nuts thrive, which, as the Malays say, grow not with pleasure beyond the sound of the human voice. The people of the village are not more indolent than other Malays. They plant a little rice, when the season comes, in the swamps behind the village. They work a little jungle produce, when the pinch of poverty drives them to it, but, like all Malays, they take life sufficiently easily. If you chance to go into the village of Ranggul, during any of the hot hours of the day, you will find most of its occupants lying about in their dark, cool houses, engaged upon such gentle mental tasks as may be afforded by whittling a stick, or hacking slowly at the already deeply scored threshold-block, with their clumsy wood-knives. Sitting thus, they gossip with a passing neighbour, who stops to chatter as he sits propped upon the stair ladder, or they croak snatches of song, with some old-world refrain to it, and, from time to time, break off to cast a word over their shoulders to the wife in the dim background near the fireplace, or to the little virgin daughter, carefully secreted on the shelf overhead, in company with a miscellaneous collection of dusty, grimy rubbish, the disused lumber of years. Nature has been very lavish to the Malay, and she has provided him with a soil which returns a maximum of food for a minimum of grudging labour. The cool, moist fruit groves call aloud to all mankind to come and revel in their fragrant shade during the parching hours of mid-day, and the Malay has caught the spirit of his surroundings, and is very much what Nature has seen fit to make him.

Some five-and-thirty years ago, when Che' wan Âhmad, now better known as Sultân Âhmad Maätham Shah, was collecting

his forces in Dûngun, preparatory to makin[g] cessful descent into the Tĕmbĕling valley, and conquer Pahang, the night was closing large house stood, at that time, in a somewha[t] within a thickly-planted compound, at one e[nd] lage. In this house, on the night of which and two women were at work on the eveni[ng] sat in the centre of the floor, on a white [mat?] plaited leaves of the mĕngkúang palm, with rice before each of them, and a brass tray, h[olding] china bowls of curry, placed where all coul[d] cross-legged, with bowed backs, supporting left arms, the left hand lying flat on the turned that the outspread fingers pointed fingers of their right hands they messed curry well into it, and then swiftly carrie[d] their mouths, skilfully, without dropping sat demurely, in a half kneeling position, away under them, and ministered to the They said never a word, save an occasion[al] they drove away a lean cat that crept too the men also held their peace. There was save the hum of the insects out of doors, bull-frogs in the rice swamps, and the un[ceasing] of mastication made by the men as they a[te].

When the meal was over the women ca[me] a corner near the fireplace, and there f[ed] viands as their lords had not consumed. I[f care-] fully, however, you would have seen that which the women ruled, still held a secr[et] consumption, and that the quality of the by no means inferior to that which ha[d] men. In a land where women wait upon none to attend to their wants, or forestall soon acquire an extremely good notion themselves; and, since they have never k[nown?] in which women are treated as they a[re]

do n[ot] brig[ht]

Th[e] taki[ng] in th[e] of Ja[va] wrap[ped] held undiv[ided]

Th[e] and t[he] condu[ct] mind. nativ[e] Che' [S]
and N[ot] the fi[eld] chanc[e] which cocoa-[nuts] which accord[ing] tails t[o] And a[s] Pôtek and th[e] becam[e] Dûngu[n] was, at success[ful] they ha[d] ing rec[ord] lack of absorbi[ng] for lon[g] merati[on] phants,

Hugh Clifford

A NIGHT OF TERROR

The glaring eyes through the brushwood shine,
  And the striped hide shows between
The trees and bushes, 'mid trailing vine
  And masses of ever-green.
A snarling moan comes long and low,
  We may neither flee nor fight,
For well our leaping pulses know
  The Terror that stalks by Night.

IF YOU PUT YOUR finger on the map of the Malay Peninsula an inch or two from its exact centre, you will find a river in Pahang territory which has its rise in the watershed that divides that State from Kělantan and Trěnggânu. This river is called the Těmběling, and it is chiefly remarkable for the number of its rapids and the richness of its gutta-bearing forests. Its inhabitants are a ruffianly lot of Malays, who are preyed upon by a family of *Wans*, a semi-royal set of nobles who do their best to live up to their traditions. Below the rapids the natives are chiefly noted for the quaint pottery that they produce from the clay which abounds there, and the rude shapes and ruder tracery of their vessels have probably suffered no change since the days when Solomon's fleets sought gold and peafowl and monkeys in the jungles of the Peninsula, as everybody knows. Above the rapids the Malays plant enough *gambir* to supply the wants of the whole betel-chewing population of Pahang, and, as the sale of this commodity wins them a few dollars annually, they are too indolent to plant their own rice. This grain, which is the staple of all Malays, without which they cannot live, is therefore sold to them by down river natives, at the exorbitant price of half a dollar the bushel.

A short distance up stream, and midway between the mouth and the big rapids, there is a straggling village, called Ranggul, the houses of which, made of wattled bamboos and thatched with palm leaves, stand on piles, amid the groves of cocoa-nut and areca-nut palms, varied by clumps of smooth-leaved banana trees. The houses are not very close together, but a man can call from one to the other with ease; and thus the cocoa-nuts thrive, which, as the Malays say, grow not with pleasure beyond the sound of the human voice. The people of the village are not more indolent than other Malays. They plant a little rice, when the season comes, in the swamps behind the village. They work a little jungle produce, when the pinch of poverty drives them to it, but, like all Malays, they take life sufficiently easily. If you chance to go into the village of Ranggul, during any of the hot hours of the day, you will find most of its occupants lying about in their dark, cool houses, engaged upon such gentle mental tasks as may be afforded by whittling a stick, or hacking slowly at the already deeply scored threshold-block, with their clumsy wood-knives. Sitting thus, they gossip with a passing neighbour, who stops to chatter as he sits propped upon the stair ladder, or they croak snatches of song, with some old-world refrain to it, and, from time to time, break off to cast a word over their shoulders to the wife in the dim background near the fireplace, or to the little virgin daughter, carefully secreted on the shelf overhead, in company with a miscellaneous collection of dusty, grimy rubbish, the disused lumber of years. Nature has been very lavish to the Malay, and she has provided him with a soil which returns a maximum of food for a minimum of grudging labour. The cool, moist fruit groves call aloud to all mankind to come and revel in their fragrant shade during the parching hours of mid-day, and the Malay has caught the spirit of his surroundings, and is very much what Nature has seen fit to make him.

Some five-and-thirty years ago, when Che' wan Âhmad, now better known as Sultân Âhmad Maätham Shah, was collecting

his forces in Dûngun, preparatory to making his last and successful descent into the Těmběling valley, whence to overrun
and conquer Pahang, the night was closing in at Ranggul. A
large house stood, at that time, in a somewhat isolated position,
within a thickly-planted compound, at one extremity of the village. In this house, on the night of which I write, seven men
and two women were at work on the evening meal. The men
sat in the centre of the floor, on a white mat made from the
plaited leaves of the *měngkûang* palm, with a plate piled with
rice before each of them, and a brass tray, holding various little
china bowls of curry, placed where all could reach it. They sat
cross-legged, with bowed backs, supporting themselves on their
left arms, the left hand lying flat on the mat, and being so
turned that the outspread fingers pointed inwards. With the
fingers of their right hands they messed the rice, mixing the
curry well into it, and then swiftly carried a large handful to
their mouths, skilfully, without dropping a grain. The women
sat demurely, in a half kneeling position, with their feet tucked
away under them, and ministered to the wants of the men.
They said never a word, save an occasional exclamation, when
they drove away a lean cat that crept too near to the food, and
the men also held their peace. There was no sound to be heard,
save the hum of the insects out of doors, the deep note of the
bull-frogs in the rice swamps, and the unnecessarily loud noise
of mastication made by the men as they ate.

When the meal was over the women carried what was left to
a corner near the fireplace, and there fell to on such of the
viands as their lords had not consumed. If you had looked carefully, however, you would have seen that the cooking-pots, over
which the women ruled, still held a secret store for their own
consumption, and that the quality of the food in this *cache* was
by no means inferior to that which had been allotted to the
men. In a land where women wait upon themselves, and have
none to attend to their wants, or forestall their wishes, they very
soon acquire an extremely good notion of how to look after
themselves; and, since they have never known a state of society
in which women are treated as they are amongst ourselves, they

do not repine, and seem, for the most part, to be sufficiently
bright, light-hearted, and happy.

The men, meanwhile, had each rolled up a quid of betel-nut,
taking the four ingredients carefully from the little brass boxes
in the wooden tray before them, and having prepared cigarettes
of Javanese tobacco, with the dried shoots of the *nîpah* palm for
wrappers, had at length broken the absorbed silence, which had
held them fast while the matter of the meal was occupying their
undivided attention.

The talk flitted lightly over many subjects; for a hearty meal,
and the peace of soul which repletion brings with it, are not
conducive to concentration of attention, nor yet to activity of
mind. The Malay, too, is always superficial, and talk among
natives generally plays round facts, rather than round ideas.
Che' Sĕman, the owner of the house, and his two sons, Âwang
and Ngah, discussed the prospects of the crop then growing in
the fields behind the compound. Their cousin Äbdollah, who
chanced to be passing the night in the house, told of a fall
which his wife's aunt's brother had come by, when climbing a
cocoa-nut tree. Mat, his *bîras* (for they had married two sisters,
which established a definite form of relationship between them,
according to Malay ideas), added a few more or less ugly de-
tails to Äbdollah's description of the corpse after the accident.
And as this attracted the attention of the two remaining men,
Pôtek and Kassim, who had been discussing the price of rice,
and the varying chances of *gĕtah* hunting, the talk at this point
became general. Pôtek and Kassim had recently returned from
Dûngun, where, as has been said, the present Sultân of Pahang
was, at that time, collecting the force with which he afterwards
successfully invaded and conquered the State. They told of all
they had seen and heard, multiplying their figures with the daring recklessness that is born of unfettered imaginations, and the
lack of a rudimentary knowledge of arithmetic. But even this
absorbing topic could not hold the attention of their hearers
for long. Before Pôtek and Kassim had well finished the enu-
meration of the heavy artillery, of the thousands of the elephants, and the tens of thousands of the followers, with which

they credited the adventurous, but slender bands of ragamuffins, who followed Âhmad's fortunes, Che' Sĕman broke into their talk with words on a subject which, at that time, was ever uppermost in the minds of the Tĕmbĕling people, and the conversation straightway drifted into the channel in which it had run, with only casual interruptions, for many weeks past.

'He of the Hairy Face * is with us once more,' ejaculated Che' Sĕman; and when this announcement had caused a dead silence to fall upon his hearers, and had even stilled the chatter of the women-folk near the fireplace, he continued:

'At the hour when the cicada is heard (sunset), I met Imân Sîdik of Gĕmûroh, and bade him stay to eat rice, but he would not, saying that He of the Hairy Face had made his kill at Lâbu yesternight, and it behoved all men to be within their houses before the darkness fell. And so saying he paddled his dug-out down stream with the short quick stroke used when we race boats. Imân Sîdik is a wise man, and his words are true. He of the Hairy Face spares neither priest nor prince. The girl he killed at Lâbu was a daughter of the *Wans*—her name Wan Esah.'

'That makes three-and-twenty whom He of the Hairy Face hath slain in one year of maize' (three months), said Âwang in a low fear-stricken voice. 'He touches neither goats nor kine, and men say He sucketh more blood than He eateth flesh.'

'That it is which proves Him to be the thing he is,' said Ngah.

'Thy words are true,' said Che' Sĕman solemnly. 'He of the Hairy Face has his origin in a man. The *Sĕmang*—the negrits of the woods—drove him forth from among them, and now he lives solitarily in the jungles, and by night he takes upon himself the form of Him of the Hairy Face, and feasts upon the flesh of his own kind.'

'I have heard tell that it is only the men of Korinchi who have this strange power,' interposed Äbdollah, in the tone of one who longs to be reassured.

* *Si Pŭdong* = one of the names used by jungle-bred Malays to describe a tiger. They avoid using the beast's real name lest the sound of it should reach his ears, and cause him to come to the speaker.

'Men say that they also possess the power,' rejoined Che' Sĕman, 'but certain it is that He of the Hairy Face was born a *Sĕmang*,—a negrit of the woods,—and when He goeth forth in human guise he is like all other *Sĕmangs* to look upon. I and many others have seen him, roaming alone, naked, and muttering to himself, when we have been in the forests seeking for jungle produce. All men know that it is He who by night harries us in our villages. If one ventures to go forth from our houses in the time of darkness, to the bathing raft at the river's edge, or to tend our sick, or to visit a friend, Si Pûdong is ever to be found watching, and thus the tale of his kills waxes longer and longer.'

'But men are safe from him while they sit within their houses?' asked Mat with evident anxiety.

'God alone knows,' answered Che' Sĕman piously, 'who can say where men are safe from Him of the Hairy Face? He cometh like a shadow, and slays like a prince, and then like a shadow he is gone! And the tale of his kills waxes ever longer and yet more long. May God send Him far from us! Ya Allah! It is He! Listen!'

At the word, a dead silence, broken only by the hard breathing of the men and women, fell upon all within the house. Then very faintly, and far away up stream, but not so faintly but that all could hear it, and shudder at the sound, the long-drawn, howling, snarling moan of a hungry tiger broke upon the stillness. The Malays call the roar of the tiger *äum*, and the word is vividly onomatopœtic, as those who have heard the sound in the jungle during the silent night watches can bear witness. All who have listened to the tiger in his forest freedom know that he has many voices wherewith to speak. He can give a barking cry, which is not unlike that of a deer; he can grunt like a startled boar, and squeak like the monkeys cowering at his approach in the branches overhead; he can shake the earth with a vibrating, resonant purr, like the sound of faint thunder in the foot-hills; he can mew and snarl like an angry wildcat; and he can roar like a lusty lion cub. But it is when he lifts up his voice in the long-drawn moan that the jungle chiefly fears him. This cry means that he is hungry, and, moreover, that he is so sure of his kill that he cares not if all the world knows that his belly is empty. It has something strangely horrible in its tone, for it speaks of that cold-blooded, dispassionate cruelty which is only to be found in perfection in the feline race. These sleek, smooth-skinned, soft-footed, lithe, almost serpentine animals, torture with a grace of movement, and a gentleness in strength which has something in it more violently repugnant to our natures than any sensation with which the thought of the blundering charge and savage goring of the buffalo, or the clumsy kneading with giant knee-caps, that the elephant metes out to its victims, can ever inspire in us. **652031**

Again the long-drawn moaning cry broke upon the stillness. The cattle in the byre heard it and were panic-stricken. Half mad with fear, they charged the walls of their pen, bearing all before them, and in a moment could be heard in the distance plunging madly through the brushwood, and splashing through the soft earth of the *pâdi* fields. The dogs whimpered and scampered off in every direction, while the fowls beneath the house set up a drowsy and discordant screeching. The folk within the house were too terror-stricken to speak, for fear, which gives voices to the animal world, renders voluble human beings dumb. And all this time the cry broke forth again and again, ever louder and louder, as He of the Hairy Face drew nearer and yet more near.

At last the cruel whining howl sounded within the very compound in which the house stood, and its sudden proximity caused Mat to start so violently that he overturned the pitch torch at his elbow, and extinguished the flickering light. The women crowded up against the men, seeking comfort by physical contact with them, their teeth chattering like castanets. The men gripped their spears, and squatted tremblingly in the half light thrown by the dying embers of the fire, and the flecks cast upon floor and wall by the faint moonbeams struggling through the interstices of the thatched roof.

'Fear nothing, Mînah,' Che' Sĕman whispered, in a hoarse, strange voice, to his little daughter, who nestled miserably against his breast, 'in a space He will be gone. Even He of the Hairy Face will do us no harm while we sit within the house.'

Che' Sĕman spoke from the experience of many generations of Malays, but he knew not the nature of the strange beast with whom he had to deal. Once more the moan-like howl broke out on the still night air, but this time the note had changed, and gradually it quickened to the ferocious snarling roar, the charge song, as the tiger rushed forward and leaped against the side of the house with a heavy jarring thud. A shriek from all the seven throats went up on the instant, and then came a scratching, tearing sound, followed by a soft, dull flop, as the tiger, failing to effect a landing on the low roof, fell back to earth. The men started to their feet, clutching their weapons convulsively, and, led by Che' Sĕman, they raised, above the shrieks of the frightened women, a lamentable attempt at a *sôrak,* the Malayan war-cry, which is designed as much to put heart into those who utter it, as to frighten the enemy in defiance of whom it is sounded.

Mat, the man who had upset the torch and plunged the house in darkness, alone failed to add his voice to the miserable cheer raised by his fellows. Wild with fear of the beast without, he crept, unobserved by the others, up into the *pâra,* or shelf-like upper apartment, on which Mînah had been wont to sit, when strangers were about, during the short days of her virginity. This place, as is usual in most Malay houses, hardly deserved to be dignified by being termed a room. It consisted of a platform suspended from the roof in one corner of the house, and among the dusty lumber with which it was covered Mat now cowered and sought to hide himself.

A minute or two of sickening suspense followed the tiger's first unsuccessful charge. But presently the howl broke forth again, quickened rapidly to the note of the charge song, and once more the house trembled under the weight of the great animal. This time the leap of Him of the Hairy Face had been of truer aim, and a crash overhead, a shower of leaflets of thatch, and an ominous creaking of the woodwork told the cowering people in the house that their enemy had landed on the roof.

The miserable thready cheer, which Che' Sĕman exhorted his fellows to raise in answer to the charge song of the tiger, died down in their throats. All looked upwards in deadly fascination as the thatch was torn violently apart by the great claws of their assailant. There were no firearms in the house, but the men instinctively grasped their spears, and held them ready to await the tiger's descent. Thus for a moment, as the quiet moonlight poured in through the gap in the thatch, they stood gazing at the great square face, marked with its black bars, at the flaming eyes, and the long cruel teeth framed in the hole which the claws of the beast had made. The timbers of the roof bent and cracked anew under the unwonted weight, and then, with the agility of a cat, He of the Hairy Face leaped lightly down, and was in among them before they knew. The striped hide was slightly wounded by the spears, but the shock of the brute's leap bore all who had resisted it to the floor. The tiger never stayed to use its jaws. It sat up, much in the attitude of a kitten which plays with something dangled before its eyes, and the soft pit-pat of its paws, as it struck out rapidly and with unerring aim, speedily disposed of all its enemies. Che' Sĕman, with his two sons, Âwang and Ngah, were the first to fall. Then Iang, Che' Sĕman's wife, fell backwards against the wall, with her skull crushed out of all resemblance to any human member, by the awful strength of one of those well-aimed buffets from the fearful claws. Kassim, Pôtek, and Äbdollah fell before the tiger in quick succession, and Mînah, the girl who had nestled against her father for protection, lay now under his dead body, sorely wounded, wild with terror, but still alive and conscious. Mat, cowering on the shelf overhead, breathless with fear, and gazing fascinated at the carnage going on within a few feet of him, was the only inmate of the house who remained uninjured.

He of the Hairy Face killed quickly and silently, while there were yet some alive to resist him. Then, purring gently, he drank a deep draught of blood from each of his slaughtered victims. At last he reached Che' Sĕman, and Mînah, seeing him approach, made a feeble effort to evade him. Then began a fearful scene, the tiger playing with, and torturing the girl, just as we all have seen a cat do with a maimed mouse. Again and again Mînah crawled feebly away from her tormentor, only to be drawn back again just when escape seemed possible. Again and again she lay still in the utter inertia of exhaustion, only to be quickened into agonised movement once more by the touch of the tiger's cruel claws. Yet so cunningly did he play with her, that, as Mat described it, a time as long as it would take to cook rice had elapsed, before the girl was finally put out of her misery.

Even then He of the Hairy Face did not quit the scene of slaughter. Mat, as he lay trembling in the shelf overhead, watched the tiger, through the long hours of that fearful night, play with the mangled bodies of each of his victims in turn. He leaped from one to the other, inflicting a fresh blow with teeth or claws on their torn flesh, with all the airy, light-hearted agility and sinuous grace of a kitten playing with its shadow in the sun. Then when the dawn was breaking, the tiger tore down the door, leaped lightly to the ground, and betook himself to the jungle.

When the sun was up, an armed party of neighbours came to the house to see if ought could be done. But they found the place a shambles, the bodies hardly to be recognised, the floor-laths dripping blood, and Mat lying face downward on the shelf, with his reason tottering in the balance. The bodies, though they had been horribly mutilated, had not been eaten, the tiger having contented himself with drinking the blood of his victims, and playing his ghastly game with them till the dawn broke.

This is, I believe, the only recorded instance in the Peninsula of a tiger having dared to attack men within their closed houses; and the circumstances are so remarkable in every way, that I, for one, cannot find it in me to greatly blame the Malays for attributing the fearlessness of mankind, and the lust for blood displayed by Him of the Hairy Face, to the fact that he owed his existence to magic agencies, and was in reality no mere wild beast, but a member of the race upon which he so cruelly preyed.

Theodore Roosevelt

LION HUNTING ON THE KAPITI PLAINS

EVERYWHERE THROUGHOUT the country we were crossing were signs that the lion was lord and that his reign was cruel. There were many lions, for the game on which they feed was extraordinarily abundant. They occasionally took the ostriches or stock of the settlers, or ravaged the herds and flocks of the natives, but not often; for their favorite food was yielded by the swarming herds of kongoni and zebras, on which they could prey at will. Later we found that in this region they rarely molested the buffalo, even where they lived in the same reedbeds; and this though elsewhere they habitually prey on the buffalo. But where zebras and hartebeests could be obtained without effort, it was evidently not worth their while to challenge such formidable quarry. Every "kill" I saw was a kongoni or a zebra; probably I came across fifty of each. One zebra kill, which was not more than eighteen hours old (after the lapse of that time the vultures and marabouts, not to speak of the hyenas and jackals, leave only the bare bones), showed just what had occurred. The bones were all in place, and the skin still on the lower legs and head. The animal was lying on its belly, the legs spread out, the neck vertebra crushed; evidently the lion had sprung clean on it, bearing it down by his weight while he bit through the back of the neck, and the zebra's legs had spread out as the body yielded under the lion. One fresh kongoni kill showed no marks on the haunches, but a broken neck and claw marks on the face and withers; in this case the lion's hind legs had remained on the ground, while with his fore paws he grasped the kongoni's head and shoulders, holding it until the teeth splintered the neck bone.

One or two of our efforts to get lions failed, of course; the ravines we beat did not contain them, or we failed to make them leave some particularly difficult hill or swamp—for lions lie close. But Sir Alfred knew just the right place to go to, and was bound to get us lions—and he did.

One day we started from the ranch house in good season for an all-day lion hunt. Besides Kermit and myself, there was a fellow-guest, Medlicott, and not only our host, but our hostess and her daughter; and we were joined by Percival at lunch, which we took under a great fig-tree, at the foot of a high, rocky hill. Percival had with him a little mongrel bull-dog, and a Masai "boy," a fine, bold-looking savage, with a handsome head-dress and the usual formidable spear; master, man, and dog evidently all looked upon any form of encounter with lions simply in the light of a spree.

After lunch we began to beat down a long donga, or dry watercourse—a creek, as we should call it in the Western plains country. The watercourse, with low, steep banks, wound in curves, and here and there were patches of brush, which might contain anything in the shape of lion, cheetah, hyena, or wild dog. Soon we came upon lion spoor in the sandy bed; first the footprints of a big male, then those of a lioness. We walked cautiously along each side of the donga, the horses following close behind so that if the lion were missed we could gallop after him and round him up on the plain. The dogs—for besides the little bull, we had a large brindled mongrel named Ben, whose courage belied his looks—began to show signs of scenting the lion; and we beat out each patch of brush, the natives shouting and throwing in stones, while we stood with the rifles where we could best command any probable exit. After a couple of false alarms the dogs drew toward one patch, their hair bristling, and showing such eager excitement that it was evident something big was inside; and in a moment one of the boys called, "simba" (lion), and pointed with his finger. It was just across the little ravine, there about four yards wide and as many feet deep; and I shifted my position, peering eagerly into the bushes for some moments before I caught a glimpse of tawny hide; as it moved, there was a call to me to "shoot," for at that distance, if the lion charged, there would be scant time to stop it; and I fired into what I saw. There was a commotion in the bushes, and Kermit fired; and immediately afterward there broke out on the other side, not the hoped-for big lion, but two cubs the size of mastiffs. Each was badly wounded and we finished them off; even if unwounded, they were too big to take alive.

This was a great disappointment, and as it was well on in the afternoon, and we had beaten the country most apt to harbor our game, it seemed unlikely that we would have another chance. Percival was on foot and a long way from his house, so he started for it; and the rest of us also began to jog homeward. But Sir Alfred, although he said nothing, intended to have another try. After going a mile or two he started off to the left at a brisk canter; and we, the other riders, followed, leaving behind our gun-bearers, saises, and porters. A couple of miles away was another donga, another shallow watercourse with occasional big brush patches along the winding bed; and toward this we cantered. Almost as soon as we reached it our leader found the spoor of two big lions; and with every sense acock, we dismounted and approached the first patch of tall bushes. We shouted and threw in stones, but nothing came out; and another small patch showed the same result. Then we mounted our horses again, and rode toward another patch a quarter of a mile off. I was mounted on Tranquillity, the stout and quiet sorrel.

This patch of tall, thick brush stood on the hither bank— that is, on our side of the watercourse. We rode up to it and shouted loudly. The response was immediate, in the shape of loud gruntings, and crashings through the thick brush. We were off our horses in an instant, I throwing the reins over the head of mine; and without delay the good old fellow began placidly grazing, quite unmoved by the ominous sounds immediately in front.

I sprang to one side; and for a second or two we waited, uncertain whether we should see the lions charging out ten yards distant or running away. Fortunately, they adopted the latter course. Right in front of me, thirty yards off, there appeared, from behind the bushes which had first screened him from my eyes, the tawny, galloping form of a big maneless lion. Crack! the Winchester spoke; and as the soft-nosed bullet ploughed forward through his flank the lion swerved so that I missed him with the second shot; but my third bullet went through the spine and forward into his chest. Down he came, sixty yards off, his hind quarters dragging, his head up, his ears back, his jaws open and lips drawn up in a prodigious snarl, as he endeavored to turn to face us. His back was broken; but of this we could not at the moment be sure, and if it had merely been grazed, he might have recovered, and then, even though dying, his charge might have done mischief. So Kermit, Sir Alfred, and I fired, almost together, into his chest. His head sank, and he died.

This lion had come out on the left of the bushes; the other, to the right of them, had not been hit, and we saw him galloping off across the plain, six or eight hundred yards away. A couple more shots missed, and we mounted our horses to try to ride him down. The plain sloped gently upward for three-quarters of a mile to a low crest or divide, and long before we got near him he disappeared over this. Sir Alfred and Kermit were tearing along in front and to the right, with Miss Pease close behind; while Tranquillity carried me, as fast as he could, on the left, with Medlicott near me. On topping the divide Sir Alfred and Kermit missed the lion, which had swung to the left, and they raced ahead too far to the right. Medlicott and I, however, saw the lion, loping along close behind some kongoni; and this enabled me to get up to him as quickly as the lighter men on the faster horses. The going was now slightly downhill, and the sorrel took me along very well, while Medlicott, whose horse was slow, bore to the right and joined the other two men. We gained rapidly, and, finding out this, the lion suddenly halted and came to bay in a slight hollow, where the grass was rather long. The plain seemed flat, and we could see the lion well from horseback; but, especially when he lay down, it was most difficult to make him out on foot, and impossible to do so when kneeling.

We were about a hundred and fifty yards from the lion, Sir Alfred, Kermit, Medlicott, and Miss Pease off to one side, and slightly above him on the slope, while I was on the level, about equidistant from him and them. Kermit and I tried shooting from the horses; but at such a distance this was not effective. Then Kermit got off, but his horse would not let him shoot; and when I got off I could not make out the animal through the grass with sufficient distinctness to enable me to take aim. Old Ben the dog had arrived, and, barking loudly, was strolling about near the lion, which paid him not the slightest attention. At this moment my black sais, Simba, came running up to me and took hold of the bridle; he had seen the chase from the line of march and had cut across to join me. There was no other sais or gun-bearer anywhere near, and his action was plucky, for he was the only man afoot, with the lion at bay. Lady Pease had also ridden up and was an interested spectator only some fifty yards behind me.

Now, an elderly man with a varied past which includes rheumatism does not vault lightly into the saddle; as his sons, for instance, can; and I had already made up my mind that in the event of the lion's charging it would be wise for me to trust to straight powder rather than to try to scramble into the saddle and get under way in time. The arrival of my two companions settled matters. I was not sure of the speed of Lady Pease's horse; and Simba was on foot and it was of course out of the question for me to leave him. So I said, "Good, Simba, now we'll see this thing through," and gentle-mannered Simba smiled a shy appreciation of my tone, though he could not understand the words. I was still unable to see the lion when I knelt, but he was now standing up, looking first at one group of horses and then at the other, his tail lashing to and fro, his head held low, and his lips dropped over his mouth in peculiar fashion, while his harsh and savage growling rolled thunderously over the plain. Seeing Simba and me on foot, he turned toward us, his tail lashing quicker and quicker. Resting my elbow on Simba's bent shoulder, I took steady aim and pressed the trigger; the bullet went in between the neck and shoulder, and the lion fell over on his side, one foreleg in the air. He recovered in a moment and stood up, evidently very sick, and once more faced me, growling hoarsely. I think he was on the eve of charging. I fired again at once, and this bullet broke his back just behind the shoulders; and with the next I killed him outright, after we had gathered round him.

These were two good-sized maneless lions; and very proud of them I was. I think Sir Alfred was at least as proud, especially because we had performed the feat alone, without any professional hunters being present. "We were all amateurs, only gentleman riders up," said Sir Alfred. It was late before we got the lions skinned. Then we set off toward the ranch, two porters carrying each lion skin, strapped to a pole; and two others carrying the cub skins. Night fell long before we were near the ranch; but the brilliant tropic moon lighted the trail. The stalwart savages who carried the bloody lion skins swung along at a faster walk as the sun went down and the moon rose higher; and they began to chant in unison, one uttering a single word or sentence, and the others joining in a deep-toned, musical chorus. The men on a safari, and indeed African natives generally, are always excited over the death of a lion, and the hunting tribes then chant their rough hunting songs, or victory songs, until the monotonous, rhythmical repetitions make them grow almost frenzied. The ride home through the moonlight, the vast barren landscape shining like silver on either hand, was one to be remembered; and above all, the sight of our trophies and of their wild bearers.

Three days later we had another successful lion hunt. Our camp was pitched at a waterhole in a little stream called Potha, by a hill of the same name. Pease, Medlicott, and both the Hills were with us, and Heller came too; for he liked, when possible, to be with the hunters so that he could at once care for any beast that was shot. As the safari was stationary, we took fifty or sixty porters as beaters. It was thirteen hours before we got into camp that evening. The Hills had with them as beaters and water-carriers half a dozen of the Wakamba who were working on their farm. It was interesting to watch these naked savages, with their filed teeth, their heads shaved in curious patterns, and carrying for arms little bows and arrows.

Before lunch we beat a long, low hill. Harold Hill was with me; Medlicott and Kermit were together. We placed ourselves, one couple on each side of a narrow neck, two-thirds of the way along the crest of the hill; and soon after we were in position we heard the distant shouts of the beaters as they came toward us, covering the crest and the tops of the slopes on both sides. It was rather disconcerting to find how much better Hill's eyes were than mine. He saw everything first, and it usually took some time before he could make me see it. In this first drive nothing came my way except some mountain reedbuck does, at which I did not shoot. But a fine male cheetah came to Kermit, and he bowled it over in good style as it ran.

Then the beaters halted, and waited before resuming their march until the guns had gone clear round and established themselves at the base of the farther end of the hill. This time Kermit, who was a couple of hundred yards from me, killed a reedbuck and a steinbuck. Suddenly Hill said, "Lion," and endeavored to point it out to me, as it crept cautiously among the rocks on the steep hill-side, a hundred and fifty yards away. At first I could not see it; finally I thought I did and fired, but, as it proved, at a place just above him. However, it made him start up, and I immediately put the next bullet behind his shoulders; it was a fatal shot; but, growling, he struggled down the hill, and I fired again and killed him. It was not much of a trophy, however, turning out to be a half-grown male.

We lunched under a tree, and then arranged for another beat. There was a long, wide valley, or rather a slight depression in the ground—for it was only three or four feet below the general level—in which the grass grew tall, as the soil was quite wet. It was the scene of Percival's adventure with the lion that chased him. Hill and I stationed ourselves on one side of this valley or depression, toward the upper end; Pease took Kermit to the opposite side; and we waited. our horses some distance behind us. The beaters were put in at the lower end, formed a line across the valley, and beat slowly toward us, making a great noise.

They were still some distance away when Hill saw three lions, which had slunk stealthily off ahead of them through the grass. I have called the grass tall, but this was only by comparison with the short grass of the dry plains. In the depression or valley it was some three feet high. In such grass a lion, which is marvellously adept at hiding, can easily conceal itself, not merely when lying down, but when advancing at a crouching gait. If it stands erect, however, it can be seen.

There were two lions near us, one directly in our front, a hundred and ten yards off. Some seconds passed before Hill could make me realize that the dim yellow smear in the yellow-brown grass was a lion; and then I found such difficulty in getting a bead on him that I overshot. However, the bullet must have passed very close—indeed, I think it just grazed him—for he jumped up and faced us, growling savagely. Then, his head lowered, he threw his tail straight into the air and began to charge. The first few steps he took at a trot, and before he could start into a gallop I put the soft-nosed Winchester bullet in between the neck and shoulder. Down he went with a roar; the wound was fatal, but I was taking no chances, and I put two more bullets in him. Then we walked toward where Hill had already seen another lion—the lioness, as it proved. Again he had some difficulty in making me see her; but he succeeded and I walked toward her through the long grass, repressing the zeal of my two gun-bearers, who were stanch, but who showed a tendency to walk a little ahead of me on each side, instead of a little behind. I walked toward her because I could not kneel to shoot in grass so tall; and when shooting off-hand I like to be fairly close, so as to be sure that my bullets go in the right place. At sixty yards I could make her out clearly, snarling at me as she faced me; and I shot her full in the chest. She at once performed a series of extraordinary antics, tumbling about on her head, just as if she were throwing somersaults, first to one side and then to the other. I fired again, but managed to shoot between the somersaults, so to speak, and missed her. The shot seemed to bring her to herself, and away she tore; but instead of charging us she charged the line of beaters. She was dying fast, however, and in her weakness failed to catch anyone; and she sank down into the long grass. Hill and I advanced to look her up, our rifles at full cock, and the gun-bearers close behind. It is ticklish work to follow a wounded lion in tall grass, and we walked carefully, every sense on the alert. We passed Heller, who had been with the beaters. He spoke to us with an amused smile. His only weapon was a pair of field-glasses, but he always took things as they came, with entire coolness, and to be close to a wounded lioness when she charged merely interested him. A beater came running up and pointed toward where he had seen her, and we walked toward the place. At thirty yards distance Hill pointed, and, eagerly peering, I made out the form of the lioness showing indistinctly through the grass. She was half crouching, half sitting, her head bent down; but she still had strength to do mischief. She saw us, but before she could turn I sent a bullet through her shoulders; down she went, and was dead when we walked up. A cub had been seen, and another full-grown lion, but they had slunk off and we got neither.

This was a full-grown, but young, lioness of average size; her cubs must have been several months old. We took her entire to camp to weigh; she weighed two hundred and eighty-three pounds. The first lion, which we had difficulty in finding, as there were no identifying marks in the plain of tall grass, was a good-sized male, weighing about four hundred pounds, but not yet full-grown; although he was probably the father of the cubs.

We were a long way from camp, and, after beating in vain for the other lion, we started back; it was after nightfall before we saw the camp-fires. It was two hours later before the porters appeared, bearing on poles the skin of the dead lion, and the lioness entire. The moon was nearly full, and it was interesting to see them come swinging down the trail in the bright silver light, chanting in deep tones, over and over again, a line or phrase that sounded like:

"Zou-zou-boulé ma ja guntai; zou-zou-boulé ma ja guntai."

Occasionally they would interrupt it by the repetition in unison, at short intervals, of a guttural ejaculation, sounding like "huzlem." They marched into camp, then up and down the lines, before the rows of small fires; then, accompanied by all the rest of the porters, they paraded up to the big fire where I was standing. Here they stopped and ended the ceremony by a minute or two's vigorous dancing amid singing and wild shouting. The firelight gleamed and flickered across the grim dead beasts, and the shining eyes and black features of the excited savages; while all around the moon flooded the landscape with her white light.

George Sterling

PUMAS

Hushed, cruel, amber-eyed,
Before the time of the danger of the day,
Or at dusk on the boulder-broken mountainside,
    The great cats seek their prey.

Soft-padded, heavy-limbed,
With agate talons chiselled for love or hate,
In desolate places wooded or granite-rimmed,
    The great cats seek their mate.

Rippling, as water swerved,
To tangled coverts overshadowed and deep
Or secret caves where the canyon's wall is curved,
    The great cats go for sleep.

Seeking the mate or prey,
Out of the darkness glow the insatiate eyes.
Man, who is made more terrible far than they,
    Dreams he is otherwise!

Charles G. D. Roberts

THE KING OF THE FLAMING HOOPS

"KING'S KIND OF ugly to-night, seems to me; better keep yer eyes peeled!" said Andy Hansen, the assistant trainer, the big, yellow-haired Swede who knew not fear. Neither did he know impatience or irritability; and so all the animals, as a rule, were on their good behavior under his calm, masterful, blue eye. Yet he was tactful with the beasts, and given to humoring their moods as far as convenient without ever letting them guess it.

"Oh, you go chase yourself, Andy!" replied Signor Tomaso, the trainer, with a strong New England accent. "If I got to look out for King, I'd better quit the business. Don't you go trying to make trouble between friends, Andy."

"Of course, Bill, I know he'd never try to maul *you*," explained Hansen seriously, determined that he should not be misunderstood in the smallest particular. "But he's acting curious. Look out he don't get into a scrap with some of the other animals."

"I reckon I kin keep 'em all straight," answered the trainer dryly, as he turned away to get ready for the great performance which the audience, dimly heard beyond the canvas walls, was breathlessly awaiting.

The trainer's name was William Sparks, and his birthplace Big Chebeague, Maine; but his lean, swarthy face and piercing, green-brown eyes, combined with the craving of his audiences for a touch of the romantic, had led him to adopt the more sonorous pseudonym of "Signor Tomaso." He maintained that if he went under his own name, nobody would ever believe that what he did could be anything wonderful. Except for this

50

glared with green, narrowed eyes at the nearest spectators, as if trying to stare them out of countenance. After the wolf came a beautiful Bengal tiger, its black-and-golden stripes shining as if they had been oiled. He glided straight to his stand, sniffed at it superciliously, and then lay down before it. The whip snapped sharply three times, but the tiger only shut his eyes tight. The audience grew hushed. Tomaso ran forward, seized the beast by the back of the neck, and shook him roughly. Whereupon the tiger half rose, opened his great red mouth like a cavern, and roared in his master's face. The audience thrilled from corner to corner, and a few cries came from frightened women.

The trainer paused for an instant, to give full effect to the situation. Then, stooping suddenly, he lifted the tiger's hind-quarters and deposited them firmly on the pedestal, and left him in that awkward position.

"There," he said in a loud voice, "that's all the help you'll get from me!"

The audience roared with instant and delighted appreciation. The tiger gathered up the rest of himself upon his pedestal, wiped his face with his paw, like a cat, and settled down complacently with a pleased assurance that he had done the trick well.

At this moment the attention of the audience was drawn to the entrance, where there seemed to be some hitch. Tomaso snapped his whip sharply, and shouted savage orders, but nothing came forth. Then the big Swede, with an agitated air, snatched up the trainer's pitchfork, which stood close at hand in case of emergency, made swift passes at the empty doorway, and jumped back. The audience was lifted fairly to its feet with excitement. What monster could it be that was giving so much trouble? The next moment, while Tomaso's whip hissed in vicious circles over his head, a plump little drab-colored pug dog marched slowly out upon the stage, its head held arrogantly aloft. Volleys of laughter crackled around the arena, and the delighted spectators settled, tittering, back into their seats.

The pug glanced searchingly around the cage, then sele

trifling matter of the name, there was no fake about Signor Tomaso. He was a brilliant animal-trainer, as unacquainted with fear as the Swede, as dominant of eye, and of immeasurably greater experience. But being, at the same time, more emotional, more temperamental than his phlegmatic assistant, his control was sometimes less steady, and now and again he would have to assert his authority with violence. He was keenly alive to the varying personalities of his beasts, naturally, and hence had favorites among them. His especial favorite, who heartily reciprocated the attachment, was the great puma, King, the most intelligent and amiable of all the wild animals that had ever come under his training whip.

As Hansen's success with the animals, during the few months of his experience as assistant, had been altogether phenomenal, his chief felt a qualm of pique upon being warned against the big puma. He had too just an appreciation of Hansen's judgment, however, to quite disregard the warning, and he turned it over curiously in his mind as he went to his dressing-room. Emerging a few minutes later in the black-and-white of faultless evening dress, without a speck on his varnished shoes, he moved down along the front of the cages, addressing to the occupant of each, as he passed, a sharp, authoritative word which brought it to attention.

With the strange, savage smell of the cages in his nostrils, that bitter, acrid pungency to which his senses never grew blunted, a new spirit of understanding was wont to enter Tomaso's brain. He would feel a sudden kinship with the wild creatures, such a direct and instant comprehension as almost justified his fancy that in some previous existence he had himself been a wild man of the jungle and spoken in their tongue. As he looked keenly into each cage, he knew that the animal whose eyes for that moment met his was in untroubled mood. This, till he came to the cage containing the latest addition to his troupe, a large cinnamon bear, which was rocking restlessly to and fro and grumbling to itself. The bear was one which had been long in captivity and well trained. Tomaso had found him docile, and clever enough to be admitted at once to the performing troupe. But to-night the beast's eyes were red with some ill-humor. Twice the trainer spoke to him before he heeded; but then he assumed instantly an air of mildest subservience. The expression of a new-weaned puppy is not more innocently mild than the look which a bear can assume when it so desires.

"Ah, ha! old sport! So it's you that's got a grouch on to-night; I'll keep an eye on you!" he muttered to himself. He snapped his heavy whip once, and the bear obediently sat up on its haunches, its great paws hanging meekly. Tomaso looked it sharply in the eye. "Don't forget, now, and get funny!" he admonished. Then he returned to the first cage, which contained the puma, and went up close to the bars. The great cat came and rubbed against him, purring harshly.

"There ain't nothing the matter with *you*, boy, I reckon," said Tomaso, scratching him affectionately behind the ears. "Andy must have wheels in his head if he thinks I've got to keep my eyes peeled on *your* account."

Out beyond the iron-grilled passage, beyond the lighted canvas walls, the sharp, metallic noises of the workmen setting up the great performing-cage came to a stop. There was a burst of music from the orchestra. That, too, ceased. The restless hum of the unseen masses around the arena died away into an expectant hush. It was time to go on. At the farther end of the passage, by the closed door leading to the performing cage, Hansen appeared. Tomaso opened the puma's cage. King dropped out with a soft thud of his great paws, and padded swiftly down the passage, his master following. Hansen slid wide the door, admitting a glare of light, a vast, intense rustle of excitement; and King marched majestically out into it, eying calmly the tier on climbing tier of eager faces. It was his customary privilege, this, to make the entrance alone, a good half minute ahead of the rest of the troupe; and he seemed to value it. Halfway around the big cage he walked, then mounted his pedestal, sat up very straight, and stared blandly at the audience. A salvo of clapping ran smartly round the tiers—King's usual tribute, which he had so learned to expect that any

failure of it would have dispirited him for the whole performance.

Signor Tomaso had taken his stand, whip in hand, just inside the cage, with Hansen opposite him, to see that the animals, on entry, went each straight to his own bench or pedestal. Any mistake in this connection was sure to lead to trouble, each beast being almost childishly jealous of its rights. Inside the long passage an attendant was opening one cage after another; and in a second more the animals began to appear in procession, filing out between the immaculate Signor and the roughly clad Swede. First came a majestic white Angora goat, carrying high his horned and bearded head, and stepping most daintily upon slim, black hoofs. Close behind, and looking just ready to pounce upon him but for dread of the Signor's eye, came slinking stealthily a spotted black-and-yellow leopard, ears back and tail twitching. He seemed ripe for mischief, as he climbed reluctantly on to his pedestal beside the goat; but he knew better than to even bare a claw. And as for the white goat, with his big golden eyes superciliously half closed, he ignored his dangerous neighbor completely, while his jaws chewed nonchalantly on a bit of brown shoe-lace which he had picked up in the passage.

Close behind the leopard came a bored-looking lion, who marched with listless dignity straight to his place. Then another lion, who paused in the doorway and looked out doubtfully, blinking with distaste at the strong light. Tomaso spoke sharply, like the snap of his whip, whereupon the lion ran forward in haste. But he seemed to have forgotten which was his proper pedestal, for he hopped upon the three nearest in turn, only to hop down again with apologetic alacrity at the order of the cracking whip. At last, obviously flustered, he reached a pedestal on which he was allowed to remain. Here he sat, blinking from side to side and apparently much mortified.

The lion was followed by a running wolf, who had shown his teeth savagely when the lion, for a moment, trespassed upon his pedestal. This beast was intensely interested in the audience, and, as soon as he was in his place, turned his head and

the biggest of the lions as a worthy antagonist, flew at his pedestal, barking furious challenge. The lion glanced down at him, looked bored at the noise, and yawned. Apparently disappointed, the pug turned away and sought another adversary. He saw King's big tail hanging down beside his pedestal. Flinging himself upon it, he began to worry it as if it were a rat. The next moment the tail threshed vigorously, and the pug went rolling end over end across the stage.

Picking himself up and shaking the sawdust from his coat, the pug growled savagely and curled his little tail into a tighter screw. Bristling with wrath, he tiptoed menacingly back toward the puma's pedestal, determined to wipe out the indignity. This time his challenge was accepted. Tomaso's whip snapped, but the audience was too intent to hear it. The great puma slipped down from his pedestal, ran forward a few steps, and crouched.

With a shrill snarl the pug rushed in. At the same instant the puma sprang, making a splendid tawny curve through the air, and alighted ten feet behind his antagonist's tail. There he wheeled like lightning and crouched. But the pug, enraged at being balked of his vengeance, had also wheeled, and charged again in the same half second. In the next, he had the puma by the throat. With a dreadful screech the great beast rolled over on his side and stiffened out his legs. The pug drew off, eyed him critically to make sure that he was quite dead, then ran, barking shrill triumph, to take possession of the victim's place. Then the whip cracked once more. Whereupon the puma got up, trotted back to his pedestal, mounted it, and tucked the pug protectingly away between his great forepaws.

The applause had not quite died away when a towering, sandy-brown bulk appeared in the entrance to the cage. Erect upon its hind legs, and with a musket on its shoulder, it marched ponderously and slowly around the circle, eying each of the sitting beasts—except the wolf—suspiciously as it passed. The watchful eyes of both Signor Tomaso and Hansen noted that it gave wider berth to the puma than to any of the others, and also that the puma's ears, at the moment, were ominously flattened. Instantly the long whip snapped its terse admonition to good manners. Nothing happened, except that the pug, from between the puma's legs, barked insolently. The sandy-brown bulk reached its allotted pedestal,—which was quite absurdly too small for it to mount,—dropped the musket with a clatter, fell upon all fours with a loud *whoof* of relief, and relapsed into a bear.

The stage now set to his satisfaction, Signor Tomaso advanced to the centre of it. He snapped his whip, and uttered a sharp cry which the audience doubtless took for purest Italian. Immediately the animals all descended from their pedestals, and circled solemnly around him in a series of more or less intricate evolutions, all except the bear, who, not having yet been initiated into this beast quadrille, kept his place and looked scornful. At another signal the evolutions ceased, and all the beasts, except one of the lions, hurried back to their places. The lion, with the bashful air of a boy who gets up to "speak his piece" at a school examination, lingered in the middle of the stage. A rope was brought. The Swede took one end of it, the attendant who had brought it took the other, and between them they began to swing it, very slowly, as a great skipping-rope. At an energetic command from Signor Tomaso the lion slipped into the swinging circle, and began to skip in a ponderous and shamefaced fashion. The house thundered applause. For perhaps half a minute the strange performance continued, the whip snapping rhythmically with every descent of the rope. Then all at once, as if he simply could not endure it for another second, the lion bolted, head down, clambered upon his pedestal, and shut his eyes hard as if expecting a whipping. But as nothing happened except a roar of laughter from the seats, he opened them again and glanced from side to side complacently, as if to say, "Didn't I get out of that neatly?"

The next act was a feat of teetering. A broad and massive teeter-board was brought in, and balanced across a support about two feet high. The sulky leopard, at a sign from Tomaso, slouched up to it, pulled one end to the ground, and mounted. At the centre he balanced cautiously for a moment till it tipped, then crept on to the other end, and crouched there, holding it down as if his very life depended on it. Immediately the white goat dropped from his pedestal, minced daintily over, skipped up upon the centre of the board, and mounted to the elevated end. His weight was not sufficient to lift, or even to disturb, the leopard, who kept the other end anchored securely. But the goat seemed to like his high and conspicuous position, for he maintained it with composure and stared around with great condescension upon the other beasts.

The goat having been given time to demonstrate his unfitness for the task he had undertaken, Tomaso's whip cracked again. Instantly King descended from his pedestal, ran over to the teeter-board, and mounted it at the centre. The goat, unwilling to be dispossessed of his high place, stamped and butted at him indignantly, but with one scornful sweep of his great paw the puma brushed him off to the sawdust, and took his place at the end of the board. Snarling and clutching at the cleats, the leopard was hoisted into the air, heavily outweighed. The crowd applauded; but the performance, obviously, was not yet perfect. Now came the white goat's opportunity. He hesitated a moment, till he heard a word from Tomaso. Then he sprang once more upon the centre of the board, faced King, and backed up inch by inch towards the leopard till the latter began to descend. At this point of balance the white goat had one forefoot just on the pivot of the board. With a dainty, dancing motion, and a proud tossing of his head, he now threw his weight slowly backward and forward. The great teeter worked to perfection. Signor Tomaso was kept bowing to round after round of applause while the leopard, the goat, and King returned proudly to their places.

After this, four of the red-and-yellow uniformed attendants ran in, each carrying a large hoop. They stationed themselves at equal distances around the circumference of the cage, holding the hoops out before them at a height of about four feet from the ground. At the command of Tomaso, the animals all formed in procession—though not without much cracking of the other through the hoops—all except the pug, who tried in the whip and vehement command—and went leaping one after vain to jump so high, and the bear, who, not knowing how to jump at all, simply marched around and pretended not to see that the hoops were there. Then four other hoops, covered with white paper, were brought in, and head first through them the puma led the way. When it came to the bear's turn, the whip cracked a special signal. Whereupon, instead of ignoring the hoop as he had done before, he stuck his head through it and marched off with it hanging on his neck. All four hoops he gathered up in this way, and, retiring with them to his place, stood shuffling restlessly and grunting with impatience until he was relieved of the awkward burden.

A moment later four more hoops were handed to the attendants. They looked like the first lot; but the attendants took them with hooked handles of iron and held them out at arm's length. Touched with a match, they burst instantly into leaping yellow flames; whereupon all the beasts, except King, stirred uneasily on their pedestals. The whip snapped with emphasis; and all the beasts—except King, who sat eying the flames tranquilly, and the bear, who whined his disapproval, but knew that he was not expected to take part in this act—formed again in procession, and ran at the flaming hoops as if to jump through them as before. But each, on arriving at a hoop, crouched flat and scurried under it like a frightened cat—except the white goat, which pranced aside and capered past derisively. Pretending to be much disappointed in them, Signor Tomaso ordered them all back to their places, and, folding his arms, stood with his head lowered as if wondering what to do about it. Upon this, King descended proudly from his pedestal and approached the blazing terrors. With easiest grace and nonchalance he lifted his lithe body, and went bounding lightly through the hoops, one after the other. The audience stormed its applause. Twice around this terrifying circuit he went, as indifferent to the writhing flames as if they had been so much grass waving in the wind. Then he stopped abruptly, turned his head, and looked at Tomaso in expectation. The latter came up, fondled his ears, and assured him that he had done wonders. Then King returned to his place, elation bristling in his whiskers.

While the flaming hoops were being rushed from the ring and the audience was settling down again to the quiet of un-limited expectation, a particularly elaborate act was being pre-pared. A massive wooden stand, with shelves and seats at vari-ous heights, was brought in. Signor Tomaso, coiling the lash of his whip and holding the heavy handle, with its loaded butt, as a sceptre, took his place on a somewhat raised seat at the centre of the frame. Hansen, with his pitchfork in one hand and a whip like Tomaso's in the other, drew nearer; and the audience, with a thrill, realized that something more than ordi-narily dangerous was on the cards. The tiger came and stretched itself at full length before Tomaso, who at once appropriated him as a footstool. The bear and the biggest of the lions posted themselves on either side of their master, rearing up like the armorial supporters of some illustrious escutcheon, and resting their mighty forepaws apparently on their master's shoulders, though in reality on two narrow little shelves placed there for the purpose. Another lion came and laid his huge head on Tomaso's knees, as if doing obeisance. By this time all the other animals were prowling about the stand, peering this way and that, as if trying to remember their places; and the big Swede was cracking his whip briskly, with curt, deep-toned commands, to sharpen up their memories. Only King seemed quite clear as to what he had to do—which was to lay his tawny body along the shelf immediately over the heads of the lion and the bear; but as he mounted the stand from the rear, his ears went back and he showed a curious reluctance to fulfil his part. Hansen's keen eyes noted this at once, and his whip snapped emphatically in the air just above the great puma's nose. Still King hesitated. The lion paid no attention whatever, but the bear glanced up with reddening eyes and a surly wagging of his head. It was all a slight matter, too slight to catch the eye or the uncompre-hending thoughts of the audience. But a grave, well-dressed man, with copper-colored face, high cheek-bones and straight, coal-black hair, who sat close to the front, turned to a companion and said:—

"Those men are good trainers, but they don't know everything about pumas. *We* know that there is a hereditary feud between the pumas and the bears, and that when they come together there's apt to be trouble."

The speaker was a full-blooded Sioux, and a graduate of one of the big Eastern universities. He leaned forward with a curious fire in his deep-set, piercing eyes, as King, unwillingly obeying the mandates of the whip, dropped down and stretched out upon his shelf, his nervous forepaws not more than a foot above the bear's head. His nostrils were twitching as if they smelled something unutterably distasteful, and his thick tail looked twice its usual size. The Sioux, who, alone of all present, understood these signs, laid an involuntary hand of warning upon his companion's knee.

Just what positions the other animals were about to take will never be known. King's sinews tightened. "Ha-ow!" grunted the Sioux, reverting in his excitement to his ancient utterance. There was a lightning sweep of King's paw, a shout from Hansen, a *wah* of surprise and pain from the bear. King leaped back to the top of the stand to avoid the expected counter-stroke. But not against him did the bear's rage turn. The maddened beast seemed to conclude that his master had betrayed him. With a roar he struck at Tomaso with the full force of his terrible forearm. Tomaso was in the very act of leaping forward from his seat, when the blow caught him full on the shoulder, shattering the bones, ripping the whole side out of his coat, and hurling him senseless to the floor.

The change in the scene was instantaneous and appalling. Most of the animals, startled, and dreading immediate punishment, darted for their pedestals,—*any* pedestals that they found within reach,—and fought savagely for the possession of the first they came to. The bear fell furiously upon the body of Tomaso. Cries and shrieks arose from the spectators. Hansen rushed to the rescue, his fork clutched in both hands. Attendants, armed with forks or iron bars, seemed to spring up from nowhere.

But before any one could reach the spot, an appalling screech tore across the uproar, and King's yellow body, launched from the top of the stand, fell like a thunderbolt upon the bear's back.

The shock rolled the bear clean over. While he was clawing about wildly, in the effort to grapple with his assailant, Hansen dragged aside the still unconscious Tomaso, and two attendants carried him hurriedly from the stage.

Audience and stage alike were now in a sort of frenzy. Animals were fighting here and there in tangled groups; but for the moment all eyes were riveted on the deadly struggle which occupied the centre of the stage.

For all that he had less than a quarter the weight and nothing like a quarter the bulk of his gigantic adversary, the puma, through the advantage of his attack, was having much the best of the fight. Hansen had no time for sentiment, no time to concern himself as to whether his chief was dead or alive. His business was to save valuable property by preventing the beasts from destroying each other. It mattered not to him, now, that King had come so effectively to Tomaso's rescue. Prodding him mercilessly with his fork, and raining savage blows upon his head, he strove, in a cold rage, to drive him off; but in vain. But other keepers, meanwhile, had run in with ropes and iron bars. A few moments more and both combatants were securely lassoed. Then they were torn apart by main force, streaming with blood. Blinded by blankets thrown over their heads, and hammered into something like subjection, they were dragged off at a rush and slammed unceremoniously into their dens. With them out of the way, it was a quick matter to dispose of the other fights, though not till after the white goat had been killed to satisfy that ancient grudge of the leopard's, and the wolf had been cruelly mauled for having refused to give up his pedestal to one of the excited lions. Only the pug had come off unscathed, having had the presence of mind to dart under the foundations of the frame at the first sign of trouble, and stay there. When all the other animals had been brought to their senses and driven off, one by one, to their cages, he came forth from his hiding and followed dejectedly, the curl quite taken out of his confident tail. Then word went round among the spectators that Tomaso was not dead—that, though badly injured, he would recover; and straightway they calmed down, with a complacent sense of having got the value of their money. The great cage was taken apart and carried off. The stage was speedily transformed. And two trick comedians, with slippers that flapped a foot beyond their toes, undertook to wipe out the memory of what had happened.

Saki (H. H. Munro)

MRS. PACKLETIDE'S TIGER

IT WAS MRS. PACKLETIDE's pleasure and intention that she should shoot a tiger. Not that the lust to kill had suddenly descended on her, or that she felt that she would leave India safer and more wholesome than she had found it, with one fraction less of wild beast per million of inhabitants. The compelling motive for her sudden deviation towards the footsteps of Nimrod was the fact that Loona Bimberton had recently been carried eleven miles in an aeroplane by an Algerian aviator, and talked of nothing else; only a personally procured tiger-skin and a heavy harvest of Press photographs could successfully counter that sort of thing. Mrs. Packletide had already arranged in her mind the lunch she would give at her house in Curzon Street, ostensibly in Loona Bimberton's honour, with a tiger-skin rug occupying most of the foreground and all of the conversation. She had also already designed in her mind the tiger-claw brooch that she was going to give Loona Bimberton on her next birthday. In a world that is supposed to be chiefly swayed by hunger and by love Mrs. Packletide was an exception; her movements and motives were largely governed by dislike of Loona Bimberton.

Circumstances proved propitious. Mrs. Packletide had offered a thousand rupees for the opportunity of shooting a tiger without overmuch risk or exertion, and it so happened that a neighbouring village could boast of being the favoured rendezvous of an animal of respectable antecedents, which had been driven by the increasing infirmities of age to abandon game-killing and confine its appetite to the smaller domestic animals. The prospect of earning the thousand rupees had stimulated the sporting and commercial instinct of the villagers; children were posted night and day on the outskirts of the local jungle to head the tiger back in the unlikely event of his attempting to roam away to fresh hunting-grounds, and the cheaper kinds of goats were left about with elaborate carelessness to keep him satisfied with his present quarters. The one great anxiety was lest he should die of old age before the date appointed for the memsahib's shoot. Mothers carrying their babies home through the jungle after the day's work in the fields hushed their singing lest they might curtail the restful sleep of the venerable herd-robber.

The great night duly arrived, moonlit and cloudless. A platform had been constructed in a comfortable and conveniently placed tree, and thereon crouched Mrs. Packletide and her paid companion, Miss Mebbin. A goat, gifted with a particularly persistent bleat, such as even a partially deaf tiger might be reasonably expected to hear on a still night, was tethered at the correct distance. With an accurately sighted rifle and a thumbnail pack of patience cards the sportswoman awaited the coming of the quarry.

"I suppose we are in some danger?" said Miss Mebbin.

She was not actually nervous about the wild beast, but she had a morbid dread of performing an atom more service than she had been paid for.

"Nonsense," said Mrs. Packletide; "it's a very old tiger. It couldn't spring up here even if it wanted to."

"If it's an old tiger I think you ought to get it cheaper. A thousand rupees is a lot of money."

Louisa Mebbin adopted a protective elder-sister attitude towards money in general, irrespective of nationality or denomination. Her energetic intervention had saved many a rouble from dissipating itself in tips in some Moscow hotel, and francs and centimes clung to her instinctively under circumstances which would have driven them headlong from less sympathetic hands. Her speculations as to the market depreciation of tiger remnants were cut short by the appearance on the scene of the animal itself. As soon as it caught sight of the tethered goat it lay flat on the earth, seemingly less from a desire to take advantage of all available cover than for the purpose of snatching a short rest before commencing the grand attack.

"I believe it's ill," said Louisa Mebbin, loudly in Hindustani, for the benefit of the village headman, who was in ambush in a neighbouring tree.

"Hush!" said Mrs. Packletide, and at that moment the tiger commenced ambling towards his victim.

"Now, now!" urged Miss Mebbin with some excitement; "if he doesn't touch the goat we needn't pay for it." (The bait was an extra.)

The rifle flashed out with a loud report, and the great tawny beast sprang to one side and then rolled over in the stillness of death. In a moment a crowd of excited natives had swarmed on to the scene, and their shouting speedily carried the glad news to the village, where a thumping of tom-toms took up the chorus of triumph. And their triumph and rejoicing found a ready echo in the heart of Mrs. Packletide; already that luncheon-party in Curzon Street seemed immeasurably nearer.

It was Louisa Mebbin who drew attention to the fact that the goat was in death-throes from a mortal bullet-wound, while no trace of the rifle's deadly work could be found on the tiger. Evidently the wrong animal had been hit, and the beast of prey had succumbed to heart-failure, caused by the sudden report of the rifle, accelerated by senile decay. Mrs. Packletide was pardonably annoyed at the discovery; but, at any rate, she was the possessor of a dead tiger, and the villagers, anxious for their thousand rupees, gladly connived at the fiction that she had shot the beast. And Miss Mebbin was a paid companion. Therefore did Mrs. Packletide face the cameras with a light heart, and her pictured fame reached from the pages of the *Texas Weekly Snapshot* to the illustrated Monday supplement of the *Novoe Vremya*. As for Loona Bimberton, she refused to look at an illustrated paper for weeks, and her letter of thanks for the gift of a tiger-claw brooch was a model of repressed emotions. The luncheon-party she declined; there are limits beyond which repressed emotions become dangerous.

From Curzon Street the tiger-skin rug travelled down to the Manor House, and was duly inspected and admired by the county, and it seemed a fitting and appropriate thing when Mrs. Packletide went to the County Costume Ball in the character of Diana. She refused to fall in, however, with Clovis's tempting suggestion of a primeval dance party, at which every one should wear the skins of beasts they had recently slain. "I should be in rather a Baby Bunting condition," confessed Clovis, "with a miserable rabbit-skin or two to wrap up in, but then," he added, with a rather malicious glance at Diana's proportions, "my figure is quite as good as that Russian dancing boy's."

"How amused every one would be if they knew what really happened," said Louisa Mebbin a few days after the ball.

"What do you mean?" asked Mrs. Packletide quickly.

"How you shot the goat and frightened the tiger to death," said Miss Mebbin, with her disagreeably pleasant laugh.

"No one would believe it," said Mrs. Packletide, her face changing colour as rapidly as though it were going through a book of patterns before post-time.

"Loona Bimberton would," said Miss Mebbin. Mrs. Packletide's face settled on an unbecoming shade of greenish white.

"You surely wouldn't give me away?" she asked.

"I've seen a week-end cottage near Dorking that I should rather like to buy," said Miss Mebbin with seeming irrelevance. "Six hundred and eighty, freehold. Quite a bargain, only I don't happen to have the money."

.   .   .   .

Louisa Mebbin's pretty week-end cottage, christened by her "Les Fauves," and gay in summer-time with its garden borders of tiger-lilies, is the wonder and admiration of her friends.

"It is a marvel how Louisa manages to do it," is the general verdict.

Mrs. Packletide indulges in no more big-game shooting.

"The incidental expenses are so heavy," she confides to inquiring friends.

Lewis R. Freeman

HUNTING WITH CHEETAHS IN INDIA

THE LONG SHADOWS of the pyramidal piles of the little Hindu temples were cutting purple triangles on the still faces of the lily tanks when Fowle and I, hot, stiff, sore and disgusted after a bootless drive for tiger in the Jammu jungles, dropped from the howdah of our kneeling elephant and started toward the gateway of the bungalow which the Maharajah had put at our disposal for the visit.

"I don't believe there's a tiger in the whole state," ejaculated Fowle weariedly, kicking the kinks out of his cramped legs. "Don't believe there's even a panther. Don't believe——"

Just what else my distinguished companion did not believe never transpired, for before the sentence was finished a tawny bolt shot over a garden wall, landed in the middle of the cleanly swept road, and bounded again into the air, this time to come down with a joyous "whouf" at Fowle's feet. Looking back from the top of the wall which I had gained at a single leap and scramble, I was just in time to see Fowle, recoiling from the attack of the giant leopard which had reared with the apparent intention of seizing his throat, trip on the coping and go rolling down the stone steps of a lily tank. An instant later a Kashmiri, turbaned and in livery, dashed out of the garden gate, dragging a second leopard at the end of a leash. The first animal reared on his hind legs again, and not until then did I see that he, like the other, was hooded and muzzled, and dangled the loose end of a leash at his neck; also that the rearing attack was nothing more than feline playfulness, the gambols of the overgrown kitten that he was. Fowle, luckily, had managed to

67

bring up at the last step at the brink of the tank, and now, bruised and bedraggled, came limping back into the road again. Fortunately he was Irish and had a keen and inclusive sense of humor; otherwise he might have followed the universal practice of Anglo-Indians and proceeded to beat the innocent cause of the diversion, thus alienating at the outset an individual who was responsible for some of the best sport we enjoyed in the course of a two-months' jaunt in the Himalayas.

The animals were the Maharajah's favorite hunting cheetahs, explained the native—whom we now saw to be very old despite his keen eye and erect carriage—and were as harmless as kittens except when their blood was up after a kill. He had been taking them out for their evening airing, and the larger one had broken away from him in the garden. He had leaped the ten-foot wall in pure fun, and his subsequent actions had been actuated by nothing more than animal spirits. All of this, of course, in Hindustani, which my companion translated to me afterwards.

Fowle was not long in recognizing the old Dogra as the most famous "cheetah-master" in the north of India, and even I, a comparative stranger in the country, had heard something of his marvelous work in animal taming, and especially the subduing, of vicious tigers. It was only natural, therefore, that we should complain to him regarding the ill luck which had attended our hunt and ask for his advice.

Our visit to Jammu, the winter capital of Kashmir, which lies at the base of the Himalayan foothills on the edge of the Punjab plains, was the result of a promise made us by that somewhat erratic potentate, the Maharajah, by whom we had been received in audience during the Delhi Durbar a few months previously, to give us some good hunting if we would pay a visit to that point later in the season. We were on our way to Kashmir and the upper Indus, but as the side trip to Jammu was the matter of but a few days we had decided to make it. On our arrival at Jammu, however, we had found the Maharajah absent on "affairs of state," and although comfortable accommodations were put at our disposal, and a couple of elephants turned over to us, the facilities were not sufficient to make anything approaching a successful hunt possible. In the heart of the Himalayan forests one may hunt with a few native beaters, or, by shooting from a platform erected over a "bait," with practically no assistance at all; but in the jungle country hunting meant numerous elephants and hundreds of beaters, and these we had not been able to secure.

We had returned to Jammu, therefore, with the intention of taking train to Rawal Pindi, thence to start for Kashmir proper over the cart road by the tonga. The old cheetah-master, however, suggested a change of plans. It was true, he admitted, that no good sport could be offered around Jammu in the absence of the Maharajah, unless we might be interested in going out with the cheetahs after buck; but by sending our heavy baggage around to Srinagar—the capital of Kashmir and the shikar base for all that part of the country—by the Rawal Pindi route, and by going into the valley by one of the pony or foot routes for which he could furnish us a guide, we would pass through one of the best panther or leopard sections of India, and might get a chance at a tiger. This we decided to do, and in a couple of days, which were necessary to get pack coolies together, had a chance of enjoying a morning with the famous old Guzra and his cheetahs.

The real sport of cheetah-hunting is, of course, reserved for the cheetah itself, with the "cheetah-master," who endeavors to control and direct the movements of that very capricious cat, coming in for the next best share of the fun. To the spectator it is a good deal like an aeroplane exhibition—interesting as a first experience, but not sufficiently exciting to induce him to go far out of his way to see it again except as an active participant. And one can learn to drive an aeroplane—yes, to volplane and "loop the loop"—in a fraction of the time that it will take him to "get results" with the average hunting leopard.

The formal cheetah hunt, which is sure to constitute a part of the entertainment provided by any one of a couple of dozen of the most prominent native chiefs of northern India for his distinguished guests, is, if anything, tamer and more tiresome than a state tiger hunt, with the latter's elaborate provisions for rounding up the torpid quarry and the still more elaborate provisions against anyone but the beaters being mauled. An informal cheetah hunt, however, where things are taken as they come, is really a very entertaining experience. On such occasions, as no Maharajah's reputation for hospitality is held to hang upon the number of slaughtered buck laid out at the feet of the guest of honor in the photographs, it is possible to give the quarry something like a sporting chance, the consequence being that the cheetah is seen far nearer the limit of its phenomenal stalking and sprinting powers than when the game, frightened and confused by a line of beaters, is driven under his supercilious nose.

It was such a hunt that Fowle and I were privileged to enjoy with old Guzra. There were no beaters, no elephants, no pomp and panoply of the regulation hunt, in fact. We simply went out at daybreak into the rolling half-open country to the west of Jammu, taking with us a pair of cheetahs in a bullock cart, and kept going until buck were sighted. Then it became a matter of maneuvering—keeping always down the wind from them, of course—to some point within the 150 to 200-yard limit, beyond which the cheetah cannot see, or at least can only with difficulty be induced to take an interest in, his prospective quarry. To approach in this manner any of the several members of the deer family in a country which was promiscuously hunted would be very difficult if not impossible, but the section in which we worked was a portion of the Maharajah's preserve which, being especially suited to the cheetah, was closed to shooting. The buck, therefore, while far from being tame, were much less wary and suspicious than those commonly hunted in the United Provinces or the Punjab.

For the first hour or two all of the buck sighted bolted away at the approach of the creaking bullock cart, and I began to understand why the native prince, anxious to insure sport for his guests, always resorted to drives to bring the game into the cheetah's range of action. Then we began to climb a gentle rise, right into the teeth of the chill Himalayan wind, which carried alike the groaning of the cart wheels and our telltale scent straight behind us. Some message of import, too, it appeared to bring to our tawny hunters, for, halfway up the hill, from the blasé indolence of end-of-the-season debutantes, they suddenly were galvanized into an avid, eager interest. Their old master, appearing to know exactly what the expanded nostrils and quivering flanks indicated, prepared for action by drawing close the hood of one of his charges and throwing back that of the other. Instantly the eagerness of the latter quickened until he was only restrained from leaping out of the cart by sharp tugs on his leash, while the former, knowing from the lowered hood that he was not elected for immediate action, relapsed into an attitude of petulant disinterest.

A half-dozen very much surprised and considerably disconcerted buck stopped grazing and stared down at us in blank indecision as we began to top the rise, quickly to break into shrill whistling snorts of alarm, and, spinning to a quick right-about, go clattering off in showers of hoof-spurned gravel.

There was no chance, nor yet any occasion, for a stalk on the part of the selected cheetah. The buck were not fifty yards away when the glaring eyes first fastened upon them, and old Guzra, for the sake of sport, let them swing about and get into full stride before slipping the straining leash. Z-rrr! Whish! There was a gasping snarl of eagerness, the rip of claws on the cart floor, a glint of yellow in the sunshine, and—a second or so later, when the action slowed down sufficiently to allow the eye to follow it— the freed cheetah appeared riding on the withers of the largest of the buck and working desperately with jaw and claw to bring it down. It was like a feat of legerdemain. Z-rrr! Whish! and the magic was wrought, wrought through the medium of the superlative quality of fluent silk and steel in the four slender legs of the remarkable beast which was now riding the faltering buck to its death. It must indeed be true that no living thing without wings is capable of a speed approaching that of a charging cheetah.

At the end of fifty yards teeth or claws—Guzra said it was usually a blow from a paw that killed—found their way to the spine of the unfortunate buck, and, collapsing in full stride, it went down in a heap, the cheetah narrowly missing being impaled on the points of the sharp, tapering horns across which his inertia carried him in the fall. We found him tearing at the throat of the buck to open the way for the draught of blood which is the usual reward of the cheetah which has made a successful kill. As there was more work in prospect, however, Guzra hooded his indignantly protesting charge at once and dragged him back to the cart.

Although we saw much more finished "cheetah work," this first kill was really the most spectacular feature of the morning's sport. This chanced to be the only occasion in which the attack was made direct from the cart, and as the other dashes were made more or less at an angle to our line of vision and at a distance which made it impossible for the eye to follow the catapulting bolt of tawny energy all the way, the effect was less startling. It was all very interesting, but there was no more of the "Z-rrr! Whish!" sort of thing.

The beasts proved marvels at stalking, dropping off the far side of the cart the instant their hoods were off, and, utilizing as cover every bush and inequality of the ground, advancing to a vantage point favorable for the final rush. More often than not, especially when the stalk had been a patient one, the victim would be taken entirely by surprise, frequently not getting under way until the enemy was on its back. On very rare occasions, Guzra told us, a buck, when taken by surprise, would receive a charge with lowered horns, in which event a more or less badly punctured cheetah was not infrequently the consequence.

I have said that we saw no more magic such as was wrought in connection with the first kill, but for the end of the morning's sport there was reserved another kind of magic which seemed to me even more remarkable. Old Guzra told, or appeared to tell, one of the cheetahs how to approach some buck that were beyond its range of vision, and succeeded in making that animal undertake what narrowly missed being a successful stalk. Coming to the edge of a broad nullah or ravine gouged out of an alluvial "fan" by a few æons of monsoon rains, Guzra's sharp eyes detected the movement of grazing buck behind the opposite rim, awed, half-querulous and wholly uncanny stare. The gestures consisted of repeated finger-stabs in the direction of the grazing buck, interspersed with full-arm sweeps evidently intended to indicate a route of approach across the nullah.

Suddenly the chirping chuckle ceased, and with quick movement Guzra snatched off the loosened hood of the cheetah, slipped its leash and pushed it roughly from the cart to the ground. Here the beast wavered undecidedly, cringing somewhat after the manner of a whipped dog and lifting half-puzzled eyes as if to assure itself of the command in those of its master.

"Jow!" ("Get out!") roared Guzra impatiently, and then, as the beast slunk uncertainly away from the cart, he relapsed again into fluent chirps and clucks, an explosively pronounced command sounding something like "hjarr!" recurring most frequently. Presently the confused beast paused, sniffed once or twice in a tentative way with lifted nose, and then, all in an instant, became one quivering bundle of single-mindedness. Down it dropped until the soft cream-golden fur of its belly swept the ground, and, seeming suddenly to have shrunk to half its original size, disappeared over the rim of the nullah.

Guzra sank back on his lean haunches with the sigh of a man relaxing after strenuous physical exertion, but his beady eyes never shifted for an instant from a spot near the dry torrent-scarred bottom of the ravine where the cheetah would have to cross to gain the farther side. A minute of tense silence passed, and then the quick pressure of a hand on my knee signaled, I took it, that the big cat was sighted. As far as I myself had been able to see, however, not a shadow had flashed across the open, and only the fact that the focus of Guzra's eyes was traveling up the opposite slope indicated that the stalk was in progress.

I have not mentioned the fact that Guzra's impatient exclamation, when the cheetah seemed to have failed to understand his "directions," had not passed unnoticed by the buck on the opposite bank, and, although they were dead to windward of us, an increasing restlessness was noticeable from the moment the stalk commenced. Every now and then a head would lift and peer suspiciously across in our direction, and presently it became appar-

at a distance of between 300 and 400 yards. To take the ca
across within a mile or more in either direction was out of que
tion, and Fowle, who had some knowledge of the limits of cheeta
action, said it would be equally impossible to send one of th
animals to the attack from where we were. To old Guzra, how
ever, the opportunity to try something out of the ordinary seeme
to act as a stimulant, and he evinced for the first time more tha
a perfunctory interest in the work at hand. Throwing back th
hood of the larger and swifter of the two cheetahs, he turned th
animal's head so that it faced across the nullah in the directio
of the slowly shifting black spots on the opposite slope. No an
swering quiver told that the round golden eyes had fixed them
selves upon the grazing buck.

"What can the old chap be driving at?" mused Fowle in Eng
lish. "Surely he can't expect to go into action at this distance.

Guzra, evidently catching the import of the remarks, replied
in Hindustani:

"He cannot see, it is true, O Captain Sahib, but I shall now
tell him whence he must proceed that he may be able to see
Will the Sahibs have the kindness to remain very quiet for a few
moments?"

Pushing back the hood well away from the animal's ears, he
took the smooth, round head in both his hands and turned the
scowling but intelligent face to his own. His deep-set beady eyes
grew fixed with concentration, and the wrinkles of his seamed
old face straightened out into firm lines of intense purposeful-
ness. The big vitreously golden eyes shifted uneasily away from
the narrow beady ones two or three times and then returned to
a submissive stare, the sullenly back-laid ears at the same time
pricking forward in awakening expectancy. Then, for a minute
or two, lost in wonder at the strangeness of the spectacle—I took
no account of the time—Guzra spoke to the grim head, which
grinned back at his own, spoke with clucks, grunts and chirrup
such as man has never used to man since the days of the Trog
lodytes. Presently he removed his twisted hands from the beast
jowls to employ them in gesture, but the golden eyes, held fas
in the mastery of the black ones, never wavered in their hal

ent that the animals were working back over a slight rise a couple of hundred yards from the rim. By the time Guzra's eyes were directed straight across on a level, indicating that they had followed the cheetah all the way up the farther slope, the last of the dark patches had drifted beyond our vision.

"Guzra says it crossed the bottom on that streak of yellow ledge that's so near the color of its own hide," muttered Fowle. "That's probably the reason we didn't see it. But watch for it now, he says, across that strip of dry grass beyond the rim."

Barely guessed through my binoculars, I had just made out a swift rufous blur against the gray-brown background, when old Guzra, shouting something to Fowle, jumped up and dived into the nullah.

Just what happened beyond the rise on the farther side we never knew exactly. The probabilities are that the buck were in flight when the big cat came in sight of them, and that, already blown from his swift stalk, the latter had given up after a short dash. At any rate, when, scratched and winded from our scramble through the ravine, we gained the field of action, it was to find only a superlatively sulky cheetah and no sign of buck within sweep of our glasses.

Ruth Manning-Sanders

THE CAGE

THEY ARE not thick, those bars——

Yet there you lie
With small grave eye
Brooding glassily,
While your heavy paws
Uncurl their claws
Lazily,
And your tail half twitches, then
Falls again.

Across those bars the people stream
In black confusion, till they seem
Like tangled thoughts that blur in dream,
You heed them not—you watch the dream.

Then spread
Immeasurable spaces,
Vast trees, garmented
With moonlight, places
Of creeping shadows, scents of blood
By dark water, where the flood
Glitters with monster stars, and you
Are crouching, quivering, bounding through
The illimitable spaces—
You with eyes
Like yellow daggers, you with claws
Like curled scythes, you with paws

Like pounding hammers, slantwise
Striking to kill. You
Free, intent,
Unaccountable, magnificent,
Bounding through
The illimitable spaces!

Black and white the people stream
Across the slim, stiff bars, and seem
Distinct as thoughts that wake from dream.

And you
Uncurl your claws lazily
And blink your eyes sleepily
And yawn as there were nought to do.

And yet they are not thick, those bars——

Emma-Lindsay Squier

THE THIRD DAY OF THE MOON

IT WAS THE THIRD day of the new moon. And in the menagerie of the great motion picture studio there were two births—and two deaths. For in adjacent cages Sarah, the lion cub, and Lady, the collie pup, sprawled inertly, blind and helpless, by their mothers' bodies. Julia, the lioness, and Lisette, the collie mother, lay silent with glazed eyes. The animal men carried them away and cleaned the cages, and two small orphans faced the world of men and make-believe from behind stout iron bars.

Perhaps you may think it strange that Lady's gentle mother should have lived in a cage, even as Julia, the amber-eyed and savage lioness. Lisette would not have been a captive but for her habit of running away from the motion picture lot just when she was needed to contribute her famous smile to a drama or an animal comedy. For the collie lady had big, brown eyes and a trick of lifting her upper lip when she was pleased. The director would praise her extravagantly until, overwhelmed with his flattery, she would turn her head on one side, roll her brown eyes up at him, and wrinkle her upper lip into an ingratiating smile. Then the camera would grind, and Lisette's smile would be transferred to celluloid.

But for the Gipsy streak in her which prompted her to roam at inopportune times, she would have been allowed the liberty of the "ranch," as the menagerie and its adjacent lots were called.

I knew both Lisette and Julia well. For I loved the menagerie, with its smell of hot, dry sand and its vague animal odors which caused strange dogs to pause and sniff questioningly, with hair bristling along their frightened spines. It was enclosed with a

78

great, high fence, and inside, the great square was flanked with rows of cages. In one long tier the lions drowsed in tawny indifference or padded the length of their cages rhythmically. Across from them lived the Malemute dogs from Alaska, who worked in northern pictures and drew sledges over fields of rock salt instead of snow. At one end of the square the monkeys chattered continually, swung from trapezes, and quarreled fiercely over peanuts and fleas. Near them lived the Russian wolves, gaunt, fierce fellows with pointed noses and pale gray eyes, and at the other end of the enclosure Charlie, the elephant, had a cement-floored barn all to himself. He lived quite comfortably, eternally munching hay and whisking bunches of it over his huge, wrinkled sides to drive away the flies.

In the center of the menagerie was the great arena cage, where palms and bamboo plants were nurtured to make a background for jungle pictures. Beside it was the smaller training cage, where the four-footed actors were trained for their parts or were let in for exercise.

"Pudgy," one of the trainers, had known me as a child on the shores of Puget Sound, where we had found a common interest in our love of the wild things. So now he let me take many liberties with his "boarders" as he called them, and would sometimes let me go with him into the cages.

Neither he nor I grieved when Julia died. It was a happy release for her proud, unbroken spirit. Although she had been born in captivity, the jungle had always called to her. She was harsh and stern, and would pace for hours, restlessly, endlessly, pausing only to sniff the air as if the next breeze might bring to her weary nostrils the longed-for scent of marshy water-holes, of hot grass lying sear and brown in African sunshine, of cool grottoes where lay the shredded bones of meat savagely and joyously killed. She was never taken into the arena cage to work in pictures, for she was dangerous. And even Pudgy, who was friend to every animal on the ranch, carried an iron prodding stick whenever he went into her cage.

But when Lisette, the gentle collie, died, he was sad, and so was I. For even in her cage she had enjoyed life in a quiet, well-bred way, and she had always smiled when she saw us coming. She was loved by all the actors, and they brought her candy when they came to work in the arena cage.

Pudgy would have reared the two orphans separately, but the powers that be of the great studio decreed otherwise. It would be a novelty, they said, for a dog and a lion to be brought up together, and they thought that for a few months, at least, the collie pup would be safe in the same cage with Julia's fat, squinty-eyed cub.

So Pudgy took the two babies, the shapeless, little collie pup and the sprawling, yellow cub, and put them in the same box, covering them warmly with flannel, for the nights were cold, and he fed them from a bottle filled with warm milk. He allowed me to hold the bottle from which Sarah drank, and the lion baby, with ears and paws much too large for the rest of her, tugged at the rubber nipple, uttering high-pitched, petulant sounds whenever I took the bottle away.

Pudgy was gently caressing the tiny, brown ball that sucked sleepily at the bottle he held in his hand.

"Poor little Lady," he was saying softly—he always spoke to the animals as if they could understand him—"you may make a meal some day for that fat daughter of Julia's. Still, if you have a smile like the one your mother had, maybe you'll win her heart and she'll spare your life."

"Oh, Pudgy," I said, "I'm sure they'll be friends. It's the third day of the moon, you know."

Pudgy smiled and nodded. Few people would have understood, but he did. He knew that the Indians of the Puget Sound country where we had lived—the Nittenats and Chinooks—have a legend which says that any creatures, two-footed or four-footed, if brought together under the same roof on the third day of the new moon, will be friends—and faithful friends, too. For long ago the Great Spirit visited the earth in the form of a deer. There came a great forest fire, and he fled before it together with all the wild things of the woods. They found a huge cave where they waited until the flames had passed over, leaving them unharmed. And the Great Spirit said to the others, "Let us make a promise each to the other, that in memory of this deliverance from death, those who meet on the third day of the new moon shall be friends." So it was agreed, and the Great Spirit set in the heavens three bright stars, all in a row, to remind those of earth of their promise. We call the constellation "the Eagle." But the Nittenats and the Chinooks call it "the Promise of the Third Day," and although many people have forgotten the ancient vow, the animals have faithfully kept the covenant made in the sheltering cave.

Perhaps you will smile at the old legend, which all the Puget Sound Indians know, but it is true indeed that Lady and Sarah grew up to be fast friends, just as if they had known of the promise of the third day. Sarah did not inherit her mother's disposition, as Pudgy feared she might. She was frolicsome and affectionate, so full of life that she often tired Lady out, and she was as gentle in her play with the collie pup as if she sensed her superior strength and curbed it so that Lady might not be hurt.

The two occupied an enclosure of liberal size, fenced around by stout wire meshes, directly across the menagerie from the central cage where the large lions were taken daily for exercise and training. And sometimes the older lions would pause in their steady pacing and stare through the bars at the enclosure where a small, fat lion cub wrestled with an equally fat, brown-and-white collie pup, the lion baby tussling silently, the collie infant combining her sallies with shrill barks and many falsetto growls. The tawny, amber-eyed ones would sniff the air curiously, as if questioning what manner of fate had brought these two children together. It was clear that they resented the familiarity with which Lady chewed Sarah's ear or dug into the rough fur of her throat. They would have liked to see Sarah turn on the presuming collie baby and make a comfortable meal on her plumpness. But such a thought was far from the little lion's mind—even when she reached the stage where milk no longer appealed to her as a completely satisfactory diet.

Sarah had round, gray eyes that would be amber when she grew up. But just now they were baby eyes, inquisitive and bright, and there was always a worried line between her eyebrows as if she were wondering about something she could not possibly understand. Her ears were too large, and she had tiny, white teeth. Sometimes she pretended to be angry, and at such times she would snarl in a high-pitched gurgle that ended with a sharp hiss. It was only then, when her ears were laid back and her eyes filled with hard, bright points of light, that we remembered that she was, after all, a lion in embryo, and we wondered just what her feelings would be toward Lady when she found that they were not of the same breed or nationality.

But Lady and Sarah, it seemed, never discovered the difference. The collie pup might just as well have been a lioness for all she knew or cared, and Sarah, if she had thought about it at all, would have contended that she was as much a collie as Lady. They romped together continually, ate together, slept together, curled up in the sun, and Sarah grew from cubhood and became heavy and unwieldy, living up to the promise of her large feet and ears. But Lady was small and dainty, like her mother, and she had Lisette's own trick of wrinkling her upper lip when she was pleased.

All the visitors to the studio menagerie wondered at the strange couple in the fenced-in space, for at sight of a friendly face and voice both the dog and the cub would come racing to the wire meshes, eager to have their noses rubbed, and jostling each other aside to get the petting which they felt was due them. Lady, by this time, had found that she could easily manage the lumbering, good-natured Sarah and would snap at her throat sharply when the lion cub tried to get more than her share of caresses. Sarah would stand back then, blinking, with that worried line between her eyes, her ears cocked at a forward slant, her tawny legs spread well apart, as if to be ready on the instant for an invitation to come to the wire netting, or to play a game of tag with Lady, if that was the capricious collie's whim.

During their brief periods of separation they were miserable. When Lady was taken out for her daily exercise, she would not frolic or rush up to bark at the monkeys as the Malemutes did when they were out for a walk. Unless taken by a leash, she would remain by the cage, sniffing through the wire meshes. And when forcibly taken away, she would sit sulkily on her haunches, contesting the going with all her strength. In her friend's absence Sarah would pace the length and breadth of the enclosure, even as the older lions did, but she had no longing for liberty. She only wanted her playmate, and until Lady returned, she would sniff the air discontentedly, watching with unshakable concentration the point where the collie had last been seen.

When Lady was brought back, the lion cub would make queer, whining noises of contentment, and the collie would bark shrilly and lift her upper lip in a delighted smile. They would greet each other in a frenzy of happiness, racing the length of the cage, licking each other's faces, and making farcical displays of combat.

So it would have continued for a long time. But as Sarah grew stronger and larger, Lady became as thin as a string, and even a course of dieting could not restore her plumpness. It was clear that too much play with a husky lion cub was telling on her health, for Sarah never knew when to stop, and long after Lady had thrown herself exhausted into a corner of the cage, the lion baby would coax her to resume the fun, springing at her in mock fury, squatting at a short distance, her body wriggling provocatively, and pushing the large, wooden ball, with which they played, up under the sleepy collie's nose. Sometimes Lady, out of all patience with her energetic friend, would bark shortly and protestingly, or snap at Sarah's eager nose. Then the tawny playfellow would back away reluctantly, more than a little hurt by this rebuff, and would blink wonderingly from the far corner of the cage.

One day Lady sickened, and Pudgy decided that she must be taken from the cage until she was well again and strong enough to compete with Sarah's vigorous playtime moods, and on the same day a new animal man came on the lot.

He was a thin, surly-looking man who had traveled with a circus and had taken care of the cages of the wild animals. He had no sympathy for them as Pudgy had. He used the double-pronged iron rod to shove them about, and he snarled at them in very much the same tone, it seemed to me, that they snarled at him.

Pudgy was not yet in charge of the menagerie, so he was powerless to curb the new man's rough ways, but he used to shake his head sometimes when he saw him driving the lionesses into the great central cage for exercise. He pushed them remorselessly with the cruel, iron prongs and shouted at them when they crouched and snarled their fear and defiance.

"You can treat a gentleman lion that way," Pudgy told me once, "but with the ladies you must be more careful. He will prod Daisy once too often with that iron rod of his, and he will be dead before they can ever get to him."

"If he ever treats Sarah so," I said tensely, "I hope you'll beat him!"

Pudgy looked down contemplatively at the lion cub, half grown now, with a tawny coat that was rough and heavy, but still with ears too big for her, and round, baby eyes with a worried line between them. "Something tells me," he said at last, "that Sarah could take care of herself."

Lady was taken from the wired enclosure where she had spent practically all her life. It was a sad day, and many sad days followed it. Lady's health did not improve as Pudgy had hoped it would, for she spent her time going round and round the cage which enclosed her playfellow, smelling the wire netting and trying frantically to dig underneath. She yelped continually, breaking off sometimes into heartbroken little howls. Then, when she was tired with her futile efforts, she would stretch out by the cage, her long, slim nose pointed into the meshes, her plumy tail draped sorrowfully upon the ground like a flag at half-mast. And Sarah was equally distraught. Pudgy could hardly make her eat, and once she went for a whole day without touching food or water. She would follow Lady in her circuit of the cage, her ears cocked forward hopefully, the worried line deepened between her eyes. And when the collie gave up in despair, Sarah, too, would stretch herself out by the wires that separated her from her friend, so close against it that her tawny fur pressed through the meshes in little scallops and circles. They were most unhappy, and Pudgy and I were sorry for them. But it amused the powers that be, and annoyed the new animal man. He had no love for either the lion baby or the little collie lady.

One day he made a mistake. I was spending the afternoon with Pudgy at the menagerie, and we were looking at the family of Russian wolves in the long cages at the north end of the lot. All at once we heard the new man's voice, loud with a sharp threat, and immediately after, a high-pitched yelp of pain. With the cry came a snarl that bellowed out into a roar of fury, and there was an ominous rattling of wires as a heavy body hurled itself against them in a frenzy of hate and wrath. Pudgy and I ran toward the sounds, and as we came around the corner of the open-air arena where the jungle pictures were made, we saw Lady limping away from the enclosure, tail between her legs, and one foot held away from the ground. Sarah was racing round and round the cage, springing up against the stout meshes, the impact shaking the whole enclosure. Her eyes were no longer baby eyes; they were the amber eyes of the jungle lioness who feels the urge of the blood lust. They were savage with fury, her tawny fur stood up in bristles, and she roared, the full-throated cry of the lioness who has come to know her power.

The new man was watching her scornfully, yet a little fearfully, we thought. The other lions in the cages across the lot began to pace fretfully and to roar in sympathy.

"What did you do to Lady?" Pudgy demanded, and I did not know his gentle voice could be so harsh.

"The cursed dog is digging up all the ground around this cage," the new man answered, sullenly defiant. "She wouldn't get away, and I pushed her with my foot. The fool lion cub went crazy. You'd think I'd given *her* the boot."

"You kicked Lady," Pudgy said again in that dangerously quiet tone. "I'm not much on carrying tales, but if you do it again, you'll be looking for another job."

He paused, and regarded Sarah with understanding eyes.

"And I'd not go in that cage if I were you," he added.

The new man snorted. "Say, you can't tell me anything about handling cats—why, she's nothing but a cub!"

Pudgy regarded him fixedly. "I'm thinking you'll find that she's a lion baby who has grown up," he answered gravely.

There was a company going out on two weeks' location, and

they wanted a dog with a trick of smiling. Pudgy recommended Lady. He would take no chances with the new man's ill humor, and he thought that away from the studio menagerie, she would become reconciled to the loss of Sarah's companionship and get well and strong again. So she was sent away, and the company made much of her. Her little wrinkly smile was so successful on the screen that had she been a human, she would have become a star at once.

But Sarah sulked in her cage. And not even the friendly overtures of Pudgy could rouse her from her apathy of loneliness. She was still as docile as ever, and the men never took prodding irons when they went in to clean or to give her food, but her eyes were amber now, and sometimes she snarled, her whiskered lip curved upward, baring white fangs.

The new man, following Pudgy's warning perhaps, kept away from her cage. But always, when scenting his presence, even across the menagerie lot, she would become restless and pad softly to the wire meshes, staring at him unblinkingly. Her tail would twist into jerky undulations, and she would begin a measured, mechanical pacing that ceased only when he had left the lot. It almost seemed as if she thought him responsible for Lady's disappearance and hated him the more.

Then, one day, it was decided that Sarah's training for pictures should begin. First it was necessary that she become accustomed to her unknown kindred and that they become acquainted with her. So six of the oldest and most trustworthy lions were driven through the runway which led into the central cage by the arena. They came padding slowly, with the utter indifference which is characteristic of the tawny ones, the males with their great, shaggy manes framing their dignified faces, the females with soft movements of lithe muscles, ears that flicked backward at a word, and with quick, hissing intakes of breath.

Pudgy stood in the center of the cage, armed only with a light whip, and spoke gently to all of them, guiding them to their pedestals without so much as raising his voice. Then he closed the iron door behind him and entered the wire enclosure where Sarah drowsed in the sunshine. He went to her quietly and slipped a leather collar around her neck. To this he affixed a chain and led her unprotesting out into the open air and into the central cage. He unsnapped the chain and threw it outside the bars. A group of studio men watched curiously. It was always to them an entertaining spectacle when a new lion was let in with the others for the first time. Often there were fights. But Pudgy was there to prevent them.

Sarah stopped in startled wonderment as the iron door swung shut behind her, and sniffed curiously at the older lions on their pedestals, staring at them with wide, inquisitive, amber eyes. They stared back, sniffing too, and one of the females snarled and moved on her pedestal.

"Keep your place, Bertha," Pudgy said warningly, and she was quiet.

Sarah pressed close to Pudgy's side as a child might do in a crowd of strangers. She was plainly perplexed by all these tawny things whose scent was so familiar, yet who seemed so strange. Perhaps if she had known they were lions, she would have been afraid, thinking herself a collie dog and therefore at their mercy. Pudgy kept his hand on her head between her big, upstanding ears, and finally, when he sat down on a camp stool, she lay down beside him, sniffing and raising her head in little, nervous jerks. Her tail made whispering noises on the floor of the cage as it twitched to and fro. But the other lions did not move. They only sniffed and sometimes snarled. Peter, the oldest of them all, went to sleep without bothering his head further about the new arrival, and Daisy, too, dozed fitfully. Bertha stared resentfully, but did not leave her pedestal.

"No excitement there," said one of the men outside regretfully. "They'll be used to her in a couple of sittings."

"Yes," said Pudgy, "if someone will take my place, I'll go to lunch."

It was the superintendent of the menagerie who came into the cage and sat down on the camp stool, and Pudgy, walking quietly, came out of the iron door and strode off across the lot to the cafeteria. But the superintendent, too, wanted lunch and he called to the new animal man to take his place, since he had just returned from eating.

The barred door slammed and clicked. It closed behind the superintendent and locked inside the circular cage the new animal man. The older lions scarcely stirred at the sound of the closing door. But Sarah moved, rising to her feet with a single lithe movement. So silent was it that the new animal man did not know. Those looking on them from the outside saw the lion baby crouch, heard a snarl that ended with a hissing spring. They saw a powerful body hurl forward in an arc of tawny fury, saw the stupid look of surprise on the animal man's face as he half turned and was hurled to the floor of the cage by the crushing impact of the lion's charge. Then someone shouted. There was bedlam of hysterical voices, hands tugged vainly at the iron-barred door; men ran aimlessly, hunting for prodding rods. Inside the cage the lions went mad. They leaped against the bars, careened against each other in a delirium of fear, snarled and struck as they passed, dashed past the prostrate man who lay screaming and fending off with clenched but futile fists the tearing teeth of Sarah, the lion baby, who had found revenge.

I saw as in a vague dream Pudgy's white face, saw him make for the iron door of the cage. He carried a gun and a prodding rod. But it would have been death to have entered there.

Suddenly the animal man's screams ceased. But it was not because death had taken him. For Sarah had lifted her head and gazed fixedly for an instant. Then, with a single bound, she left the torn body of the man she hated, and was pressed against the bars of the cage, jostled by the bewildered lions as they circled the space with only the thought of escape in their frightened minds. She did not notice. For there, outside the cage, sniffing, wondering, and with daintily wagging tail, was Lady, plump and sleek, her brown eyes mirroring astonishment at all the commotion. Then her upper lip lifted in a delighted smile. She yelped feverishly. For she had caught sight of Sarah. The two smelled noses through the bars, Lady jumping about in a frenzy of delight and her plumy tail waving madly. Sarah was whining softly with a baby note we thought she had forgotten.

So Pudgy opened the door of the runway, and the lions entered it gladly, padding swiftly back to the peace and quiet of their individual cages. Willing hands lifted the animal man from the floor and carried him, bruised and bleeding, to the hospital near by.

Sarah did not even know he was gone. She was telling Lady, as well as she could, of her loneliness during the past weeks, of her joy at the return of her friend.

Pudgy stood looking down at her, and there was something of respectful wonder in his gaze. I wondered if he was thinking of the third day of the moon. I was.

The animal man lived, but stayed no longer at the studio menagerie. And it was due to Pudgy's influence that Sarah and Lady were put together again in the wired enclosure. For Sarah had outgrown her sportive cubhood and was content to lie quietly stretched out in the sun with Lady curled up beside her.

The lion baby is full-grown now; her eyes are the color of pale amber, and the worried line between them is gone. Her tawny coat is rich and thick; her paws are huge and padded. But still she is Lady's devoted slave. She is a willing pillow for the sleeping collie to sprawl upon; she allows Lady to have the sunniest corner of the cage. And the daughter of the gentle Lisette is not to be coaxed from the enclosure with flattering words or bribes of juicy meat. She will cock her ears, thump her tail in pleased acknowledgment of the compliment, and wrinkle back her lip in a deprecatory smile. But from Sarah's side she will not stir.

People seeing the two together marvel at their friendship. Some of them make dire prophecies that Sarah will one day take Lady for a meal. But they do not know of the promise of the third day, for humans have forgotten the ancient agreement. But the animals remember it, and Lady and Sarah will keep the covenant.

Llewellyn Powys

A LEOPARD BY LAKE ELMENTEITA

> When the stars threw down their spears,
> And water'd heaven with their tears,
> Did He smile His work to see?
> Did He who made the lamb make thee?

Is THERE ANY animal more astounding, more amazing than a leopard? With what terrible precision his gilded limbs have been designed to deal out death, and in what a wonderful way his furtive and treacherous beauty symbolizes the soul of the strange continent which he inhabits!

"Bwana, bwana, chui n'kwesha pigga m'toto gombi!" "Master, master, a leopard has killed a calf!" Well do I remember how those words came to me from the cattle yards as early one morning I emerged from my hut in the highlands of British East Africa. I had been in the country only a few weeks and it was the first time an open attack had been made on the homestead by a leopard. I had heard leopards about often enough. The house I lived in was situated on the edge of a great forest and almost every night I would lie awake listening with awestruck intentness to the sound of their barking as it went echoing between the white pillar-like tree trunks. Until the sound was over, all else would be silent, the very tree hyraxes remaining mute as with small blinking eyes they waited for its menace to die down into the circumambient darkness. With padded footfall to and fro these great cats would steal over the maidenhair ferns and moonlit mossgrown stones of the forest floor, but until this particular night none of them had approached the farm buildings which were built out upon the open veldt. I went to the shed and was shown the place between two rough cedar logs through which the leopard had crept. There had been rain in the night and with the help of some natives I tracked it by its spoor for a considerable distance until the grass grew so thick that we could no longer find any trace of it. I concluded that it had got away for good and returned to my house. At noon however a Masai herder came in to say that he had discovered the half-eaten body of a calf near the shore of Lake Elmenteita. He conducted me to the place and there under the shadow of a high cliff which jutted out over the water I found the mangled animal. Very little of it had been devoured, so that there seemed every prospect of the leopard returning to the kill as soon as darkness fell. I therefore made up my mind to wait for it.

The late afternoon found me clambering about the rocks of the escarpment looking for a good position in which to pass the night. I found what I wanted at last, a flat, inaccessible ledge some forty yards above where the calf lay. The moon I knew was almost full, so that if the sky remained clear it seemed that there was a good chance of my taking my revenge. I stuck a tiny piece of white paper on the sight of my rifle so as to render it visible even in a dim light.

It was a weird and isolated place, that escarpment, and as I sat watching the sun slowly sink towards the rim of the mountain range beyond the Rift Valley, I became aware of a strange thing. It was as though all Africa at that enchanted hour was under some curious influence, as if it waited expectantly with indrawn breath for this half of the earth's globe to turn itself once again towards the spangled darkness of ultimate space. Unfamiliar noises rose from the water before me, and it was not till several minutes had passed that I realized their origin. Slowly, surely, from every quarter of the lake the monstrous amphibia were drawing in towards the shore. Presently I could see their colossal hippopotamus-heads rising to the surface, now here now there, as they lolled and yawned together in fabulous droves waiting impatiently for the fall of darkness when they would be able to come up out of the water and graze upon the cool dew-drenched grass of their midnight pasturage. The sun went down at last and from where I crouched I watched their huge unforgettable forms slipping and floundering through the rushes which bordered upon the edge of the lake where the silver froth lapped against the strand.

With the coming of the night the whole air became vibrant, quivering, palpitating. From innumerable minute scaly throats a song of praise rose to the creator of the world. In shrill and high tones that fantastical chorus throbbed and hummed against my ear drum. Now and again far above my head would sound the romantic alien call of some wild fowl winging its solitary way through the night. I waited and waited. A damp air, chilling and invisible, rose from the lake. It had about it the smell of thousands of unrecorded years that had passed in quiet procession over these remote waters, while century after century trees grew to their prime and rotted to water-logged decay, while century after century the bones of fabulous equatorial animals accumulated upon the slimy mud of the lake's bottom. It had about it the smell of water-pythons, of incredible crustacea, and of the fecund spawn of insects.

Then suddenly, loud and clear, breaking in upon the stillness of that wide moonlit stretch of water till every flag and every reed seemed to tremble, sounded the harsh note of a hungry leopard. And not only the reeds trembled, for scarcely had the first echo subsided than, like a city slum waked suddenly from sleep, a deafening clamour rose to the stars. The baboons which roosted in the rocks amongst which I sat had heard it. Turning my head I could see them clambering higher and ever higher in the dim light, clinging with their muscular black hands to the stony shelves or huddling one against another, hairy limb against hairy limb, in the deeper recesses of the cliff. It was then for the first time that I realized how nightly the barbarous imaginations of these hideous monkeys are haunted with panic fear of their crafty and subtle enemy, which leaps suddenly upon them out of the darkness and tears out their eyes! Gradually the barking of the leopard grew nearer. I got my rifle ready. I surmised that the animal was coming along a narrow game-path which threaded its way between the boulders at the foot of the escarpment. All now was once more silent. Not a rustle, not the cracking of a twig to tell of the animal's approach, or to disturb the spellbound stillness of that amazing midnight landscape which under the liquid light of the moon lay extended in agonized suspense.

Like some wide plain of abandoned polar ice the tropical lake lay silent and immutable, and from the depths of the dark forest away on the left no sound rose. What had come over the baboons? I wondered. Were their superficial brains once more clouded in a nervous sleep? or were they, with narrow wide-open antique eyes, peering over their grotesque snouts in abject alertness for their enemy?

Suddenly the leopard, elongated and serpentine, was crossing an open space below. There was something horrible and uncanny about the absolute silence of its movements. For a few moments I watched it. Delicately, daintily, it nibbled at the carcass, stepping round the mutilated body with fastidious tread. I pulled the trigger at last. Undoubtedly I had missed, for look as I might through the uncertain light I could see nothing. It was just as though at the report of my rifle a ghost-leopard had vanished into the air.

Slowly the time dragged by as I waited for the dawn. In the small hours of the morning I fell asleep. When I awoke it was already past six and the first rays of the great equatorial sun were glancing down upon Africa. Cold and stiff I stood up and looked about. Shafts of fine golden light were slanting down upon the basalt rocks, upon the flamingoes in the shallows,— and upon the miraculous spotted body of a dead leopard which, outstretched in all its bizarre beauty, lay by the edge of those far-off mysterious waters which are called by the natives El-menteita.

John Eyton

THE HOLY TIGER

SOMETIMES MEN RETURNING at dusk by the hill path to Kala-dunghi would come in with trembling bodies and starting eyes and babble of a white tiger, bigger than a buffalo, crossing the shingle that makes a bed by the Koshi River. Strangers would wonder, but wise men would nod their heads and say—

"Ah, the Ancient One." Or—

"Ah, the Holy One of the Gorge."

He was white, they would say, as the snow on Nanda Devi, and older than mankind. The most ancient man in the Terai—old Moti Singh, who had begotten sons before the Mutiny and had lived a hundred years—gave precedence to the Holy One, who was old even when he was born. No bullet could pierce the Holy One—(whispers here)—because he had no body to pierce, or because, as others held, his spirit could leave his body at will and repair to the temple in the forest on the slope of the gorge, known to all men as the Holy Tiger's temple. Sahibs had come and gone—the commissioner, and the Lat Sahib, and Ramsay Sahib, and even he that had been before Ramsay Sahib.

They had tied up twenty buffalo calves on a night for him to kill, and on a night he had killed them all. They had ringed him with a hundred elephants and two hundred men perched in trees, and he had slipped through the net. They had thrown balls of fire at him as he had lain in a cane-brake and the fire had not even singed his coat. But on that day an elephant had been swallowed up in the mud, howdah and all. A full-grown elephant had been sucked in, and the mud had closed over his head as it would close over a stone—did not Abdullah Khan, the mahout, live to tell the tale?

But he was good to the men of Kaladunghi, the wise men would say; for though he passed nightly by and nightly returned, he never killed within the confines of the village—only in the forest above or the forest below. Woe to any man who interfered with his killing there. Evil would come on that man.

So, over the long black pipe and the wood fire, the beards of the wise would wag. And if on the morrow the stranger wished to verify the tale, he had only to walk up the river bed to the place where the gorge overhangs it steeply and where blue rocks jostle the trees, and see for himself. Great pug-marks he would see, splayed out broader than his hand and sunk deep in the wet sand by a clear pool.

"There he drinks," he would murmur, and glancing quickly round—for it is a silent place—he would go on his knees and bend his head till it touched the sand, doing pooja * to the drinker. Then he would take the hillside path and pass among the trees to a squat temple with a shaven priest in faded yellow brooding outside. There he would lay a few flowers ere he journeyed on.

No matter when he should chance to return that way—six months, a year, ten years—he would hear the same tale. The Holy One still walked.

II

Like most legends, that of the Holy One was partly true. For close on a hundred years there had been a great tiger of the gorge—but not the same tiger, for three generations had haunted the place. The first, the grandsire, might have seen the flames of the Mutiny in his middle age. The second, the sire, might have seen them when he was but a stripling *pattr* † ambling behind his dam, but the third could not, with all deference to the ancient Moti Singh, have seen them at all. But he had seen change. He had seen the redcoats march up the old road to the

---

* Worship.
† Grown cub.

hot barracks by the side of Kurpa Tal, the little dead lake. He had seen some of them dead of fever, and the barracks crumbling into empty shells and rubble heaps, for black snakes to dwell in. He had seen the palms and the fields of the Terai making ever greater rifts of young green in the yellow grass and the ground bushes of the jungle. For he was old. He was as old as a tiger might be.

His grandsire had died in a drought, lying helpless, beside the very deer he had come to kill, on the cracked mud of the last pool—and the vultures had picked him clean. His sire had died in a thick tangle of grass by the little stream called Bulbul, and his body and bones, found by none, had melted into the soil.

Thus there had been no dead body to prove the passing of one and the coming of another, and the legend had held.

They called him white, but he was not quite white; his coat was the colour of silver sand, faintly pencilled with black. He lacked altogether the royal gold and the ebony, and at dusk or by moonlight or in the half-light before dawn he looked utterly white. He was seldom seen in the full light of day, for by day he slept in a thorny cleft of the hillside, not far from the temple. When the sun was about to set, and the hill lay in shadow, he would take his downward path, passing in full view of the temple, and by dusk would come to the river.

There, in a clear pool under a blue rock, he would drink, and, having drunk, would ford the shallows below and creep into the strip of jungle which skirts the village and joins the upper and the lower forests. Thence he would take one of the many forest rides and walk far into the Terai to Gularbhoj, to Burhaini, to Dalpura—twenty miles at least, going and coming. On the way he would kill and eat, but he never came back on the second night to what he had killed—which fact concerns the legend.

Once, in that strip of jungle, he had killed a *khattra* * and had been disturbed by woodcutters ere he had eaten. The next

* Buffalo calf.

night he had returned by moonlight to eat, but he had hardly touched the calf when the sun had seemed to burst on the night, with thunder from above and a strange smell, and something had burned a furrow in his shoulder. Thereafter he had never returned to a kill, although on one night he had indeed killed twenty buffalo calves. Also, he had never since killed in that strip. So the men of Kaladunghi held that he was good for them.

As if to brand the memory of the day, he had since carried across his right shoulder a long bare furrow. But as the skin had not been broken, the saying that no bullet had pierced him was true.

He had a great head set close on the shoulders; yellow teeth in a slobbering jowl; smouldering yellow eyes; and worn, splayed pads. He was long and lean, and he walked slowly, lumbering with his head low. If men heard the song of a tiger in the gorge they knew that it was not he, for he was always silent.

Though his teeth were splintered and his muscles stiff, and though man was easy game, he had never killed man. Even as his sire and his grandsire had seen men dead by the road and had passed on—so nightly he, brooding outside the temple, washing in the river, sleeping in the grass, riding on the road— was aware of man and ignored him. Nightly, too, he heard the cries of the children of man and saw little brown bodies flitting in the firelight, but the sight and the smell and the sound of them never gave him pause or stirred him to kill. Perhaps the faith in his holiness was due to some dim knowledge of this abstinence.

The years passed, and he still walked. If in one sense he was sacred to the villagers, in another he was sacred to the hunters, for to them he came to represent the supreme prize. According to their purses they hunted him, and according to their natures they dreamed of him—some, in feet and inches, as a record to be inscribed in a book and stretched on a wall; some, in flesh and blood, as a noble thing to kill; some, in craft, as a match for craft.

But, whoever dreamed and came and spent, the wise men only shook their heads.

"He will never die," they said.

III

John Tarbutt swore he would have him. He took the shooting block for a month, brought six elephants, pitched a tent in a clearing on the river bank, and swore that it should be a duel to the death—which meant something on his side. He had money and leisure and, above all, woodcraft; he had the trick of silence; and he had shot tigers everywhere from the Nilgiris to Nepal. Indeed he lived for nothing else, and he did not mind how he hunted—afoot, on an elephant, on a tree, under a rock— so long as he got on terms with the one animal he deemed worth hunting. He was a silent man, and he hunted alone. A duel without spectators, craft against craft, filled the want of his nature.

He sat down outside the tent and looked at the country, pipe in mouth. From where he sat he could trace the river, a ribbon of blue set in silver shingle, to the gorge, where its bed was confined between precipitous banks. A feathery wood clothed the gorge and spread along the hills till it melted in blue distance. Among the trees, a dot of white, was the little temple. When his eye lighted on it, he smiled to himself, for he was aware of the legend. Springing from the gorge, passing him, melting into the great forest behind him, was the strip of jungle—a mile wide—where they said the tiger walked. Indeed, there was nowhere else for him to walk if he desired to leave the hills. John Tarbutt looked it up and down.

"Seems almost too easy," he said to himself.

For a week he seemed to do nothing. He fished, he passed the time of day with the priest at the temple, who informed him politely that, if he had come for the Holy One, he was wasting his time. He mooched about the strip of jungle with his pipe in his mouth, till the villagers, who had been agog with interest at his arrival, ceased to pay any attention to him.

He was a sleepy sahib, they said, who forgot even to take a rifle with him.

But by that time he knew every track in the country. He knew that there were six tracks leading through the strip, and that the tiger used them all impartially. He knew that he did not kill there, for he had quietly sowed the place with buffalo calves. He also knew that he did not lie up there, for he had beaten out all the likely patches with his elephants. In fact, he ruled out the strip, and began to follow him—afoot, or on a pad elephant—in the deep jungle below.

"If only I could see him!" became his constant thought—for that was just what he failed to do.

There was no great difficulty about following him. There were the splayed *punjas* * on the dusty tracks, and, when the *punjas* failed, bent grasses and turned leaves—once, even quivering grasses and leaves. There were all the warning sounds—deer and monkeys and peafowl and jungle fowl signalling to their kind. But get a view he could not. He heard the tiger moving. He heard him drinking. He heard him killing. But he was always a moment too late.

After a fortnight it began to get on his nerves. He began to dream of a white tiger always ahead of him at dusk on a long track between trees. The chance would come. He would align his sights, and—the road would be empty.

He was not superstitious. He had encountered tiger tales by the dozen—tigers with an alleged human spirit inside them, tigers that changed into magicians, tigers that turned away bullets, ghost tigers, impalpable tigers—but he had again and again given the lie to the tales by bringing in dead tigers. Knowing that almost all old tigers achieve a halo of romance, he pooh-poohed the legend of this one, based as it was, he thought, on stupendous luck, unusual cunning, and the accident of a temple. Yet he had to admit his antagonist elusive and to reflect sadly that he was not even in a position to say definitely that he was not white. Tarbutt left the vicinity of the temple to the

* Footprints.

last. Superstitious or no, he had no great hopes of the temple.

He had many vigils, as often as not eating and sleeping under the trees. He haunted the forest paths. But invariably, though nothing but second sight or colossal luck could have accounted for the choice, he would find the prints on the wrong road. Sometimes he would look himself up and down, as if to ask himself what there was about him to betray him. But from his khaki helmet to his rope-soled shoes, he was of the colour of the undergrowth. He had the movement and intuition of an animal. There was no explaining it.

After three weeks he sent his elephants away, and concentrated on the temple slope.

The temple stood on the side of a little depression, where a path ran and the trees stopped short. In the rainy season water collected there, but at that time the place was dry. The caked mud below the path, as well as the dust on the path, held a vivid record. There were innumerable splayed tiger prints, coming and going, and they all led to impenetrable thorn. There was no hope of following the tiger to his lair, even if it could be known that he had any settled lair. Tarbutt tied up a buffalo calf in the hollow below the temple, and, for the first time, scored.

The calf was killed, but not eaten. Nor did the tiger return to eat it on the second night, though Tarbutt held aloof and let the calf lie.

"You know something," was his tribute to his quarry.

A second calf shared the fate of the first, with the same result.

"Tie up a hundred, and a hundred will perish," said the priest.

"So much the better," said Tarbutt, and tied up a third.

This time he climbed into a tree which commanded the hollow and prepared to spend the night there.

The moon was at the full, and by nine o'clock it made day of the ground, silvering the white path and the humped temple. Tarbutt, with an empty pipe in his mouth and his rifle across his knees, watched the calf as it browsed in the short grass—its outline clear as in daylight. The only sounds were the rustling of dewdrops from the trees, the night-jars' call, and the occasional "barks" of a suspicious deer.

Slowly the moon rose to its height. For an hour, maybe, it seemed to stand still in the heavens; then began to sink. But as it sank, the black shadow of a clump of pines stole over the path till the animal was blotted out in a creeping river of black, all the more intense for the light that lay around it. There was a complete inky way, whereby the tiger could come, and kill, and go.

"Anyway, he can't know *that*," thought Tarbutt.

But he had hardly formulated the thought before he was aware of something. He was an expert in sounds. Some obscure instinct in him could be relied on to distinguish between a significant sound and a sound that meant nothing—even to the rustle of a straw or the crackle of a leaf.

He had caught a sound.

It was something slighter than either a rustle or a crackle—the slightest conceivable sound, in fact—a stirring no greater than that which a mouse or an insect would make. But it was significant. At the time, in the place, it meant everything. He knew, as certainly as if he could see it, that in that patch—which looked much as if a large inkpot had been upset on the ground—a tiger was standing; and that tiger could be only one tiger.

In his mind's eye he could trace his actions—the eyeing of the calf, the planted forefeet, the listening poise, the tail tip just flicking. He would have bet a hundred rupees to an anna on it. He waited, tense.

The calf was seemingly lacking in instinct, for it was still browsing and blowing on the leaves.

Then—in an instant—all was over. A scurry; an impact; a little crack; a loud fall; silence. Utter silence!

Tarbutt sat like one carved in stone, his eyes straining to see some sign of movement within the dark patch—or, better still, outside.

A minute passed—five minutes—ten. Still not a sound.

The shadow was beginning to shift. Soon the head of the calf was visible in a silvered place. It was oddly pulled out—neck broken.

Gradually the body, crumpled and hunched still, came into view—till Tarbutt was looking down on a black corpse.

Then, beyond the temple, where the path wound among the trees, he saw the movement of something white.

The tiger had come by the shadow, and killed in the shadow. Then he had taken the open path.

"One up to you!" said Tarbutt.

IV

By the last night Tarbutt, almost in despair, decided on an all-night chase. To relax his mind, he would fish, leaving his rifle with a servant at an appointed place on the bank; then, at the first warning call of bird or beast, he would take up the trail.

In the afternoon he took a light rod and fished towards the gorge. The water was in good order—clear, but with a mild ripple—and he caught half a dozen clean, lively mahsir before he turned. He had fished by them right up to the jaws of the gorge, but the sun was still high and no shadow had touched the hillside. He knew that he had plenty of time.

It was a hot day—the first day, in fact, of the hot weather—and he walked slowly. The water was dazzling. The stones radiated heat. The hills shimmered, and the jungle seemed to drowse. When he came to a shady place—a strip of clean sand at the edge of a pool, with a blue rock to lean his back against—he sat down for a pipe. A quarter of a mile below him he could see his man waiting under a tree at a bend of the river. Feeling that he had half an hour to spare, and that he was in easy reach of his rifle, he sat idly, puffing at his pipe and examining the familiar *punjas* at his feet. For he was clearly sitting by the tiger's favourite drinking pool. There were caved-in prints a month old, as well as the clear impression of yesterday. The sand was full of history.

"A very good choice, old friend," said Tarbutt, scraping the prints over with his foot, "a very good spot indeed."

Then suddenly his pipe dropped out of his mouth and clattered on the pebbles. He sat bolt upright, every muscle of him tense.

The great tiger was within a yard of him.

In the life of every animal, and man, too, for the matter of that, there comes, the wise men say, an hour called *Kaza*—the hour of fate. It is the hour when he is off his guard and for once departs from his protective routine. It is the hour when God wills that he should die, and until that hour he will not die, whatever the odds against him. Thus would the wise men have explained the fact that on this day and this day only the Holy Tiger left the hillside before the shadow covered it and came down to drink an hour before his time.

John Tarbutt, on the other hand, put it down to the first hot-weather thirst. But, whatever may have been the explanation, the fact remains that he looked up from the prints into the eyes of the tiger.

Across a tiny basin of still water where minnows wheeled glinting was the head of the biggest tiger he had ever seen. It was almost white, faintly pencilled with gray lines. The jowl was black and slobbering; the eyes livid. They mesmerized him.

More than half the body was hidden behind the buttress of rock, but the shoulder showed a long bare scar.

The tension was terrible. He was feeling suffocated, as if his clothes had shrunk to pinion him. He could not move. Even if he had not been imprisoned by rock, he could not have moved. Power had left him.

Once before he had met a tiger face to face. But both had sprung aside, and the movement had steeled the nerves. But this tiger never moved or shifted his gaze. A curious thought passed through Tarbutt's mind—was he blind?

Mentally he gave himself up. To his own surprise, he was not afraid. He was merely numb. But his mind was clear, and working rapidly. He noticed things. He had time to wonder who had scored that furrow in the shoulder, and to think what a double-headed monster the reflection in the water made.

Hours seemed to pass.

Then, with infinite deliberation, the great tiger raised its head; gave one last look which seemed to have disdain in it; and drew slowly back behind the rock.

There was no sound of a footfall. The song of the river, lost awhile, came back. There was a lapping of tiny waves at Tarbutt's feet. A fly whined past his ear, and he saw a little whorl of blue smoke creeping from his pipe among the pebbles. Gradually, calculating every fraction of every movement, he raised himself and looked over the buttress of rock—ready any second to plunge into the pool.

Along the shining shingle to the narrow jaws of the gorge, was no sign of life.

He stood up and wiped his forehead. Like a man in a maze he groped for his rod and net. Then, muttering:

"Thank you, my friend, you win," he started to walk downstream.

He had definitely decided to give up. He had never had the impulse before, and could not have explained it. It was not due to fear, but rather the result of complex feelings in which fear was mingled with gratitude and superstition and something of respect. In fact, there was so little fear in it that he was not ashamed of his impulse. He had been beaten—that was the long and short of it.

He walked up to the tree where his man was waiting, and was about to tell him that he was, after all, going back to camp, when he was pulled up short by the very last sound he would have expected—the sound of a fusillade.

It came from across the river, from the strip of jungle which he had come to know like a book. It was a ragged volley, sounding like the fire of a shooting party at a straggling covey of partridges, and it was succeeded by a babble of conversation.

For a moment he stood still, looking round foolishly, for it had been a shrewd blow at his jangled nerves. Then, scenting trouble, he plunged into the river and made for the other side.

As he ran up the beach, he swore doggedly and persistently, for something told him that the trouble might be a wounded tiger. There was no doubt as to his direction. He could hear shouts under the trees and see figures.

He dashed through the bushes, and ran full tilt into a party of youths, who were babbling excitedly and looking at the path. They were obviously schoolboys—not one over twenty—and were diversely armed, three with shotguns, two with Winchesters, and one with a muzzle loader. They were looking at a small round patch of frothy blood in the path.

"What in the devil's name have you done?" Tarbutt gasped.

They told him in snatches.

They were on a mid-term holiday from some college. They always camped here. They had arrived that morning and had sat up in the first likely place they had found on the chance of seeing a stag on its way to the river, or a pig. They had not been ten minutes in the trees before they had seen a bush quiver. Some animal, they had thought, lay down. There had been rustles. Then, thinking that it was a pig rooting, one of them had fired into the bush, and they had all followed suit.

"What happened then?" asked Tarbutt grimly.

"Nothing."

"You saw nothing?"

No, they had seen nothing. One or two of them had thought that they heard something creeping away. So they had all come down and investigated. Then they had chanced on the patch of blood, twenty yards or so on.

"H'm," said Tarbutt. "Show me that bush."

They led him up the path and pointed out the bush, a thick brier at the side of a little deer track, which branched off from the path. On the smaller track, faint on the hard ground, were the splayed *punjas* which he had dreamed of and followed so often. With an inward groan he turned and faced the party.

"Go home, the lot of you," he said. "Cross the river and take the main road and don't stop till you're home. And bear this in mind—if you shoot at something before you have seen what it is, you deserve to be flayed. You might have committed manslaughter. As it is, you've wounded a tiger. You've made trouble. Get!"

They went. He heard subdued conversation as they crossed the river. But he was listening for something else. The jungle was very still, but, far down the strip to the south, a Langur ape was scolding. The sound, much like a cough, was repeated again and again. It meant tiger.

Tarbutt hurried down the path in the direction of the sound.

V

A villager, driving a bullock cart home in the dusk, saw, at a turn in the track, a great pale shape ahead of him—standing still and seeming to shake. At the same moment his pair of bullocks swerved into the ditch and overturned the cart. So once more a trembling man ran into the village and babbled of the white tiger. But he had not seen the blood on the track.

Tarbutt saw it. Patch by patch he marked it, and at every patch he swore.

The irony of it! To have struggled and schemed for a month, day in, day out; to have given his best; then to have heard a parcel of boys with pop-guns down a great tiger—it was too much!

He knew what had happened. A chance bullet from one of the Winchesters had gone well forward, and, finding by a miracle some chink in the mighty mass of muscle, had pierced a lung. But what puzzled him was the doggedness of the wounded animal. Half a mile he would have expected—but that overturned bullock cart was three miles down the road. Where could he be making for? And why?

At every turn of the track he expected to come on a dead tiger, and at every turn he saw only a dim, empty path between dark walls of trees, and here and there that frothy stain in the dust. Whence came that incredible power of holding on?

He was out of the strip now. The little fires that marked the village were behind, while ahead loomed the deep Terai forest, pitchy black. Still on.

The new moon came up and made shadows ahead which seemed to limp and halt. Still no end. The track was straight now, stretching forever between pitchy walls of foliage. But nothing moved on it. Yet the tracks and the pools of blood were still there.

The moon had given place to darkness before Tarbutt weary with following, found that the tracks had ceased to follow the road. The tiger had at last turned aside into the grass. So much he could see with the aid of matches. But he dared not follow farther in the dark.

He lay down and waited for the faint light that heralds dawn.

When the light came, he saw that the jungle was open here—grass, as far as the eye could see, dotted with clumps of trees, and intersected by streams that lay deep between immense banks of reeds.

Very warily, with the dawn, he crept into the grass. It had been trampled, he found, and broken, and in places was flecked with blood as from a coughing fit—but the tiger had not lain down. Soon the grass was over his head, and in front he could see rushes rising still higher. The ground, firm no longer, quaked under his feet. Then his left foot went deep, and it was all he could do to recover. There was no going on. Ahead was a morass and a stream.

But the end was written in the grass.

The great tiger had rested a long time at the edge of the firm ground. Five feet, ten feet on, was a bottomless pit of mud, guarded by green reeds. His head had lain that way.

At last he had risen to his feet, gathered himself for his last spring—and had leapt. Where he had fallen the reeds were parted and torn. But none could follow.

There are no footprints now in the gorge, or at the drinking pool, or on the road. But wise men say that the white tiger, the ancient and the holy one, still walks at night. And, if strangers doubt, they only nod their heads and say:

"No man has seen him die. He is not dead."

John Galsworthy

NEVER GET OUT

I KNEW a little Serval cat—
   Never get out!
Would pad all day from this to that—
   Never get out!
From bar to bar she'd turn and turn,
And in her eyes a fire would burn—
(From her Zoology we learn!)—
   Never get out!

And if by hap a ray of sun—
Came shining in her cage, she'd run
And sit upon her haunches where
Into the open she could stare.
And with the free that sunlight share—
   Never get out!

That catling's jungle heart forlorn
Will die as wild as it was born.
If I could cage the human race
Awhile like her, in prisoned space,
And teach them what it is to face
   Never get out! . . .

Samuel Scoville

LODI

SLOWLY, GRAY-BLACK thorn trees deepened to ashy silver; the flaming African stars paled; and the lilac of the sky changed to violet. Then the full moon wheeled above the baobab trees which stood here and there upon the plain like lurking monsters. At first it was a pale, pale bubble of light, then a shield of burnished gold, to hang at last in mid-sky, an incandescent mass of white fire which made lanes of light through deep dongas and kloof alike. Deceived by the false dawn, hornbills began to mourn from the thickets, and the hollow, liquid crooning of little wood doves sounded from the mango trees.

Suddenly in that strange, still moonlight which had the trick of transmuting all colors into charcoal and old silver, there sounded a wailing cry, "M-wa, m-wa, m-wa." The next moment a long-legged cat with glaring eyes and an orange-tawny coat blotched with black stood in the veldt and sniffed the air hungrily.

Rarely enough does that bush-cat the serval, appear in the open. That one, however, had excuses for being bold—four round, chubby ones, denned in a hollow limb of a yellow-wood tree. Wherefore, when her unerring nostrils brought the news that a lion had killed a sassaby, that swiftest of all antelopes, and cached its carcass back of a big mimosa bush, she came out to investigate.

Ordinarily that tiger cat would no more have ventured to interfere with a lion's kill than she would have crossed the ten-foot dead line which surrounds a rock python in coil, or entered the haunted waters of one of those rivers where crocodiles lurk.

Hunting, however, had been bad with the spotted cat the night before; and the double task of nursing and guarding her cubs made it necessary for her to secure food at once. So, with every muscle tense, ready to vanish like the shadow of a flickering leaf at the first sign of danger, she crept foot by foot toward the spot where the half-eaten body of the buck was hidden.

As she came nearer to the bush her nose caught a hot, raw reek, and that little alarm-bell which beats for all of the wild-folk clanged, "Lion! lion! lion!" against her brain. Perhaps it was the fierce hunger which gnawed at her entrails like a rat which made her disregard that warning for the first and last time in her life. With a fixed stare, she searched every shadow before she crept in toward the torn carcass; but even her flaming eyes could not see the tawny death which lay hidden in the yellow grass. With the terrible craft of his clan, the lion crouched beside his kill, to make an example of any of the lesser breeds who dared to molest it.

The strained, lithe figure of the cat crept forward until with a little growl of satisfaction she sank her teeth deep into a haunch of the dead buck. As if her touch had released some fatal spring, there was the flash of a great paw, and a second later the spotted body of the bush-cat lay stiffening beside the plum-colored one of the sassaby—a warning to all jungle thieves to beware the kill of their king.

Yet death still lurked in that thicket, unsated with his double toll. As the lion lay down again in the hollow which his body had made in the long grass, the lithe figure of a man scarce four feet high showed for a moment in the moonlight. The pale-yellow skin, gaunt frame, and scanty hair growing in pepper-corn tufts marked him as a Bushman, one of that strange race of tiny warriors who drove out the men of the Stone Age who first peopled South Africa. In spite of their size the Bushmen are among the best and bravest hunters in the world, for they alone dare to ambush the lion in his lair or beside his kill and slay him for the sake of his skin and the glory of the deed.

That particular pygmy, washed in a decoction of wild cassia so that the lion might not scent him, had lain since sunset hidden near the dead antelope, waiting with the inexhaustible patience of his kind for the great cat to show some consciousness of his presence. Armed only with a small, weak bow and unfeathered reed arrows with bone heads, it seemed impossible that he would dare to attack the king of beasts—yet when the lion once showed himself, the Bushman never hesitated. There was a twang from the thicket where he stood, and an arrow buzzed through the air like a bee and pierced the lion's tawny shoulder. With a growl, the great cat struck at the shaft with his paw, breaking it off short, but leaving the bone head imbedded in his flesh. The little hunter did not shoot again, but crouched down to wait, knowing that nothing living could long survive the stab of an arrow-point which had been thrust into the body of a devil caterpillar and then smeared with the gum of the poison tree.

For long minutes the lion gave no sign. Then he suddenly stood up, and towering to his full height, gave that dreadful, full-throated roar which shatters the air like a clap of thunder. The great body swayed slightly where it stood, the fierce eyes blazed with a yellow flame, and with another tremendous roar the king of all the killers of the veldt pitched over—dead.

All that night four soft, woolly little serval cubs waited in vain for their mother to come back. The next day three of them cried loudly from hunger. The fourth cub did not cry at all. By mid-afternoon, when his mother had not appeared, he thrust his round head out of the hollow limb and tried to climb down the tree, whereupon he promptly lost his balance and pitched to the ground below. There Baas Vogel found him while on his way across the kloof to his plantation, the largest in that part of South Africa. Though faint and frightened and shaken by his fall, the serval kitten faced the old Boer bravely, hunching up his back and giving tiny growls as a warning of the terrible things he would do if molested. Baas Vogel was much amused.

"Come you home with me, little rascal," he said, in the peculiar brand of English which he always insisted upon using. "It may be that thou shalt help kill some of those verdammt cane rats which eat up my crops so fast as I sow them."

By the time the Boer reached the plantation, the little tiger cat was too weak to stand; for he had been a night and a day without food. It was evident that unless he were fed at once, the last fierce spark of life which he had left would flicker out. There was no milk in the house nor any other food suitable for an unweaned kitten, and no one seemed to know what to do. At that critical moment Spot, the house cat, happened to be crossing the verandah on her way to where a litter of kittens were awaiting her visitation. Purring loudly with her tail arched high above her back, she pushed her way contemptuously through the group of helpless humans, stood over the starving cub, and in another moment that orphan of the veldt was drinking life and strength in eager gulps from the unfailing fountain of warm milk so hospitably offered him.

From that day the serval cat became an important member of the plantation household. Tali, the native overseer, christened him Lodi, which in his Bechuana tongue signified "luck."

Under Spot's nursing, he grew apace and was weaned long before her own kittens. The first that the plantation knew of Lodi's change of diet was one morning when he followed Baas Vogel into the poultry yard. As a flock of pigeons settled on the ground to pick up the strewn grain, Lodi, who had hidden behind the Boer's great bulk, sprang at one bound clear across his master's head and landed, like the little tiger he was, among the feeding birds. Before the flock could take to flight, he had struck down no less than four with swift, dabbing strokes of his armed paws. That was the end of Lodi's liberty for many a long day, for thereafter he was kept on a chain.

A few months later, he had grown into a magnificent cat, two feet high at the shoulder, while his lithe, orange-colored body, inked with round black spots, was a good three feet long, and his ringed tail accounted for another foot. He had eyes like flaming topazes, and his feet and pads were shrimp-pink.

Sometimes, as a special treat, the Baas would take him out on the veldt, unchained, to hunt for himself. Long-legged, lithe, and lean, it was a pleasure for the old Boer to watch the in-

credible speed and certainty with which his pet would catch
field mice and cane rats. Before long he was stalking nobler
quarry. Once the two walked into a covey of partridges, and as
they whirred up from the grass, Lodi sprang six feet into the
air and caught one in mid-flight, although an African partridge,
like his American relative, buzzes through the air like a bullet.
Another day Lodi saw a bush-pigeon preening itself on a near-
by tree. Crouching low, the serval slipped along the ground like
a snake, taking advantage of every bit of cover, his tawny body
blending perfectly with the yellow grass and dry fern about
him. Crouching until almost flat on the ground, the great cat
suddenly shot up fully ten feet straight into the air, snatched
the bird off the limb, and brought it back to the Boer to be
broiled for luncheon.

Then came the unlucky day when, in his master's absence,
old Tali took Lodi hunting. In the late afternoon, when the
trees that fringed the horizon were etched in inky purple
against a blazing orange sky, the two plodded homeward empty-
handed through the cool green light.

Suddenly, out of a great reed-bed full of golden finches and
malachite sunbirds, burst a blue duiker, smallest of all South
African antelope and only about the size of a hare. So fast did
he move that he showed only as a blue-brown blur against the
yellow grass. Instantly a tawny streak shot toward him, and before the startled Tali could stop him, the serval cat was gone.
In vain he gave the long, wailing cry of the bush-cat, with
which he was accustomed to call Lodi back. There was a crack-
ling of the reeds, a waving of distant ferns, and the little duiker,
racing for his life with the tiger cat hard at his heels, had disappeared. Tali hunted and called until dark before he returned
home and reported the loss of the old Boer's pet.

Baas Vogel was greatly incensed at the news.

"Verdammt esel!" he thundered. "Be off tomorrow and come
not back without my Lodi, or I break every bone in thy worthless black body."

As always, the old Boer's bark was worse than his bite, but
the Bechuana took the threat seriously. Early the next day, with

his tin billy and a sack of mealie flour, he disappeared into the veldt.

For the whole of a long day he quartered back and forth mile after mile over the plain, hunting and calling for the lost Lodi. There was no sight of the serval until late in the afternoon, when there was a sudden rustle in the reeds near the old man, and out into the open sprang Lodi, with the dead duiker flung across his shoulder. Bechuana and bush-cat returned to the plantation in triumph, and the Boer was so pleased over his pet's exploit in running down a blue duiker that he not only forgave the old native but presented him with an extra ration of snuff to make up for his hard words of the day before.

Baas Vogel's joy over the return of the prodigal was somewhat tempered by an incident which happened a few days after Lodi came back. He had been placed on a chain outside of an enclosure screened by wide-meshed wire, intended to protect the poultry from any more of his sudden attacks. One old rooster, an imported white Wyandotte, used to exasperate Lodi by thrusting his head in through the screen and stealing scraps.

One morning Lodi's food-dish happened to be placed less than a foot from the netting. Watching his chance, the white cock would thrust his head through the screen and snatch up bits from the plate. Hissing with rage, the serval each time sprang at the Wyandotte; but the old rooster had calculated the length of the chain to an inch, and at every spring the tiger cat was jerked painfully back, while the thief went on calmly gobbling up his dinner.

After a third unsuccessful attempt, Lodi ostentatiously gave up all hopes of catching his unwelcome visitor. Crouching down as close to the dish as the chain would permit, he closed his eyes, and doubling up his paws beneath him, apparently went to sleep under the shade of a pyramid cypress tree which towered above him, black-green against the summer sky.

The old rooster eyed him suspiciously for some time. At last he pretended to thrust his head in and pick at the plate. The tiger cat did not move or even open his eyes. Half a dozen times the crafty cock repeated this feint, with no sign of life from

Lodi. At last, evidently convinced that the big serval was really asleep, the rooster poked his head clear through the mesh, snatched a morsel from the plate, and gulped it down, chuckling deep in his throat as he did so. Again he repeated the theft. When for the third time his red comb and wattles dipped into the dish, a long, spotted paw shot out like a flash; and the next instant the cock's headless body was tumbling about outside of the enclosure, decapitated instantly by the cat's keen, retractile claws.

The Baas exploded with a loud report when the news came to him of the passing of his prize Wyandotte.

"Wicked little spotted devil!" he thundered. "First it is that you run away and my best man loses for me a day's work. Then you pull, from his body off, the head of my fine, big white rooster, who is worth a thousand bush-cats. Now I fix you."

Lodi only blinked his gooseberry-green eyes and rubbed his head disarmingly against the Baas's leg. His caresses availed him nothing, for the next day he was shut up in a cage made of close-meshed wire and no longer allowed to run about the enclosure even on a chain. Those cramped quarters soon had a bad effect upon his temper, and before long he would snarl whenever anyone approached. One morning Kosi, the Kafir boy, whose duty it was to clean out Lodi's cage, teased the fretting animal with his broom. The serval hissed murderously, but the Kafir kept on until, with a growl which sounded like the rasping of rough iron, the tiger cat sprang through the half-open door, dodged the broom which the boy flourished in front of him, and like the flash of a brandished blade, sprang for Kosi's throat. If Baas Vogel had not happened to be passing just at that moment, the furious animal would have killed his tormenter. It was old Tali who secured the acquittal of his pet.

"With my own eyes," he testified, "I saw that worthless lump of Kafir mud poke the Spotted One with his broom. The evil son of an aard-vark deserved far worse than he got."

It had been Spot who first saved Lodi's life, and it was the last and least of her kittens who secured his liberty for her foster child.

That kitten was a tiny mite of a thing, black as a blot of ink except for a snubby white nose. The first time that she chanced to wander near Lodi's cage, it was a case of love at first sight with her. Running up to the netting, with tail arched high, she mewed and tried in vain to rub her snowy nose against the tiger cat's black one. Lodi growled furiously and would have killed her instantly if he had been able to reach her. Undiscouraged by this reception, Blackie kept on making friendly advances until at last Lodi responded to her untiring efforts, and the great cat and the tiny kitten would lie for hours at a time as close to each other as the wire netting would allow, crooning and purring as if carrying on long conversations in cat fashion.

At other times they would play games together, leaping around on different sides of the netting and occasionally pretending to dart at each other through the wire meshes.

At last one day old Tali opened the door carefully and set the kitten inside. Lodi advanced with arched back, purring loudly, and leaped delightedly up and down and over and around his visitor in a great demonstration of delight. Then he lay down and licked Blackie all over gently with his long rough tongue, burrowing his nose into her soft fur caressingly.

When at last Tali tried to take the kitten out, the tiger cat instantly gripped Blackie by the loose skin at the back of her neck as a mother cat might, and throwing a protecting paw around her, gave such a murderous growl that the old native instantly decided to leave the kitten where she was.

From that moment Lodi became a changed character. He growled no more at visitors nor yowled through the night, and the hens and ducks fed about his cage unaffrighted. Before long his conduct became so irreproachable that the Baas decided to give him once more the freedom of the plantation. Accordingly Lodi left the cage one morning, free and unchained, accompanied by the kitten.

Blackie, in spite of her youth, had been properly brought up by Spot in all the traditions of a well-trained house cat, and in some way known only to herself, she soon convinced her companion that pigeons and poultry were to be regarded as allies and not enemies.

Lodi made up for his enforced virtue during the day by his activities at night in the Dene, that wooded strip of jungle surrounding the plantation. There and on the adjacent veldt he would hunt night after night, always bringing his kill through an open window into his master's bedroom for the latter's inspection and approval. Sometimes it was a cane rat big as a rabbit, or a rock dassie, or a six-pound springhare, which jumps like a kangaroo and bites like a weasel. Whatever his catch, Lodi would crouch with it beside the Baas's bed and purr like a coffee mill until the latter woke up and patted and praised him, whereupon he would depart through the open window, taking his catch with him.

Then there came the fatal night when he caught a striped musihond. The musihond is Africa's reply to the challenge of the American skunk, and though dead a musihond speaketh—loudly. When Lodi brought that one into the bedroom the Baas left it at one jump, burying his face in his pillow as he went, not to return until the room had been scrubbed and fumigated over and over again. That unfortunate occurrence was the last straw which broke the back of his patience.

"That verdammt cat, he leaves now," he spluttered as soon as he could get his breath.

"Send him not away," pleaded Tali. "The Spotted One is a luck cat."

"Yes—a bad-luck cat," returned the Baas grimly. "First it is my pigeons and then my big rooster and now me myself. Luck cat or no, he goes."

Wherefore the next day Lodi left by train in a covered basket, from which came indignant yowls, on his way to another plantation two hundred miles down the coast.

The Baas missed the great cat more than he had supposed possible. Night after night he would wake with a start, thinking that he heard Lodi's resonant purr beside his bed—or would find himself expecting to feel his lithe body rub against him as he walked across the plantation. Always, however, there was neither sight nor sound of his lost pet.

At last, musihonds or no musihonds, the Baas could stand Lodi's absence no longer and traveled clear down to the other plantation to bring him back, only to find that he had disappeared from his new home the day after his arrival there. He went back without his cat, feeling remorsefully that perhaps he had driven away forever the luck of the plantation, even as Tali had said.

The night after his return was peculiarly hot and stifling, and it was only after long tossings on his hot pillow, that he at length fell into a troubled sleep, to be suddenly awakened by a curious rubbery thud on the matting by the open window, as if someone had dropped there a piece of heavy garden-hose. For a moment the Baas thought that Lodi had come back, but the sound was entirely different from the light thump with which the cat's padded paws used to strike the floor. Half asleep, he switched on the light and found himself looking into a pair of deadly, staring eyes set like fatal jewels in a heart-shaped head. Below them he recognized the bloated body of a huge puff adder, some five feet in length and as thick through as a man's leg. In the sudden light, the sooty chevrons and cream-colored crescents blotched with yellow-lake showing on its scaled skin made a blended pattern like a strip of some sinister eastern carpet woven on the loom of death itself.

As the Baas shrank back there was an intake of whistling breath followed by a fierce hiss as the great snake's swollen body moved itself a foot or so nearer the bed.

The Boer had seen puff adders in action before and knew that in spite of their seeming sluggishness, nothing that lives can surpass in swiftness the flashing stroke of that deadly viper. Bracing his sweating back against the wall the man waited, holding himself rigidly still. Hissing again, the great serpent pushed forward another foot; and the cruel head raised itself above the bloated coils. At any moment that ghastly demon of the night might start the rush forward which could end in only one way.

Then, as the Baas clenched his hands so tightly that his nails cut into his wet palms, there came a scratching and a rustle just outside the window, and into the room with a bound sprang the lost tiger cat. His sides, which had been so sleek, were sunken, and every rib showed gauntly beneath his silky skin, while bloody welts here and there spoke of the dangers through which he had passed on his long journey home.

Turning like a flash as it felt the vibration of the cat's landing, the great serpent faced the newcomer, hissing horribly. At that breath Lodi crouched; his eyes flamed green-gold in the shadow, and deep in his throat he growled, while his coral gums showing over the white stiletto-like teeth changed his face into a snarling mask of rage like those lion heads which Assyrian sculptors used to cut in black basalt on the plains of Nineveh six thousand years ago.

For an instant, as cat and snake crouched and coiled, the flaming eyes of the beast met the dreadful lidless gaze of the serpent. It was Lodi who attacked first. Springing forward, he feinted a lunge with his right forepaw, and even as he did so sprang to his left, as if shot forward by an uncoiled spring. As he moved, the mouth of the snake opened, and from white ridges of gum two crooked, glistening fangs suddenly thrust themselves out from the upper jaw, keener than the sharpest needle ever made by man. As the horrid mouth gaped wide, the inch-long weapons showed tiny openings in their sides, like those in a hypodermic needle, through which the venom would ooze when once their points were sunk deep into the flesh of a victim. Then, just as the cat's body flashed away, the head of the puff adder shot two feet through the air with a motion so swift that no human eye could have followed it and struck the floor a scant inch from the cat's paw. At the stroke the muscles surrounding the capsule containing the poison ducts contracted, and little jets of a limpid yellow liquid bedewed the silken fur of the cat with the very essence of death. Then, like the return of a released spring, the grim head snapped back into the center of the adder's coil once more. Again and again, the great cat advanced and retreated, feinting, snarling, springing, until he had provoked the enraged serpent into striking a score of times. Each time only the animal's exquisite sense of distance saved his life, since stroke after stroke of the snake just missed the cat's outstretched paw by a fraction of an inch.

Springing, darting back and forth, and continually circling the bloated body of the huge adder, never once during the first rounds of this duel to the death did Lodi sink teeth or claw into the patterned, scaly skin of the snake, or take chances with the fatal backlash with which a puff adder so often catches an opponent unawares.

At last the great serpent began to refuse to strike. Still the cat moved around it in swift circles, forcing the adder to move with him in order to keep facing its antagonist.

For some fifteen minutes Lodi feinted and circled until the puff adder, not built for a long battle, began to move more and more slowly and to show signs of weakness.

At last there came a time when the heavy body was so slow in recoiling that the cat stopped his circling tactics and stared for an instant at the great snake, with an almost human calculation in his flaming eyes. Then he feinted a last reckless rush, which the viper countered by a lunge which just grazed the cat's outstretched paw. For an instant the fatal head lay flat on the floor. Before it could snap back into place, the cat for the first time struck two lightning-like blows with either paw, ripping his curved black talons through the serpent's skin with a sound like that of tearing silk. Once again the puff adder went back into coil and for the last time struck as the cat plunged in and out. As the serpent lay exhausted, Lodi dabbed at it again with his left forepaw, pinned the deadly head down, and with a lightning-like spring drove his four long fighting teeth through and through the snake's spine, and with teeth and claws tore the grinning head clear off from the paralyzed body. Then, purring proudly, with arched back, he rubbed his silky side against Baas Vogel's shaking hand.

The Luck of the Plantation had come back—and this time to stay.

Herbert Ravenel Sass

LYNX-HAUNTED WOODS

EARLY ONE MORNING a hunter went down to the edge of a swamp in the Carolina Low Country in search of wild turkeys. About fifty yards from the swamp, he found a big log with an oak in front of it and another behind it. Leaning his gun against the log, he sat down with his back against one of the trees to wait for daylight.

At day-clean, as the Low Country Negroes term full dawn, he began calling. It was just the hour when the turkeys should be coming down from their roosts in the tall trees to feed, and the hunter yelped several times, then listened eagerly for an answer. Almost at once he heard a faint sound. Something had come out of the strip of reeds along the edge of the swamp about forty yards away. He saw it, or believed that he saw it, for an instant amid the scattered blackjack saplings; but in the dim light this brief uncertain glimpse told him little, and he concluded that it was only a rabbit.

He continued yelping; and listening intently for the reply that he hoped to hear, he heard the rabbit come a few feet nearer. Thinking only of turkeys, he did not realize, until the intruder was within eight feet of him on the other side of the log, that rabbits do not ordinarily behave as this animal was behaving.

The hunter was still sitting on the ground, his feet against the log, his knees drawn up under his chin. He leaned to his left to look over the log and behind the oak just beyond it, at the same time extending his arm toward his gun. He gazed straight into the eyes of a bay lynx, or wildcat.

121

For two seconds neither man nor wildcat moved. Then the man, still sitting, seized his gun and tried to tip the barrel over the log for an arm's-length shot.

Instantly the lynx sprang, launching itself at the hunter's throat. The man jerked his head and body aside and threw up his arm to ward off the blow. The leaping cat passed between the hunter's face and the gun held in his right hand, slashing the man's thumb and knuckles, and made off into the woods at top speed, its flight hastened by the load of turkey shot that went crashing after it. The encounter was merely a remarkable instance of mistaken identity. But, although the hunter did not look at it in just that light, it was, too, an illustration of the wild charm of lynx-haunted woods, where in any green bay or dense thicket the most mysterious and elusive of all the four-footed wild creatures may be lurking.

In this sense, all these woods of the Low Country are lynx-haunted. Not that at any moment in these woods one is likely to have a wildcat adventure as exciting as that which befell the turkey hunter. There is not by any means a lynx in every thicket; the point is that in almost any thicket there may be one. Not so clever as the fox, the wildcat—or bobcat, as he is known in the West, though bay lynx is his proper and much better name—makes up in mystery what he lacks in personality. Even in places where he is most abundant he is very seldom seen—so seldom that to most people the animal is little more than a myth, a phantom denizen of the mystical, moss-tapestried swamp forests, a legend rather than a reality. Preëminently a creature of the night, he never shows himself to man if he can avoid it; and when he does show himself, he can appear and disappear so swiftly, so soundlessly, that there seems to be magic in it. He is thus, in a sense, the wildest of all the wild inhabitants of the plantation region; and the Low Country woods and swamps owe something of their allurement to the fact that almost anywhere in them this little kinsman of the tiger may be watching you or listening to your footfalls as you pass by.

The thought that a fierce-eyed, silent, hungry watcher, a

hater of mankind, may have you under his gaze need inspire no nervousness in anyone who knows the creature. Nothing on earth could have made that lynx of the Low Country stalk the turkey hunter if the animal had suspected that the sounds issuing from behind the log came from a man and not from a turkey. Yet arrant coward though the wildcat is, even the oldest woodsman finds something both sinister and uncanny in this invisible, almost intangible presence which glides along the dim forest paths on padded feet and prowls about the plantation outhouses in the darkness, unknown and unrecorded, unless some turkey, goose or pig is missing in the morning and certain rounded tracks in the sand reveal the nature of the marauder.

On a dim, shadowy night some years ago, at Magnolia on the Ashley—once one of the finest of the old plantations and now a wonderland of azaleas—a long, slim, slinking shape stole out of the woods and passed swiftly across an open space near an outbuilding. It made for a large leaning mulberry tree and ran rapidly and with perfect ease up the stout trunk. At a height of about twenty feet it fastened itself upon a sleeping hen turkey, leaped or fell with the turkey to the ground, and, somewhat less swiftly than it had come—for the turkey weighed nearly ten pounds—passed like a ghost across the clearing and vanished in the blackness of the woods.

Several nights later this same long, slinking shape came stealing through the forest near the river. Presently it stopped. Ahead of it in the darkness it saw something that was not there when last it had passed that way. Probably it reconnoitered the strange object with great care, but did not find it sufficiently formidable to excite serious alarm. Soon the dim shape moved forward again. It had a special reason for desiring to reach a certain spot within a few feet of this strange object, which resembled a square wooden box about a foot and a half high. So the dim shape drew nearer and nearer, probably by a more or less circuitous route, and certainly keeping a watchful eye on the boxlike object all the while; and suddenly, when it had come almost within leaping distance of the object, something

snapped, and one of the largest bay lynxes that ever roamed
the woods of the Low Country was caught by the foot in a steel
trap.

Early next morning some of the Negroes at Magnolia, coming
to examine the traps, found the captive. He had returned, as
they had believed that he would, to the place where he had
buried the carcass of the turkey, after eating as much of it as he
could hold. They had concealed their traps about the place, and
in the midst of them, near the spot where the half-eaten body of
the turkey was buried, they had placed a live rooster in a slatted
coop, hoping that the crowing of the rooster would hasten the
raider's coming.

They spent little time wondering whether it was the rooster
or the turkey which was chiefly responsible for the lynx's pre-
dicament. What interested them at the moment was the amazing size of the creature; and so forbidding was his aspect, and
so ferocious were his deep growls and snarls, that, although he
was evidently held securely by the trap, none of the Negroes
would go near him. After some moments one of them picked
up a stick and threw it at the animal. The wildcat, apparently
holding the rooster responsible for this assault, sprang furiously
at the coop and smote so fiercely with his paw as to smash one
of the slats and rake the terrified bird with his long claws. A
little later the cat's career was ended with a bullet. His skin
was brought to the city by the owner of Magnolia. The Negroes
pronounced the rest of him delicious.

This wildcat of Magnolia, which came to his death on the
morning of October 10, 1921, deserves some special notice. He
was not weighed and his measurements were not properly taken;
but though he was probably not a record breaker, he was an
extraordinary specimen of his kind. Experienced hunters who
saw his skin estimated his weight at between sixty and seventy
pounds; and though their estimates were certainly excessive,
they may not have been so wildly extravagant as many will be
inclined to suppose. Naturalists of the North and East will
smile at those figures; but the fact is that naturalists of the

North and East do not know much about Low Country wild-cats.

Here undoubtedly the animal attains a size far in excess of Northern and Western averages. Dr. William T. Hornaday, director of the New York Zoölogical Park, certainly a first-rate authority, says:

"The largest specimen that ever came into my hands weighed eighteen pounds"—this figure is so small that one wonders whether it is not a misprint. "The largest of nine specimens killed by Mr. Roosevelt's party in Routt County, Colorado, in 1901, weighed thirty-nine pounds. One killed near Asheville, North Carolina, in 1900 is reported to have weighed fifty-one pounds."

The Low Country can beat the best of these, even the Asheville record, which Doctor Hornaday evidently regards with doubt. In November, 1900, Ferdinand Gregorie, a planter, killed at Grog Pond, near Oakland plantation, a male bay lynx which tipped the scales at a trifle more than fifty-one pounds. This monarch of wildcats was weighed by Arthur T. Wayne, an ornithologist of national note, whose testimony will be accepted by scientific men everywhere. It was the largest lynx of which there is authentic record in this region; yet thirty-pounders are not very rare here, and it is easily possible that an even bigger wildcat than that Oakland monster is lurking now in some Low Country swamp.

To the many swamps, which afford excellent cover and safe refuge for the rearing of the three or four kittens which the female brings forth each year, and to the abundance of the wild life on which he subsists—mainly rabbits and other rodents and many sorts of birds—the bay lynx owes his survival in such large numbers in the Low Country. In some respects the coming of civilization has actually favored him. The puma and the great packs of wolves which formerly ranged through these forests have gone, and though man is a far more dangerous enemy to the wildcat than these former masters of the wilderness ever were, their elimination is one thing for which the lynx must thank his most hated foeman.

There are other man-made compensations besides this one
to console the lynx for the passing of the halcyon days of the
Low Country's early youth. He is quite as fond of quail as he
is of turkey as an article of food; and though there are fewer
turkeys now than in the Indians' time, there are probably more
bobwhites. It seems likely that the bobwhite was a compara
tively rare bird in the primeval forests, and that it followed the
white man and throve upon his handiwork, instead of with
drawing before him. The call of the partridge, like the hum of
the bee, says one of the old historians, was a signal to the In
dians of coming white men and the approach of civilization
It was, too, a signal to the lynxes of those times, though they
could hardly have known it, of the coming of a new and suc
culent species of prey, destined to take the place, in large meas
ure, of the wild turkey, which seems to have been those early
lynxes' favorite form of provender.

The bay lynx has to work harder now for a turkey dinner
than the lynxes of the early days; yet such a dinner may be had,
and is probably often had, in the seclusion of the canebrakes
and thickets where no hound or hunter is likely to interrupt
the feast. The wild turkey survives in fair numbers in the Low
Country. I heard the other day of a man who had recently
counted more than forty of these splendid birds in one old
field, and it is not a very unusual experience to flush them as
one drives along the less frequented woods roads.

To see the great gobblers, tall and slender of build, their
heads held high, their bronze bodies glinting in the light, striding through the open woods of the pineland at the moment
before they take flight, and then to watch them sailing swiftly
away amid the trees, rising higher and higher until they have
topped the feathery summits of the pines, is to enjoy one of the
most thrilling spectacles which the Low Country woods afford
and to receive a vivid reminder of the old days when all the
woodlands swarmed with turkeys.

"Having rested very well during the night," wrote William
Bartram, the botanist, describing his journey through Carolina
about a century and a half ago, "I was awakened in the morn-

ng early by the cheerful converse of the wild turkey cocks
aluting one another from the sun-brightened tops of the lofty
ypresses. They begin at early dawn and continue until sunrise,
rom March until the last of April. The high forests ring with
he noise, like the crowing of the domestic cock, of these social
entinels; the watchword being caught and repeated from one
o another for hundreds of miles around; in so much that the
vhole country is, for an hour or more, in an universal shout.
A little after sunrise they quit the trees, and alighting on the
arth, strut and dance around the coy female, while the deep
orests seem to tremble with the shrill noise."

What marvelous turkey feasts the lynxes of that period must
ave enjoyed, following the great flocks as they roamed through
he vast forest that stretched from the ocean to the prairies, and
carcely ever out of sight, sound or scent of turkeys from one
ay's end to another!

Those days have gone, but something of them remains. The
ay lynx is one reminder of them and the wild turkey another,
hough the fear of man has settled over the woods, so that the
morous gobblers no longer welcome the dawn with so cheer-
ul a clamor. Yet to-day, just as in the early days, these two
ereditary foes often match wits in the woods; and sometimes
he turkey, in spite of the amazing keenness of his senses, is the
oser in the deadly game. Few and far between are the human
unters who can walk or crawl up to a gobbler feeding on the
round; but the soft-footed, serpentlike lynx—serpentlike in his
inuousness and slender symmetry and in his possession of the
ame sinister craft and cunning which, rightly or wrongly, we
ttribute to the serpent—is a still-hunter and stalker whose skill
ven the most practiced of two-legged woodsmen can never
ope to approach.

Not only the turkeys but the deer also fear him. Perhaps the
irst explorers overdrew their spirited accounts of wildcats rid-
ng through the woods on the backs of full-grown deer and
ucking the blood of their victims while they were yet in the
hroes of death; but there can be little doubt that the wildcat
vas a destructive enemy of the deer when the latter grazed in

hundreds in all the forests, just as there is no doubt that the
wildcats of to-day sometimes dine on venison. As a rule only
young fawns are taken. As a matter of fact, an adult buck, un
less the lynx could contrive to drop upon him from some over
hanging bough, would be more than a match for any wildcat
Only the other day, however, a negro woodsman came upon the
body of a yearling deer which had just been killed by three
wildcats, seen close by the carcass.

A friend of mine who is a mighty deer hunter captured a
young fawn in the woods some time ago and reared it in a small
enclosure in his yard. The fawn became very tame, and being
admitted often to the house, made itself almost a nuisance by
its importunate and incessant desire for tidbits of various kinds
accepting eagerly whatever was given it, including even shrimps
and cigarette stumps. Of only one thing was it afraid. If a cat
came anywhere near it, it was seized with a paroxysm of terror
and sometimes its frenzied efforts to flee were so violent that
its owner feared it would break its neck.

This fawn, having been taken so young, within a few hours
after birth, could hardly have had any actual experience of
wildcats, and during its life in captivity no domestic cat had
ever made an attack upon it. Its fear must have been purely in
stinctive, the result of long centuries of warfare between the
bay lynx and the white-tailed deer in the Low Country woods;
and it is interesting to note that this instinct, based upon the
bobtailed tawny lynx, was aroused so swiftly and powerfully
by the long-tailed, variously colored and much smaller cousins
of the lynx, which roam our fences at night and occasionally
make a pretense of paying their board by catching a few mice
for their owners.

It is possible that two hundred and fifty years ago the wildcat
was not so desperately afraid of man as it is to-day. The twen
tieth-century wildcat, which has to deal with shotguns instead
of bows and arrows, has learned wisdom. I know of only one
instance in which a bay lynx has deliberately attacked a human
being in this region, and in that case the victim was a very small
negro boy. To-day, when a wildcat is started by the dogs in the

ourse of a deer hunt, the hunter is in less danger from the cat han from the deer, for there have been cases in which a hunted uck has charged a hunter.

For the dogs, however, the cat may prove an exciting cus- omer, at least in those instances when it is brought to bay be- ore it has an opportunity to climb a tree. Coward though it s, the lynx will fight hard for its life when the hounds close n for the death grapple, and its fangs are long and keen and ts claws as sharp as needles; but it will not fight the pack, or ven one dog of the pack, so long as there is any possibility of scape by flight or concealment. One startling exception to this ule is an incident related by William Elliott, most famous of Low Country sportsmen, who hunted these woods and fished hese waters some three-quarters of a century ago.

"A full-grown wildcat," says Elliott, "will sometimes succeed n beating off a half dozen dogs; though I once owned a noble ound that would kill a cat single-handed. I was witness to uch an exciting contest. I was hunting cats with my two well- rained cat hounds, Rowser and Black, and had given the cat chase of a couple of hours, when, Black having been thrown ut, Rowser brought the chase to bay in a hedge. Seeing but ne dog in pursuit, he determined to give battle, and after a growl of defiance, left the cover of the hedge and leaped out nto an open field. Rowser sprang after him, and the cat, in- tead of flying, threw himself upon his back, raised his head nd extended his forepaws in the attitude of a pugilist on guard. The dog approached—his hair bristling upon his back—and tood almost over his recumbent foe. There was a pause of sev- ral seconds, during which they glared at each other with in- onceivable fury, before they closed in the death struggle.

"The dog seized the cat on its breast, between the forelegs, he cat at the same time burying its fangs in the shoulder of he dog. Though bitten through and through he uttered no cry f pain, but pressed down upon the cat—nor relaxed his hold ntil his foe was dead. He killed him by dint of pressure, for is teeth had never entered the skin of the cat—nor have I ever vitnessed an instance in which, when killed by dogs, their skins

have been torn by their teeth. When the cat was dead his fang
still remained clinched in the shoulder of the dog; his jaws had
to be separated by force, and the victor, released from his grip
was unable to move, and was taken home on the back of a
horse. I need hardly add that I never suffered this gallant hound
a second time to engage single-handed in so serious a conflict."

I have come upon one other remarkable instance, which
though it is less noteworthy than Elliott's, should perhaps be
mentioned here. Some years ago, at Old Town Plantation—his
toric ground, because it was there that the first Charleston
stood—two boys about twelve or fourteen years of age were
hunting rabbits, with a little mongrel as their assistant, on a
wooded point of land extending into the marsh. Suddenly they
heard the dog yelling in pain and terror. Hastening to the spot
they found that a big wildcat had him on his back and was
mauling him unmercifully.

The boys were too small and inexperienced to be trusted
with shotguns and their only weapons were stout sticks. They
were not wanting in pluck, however, and they rushed instantly
to the rescue, delivering such telling blows upon the lynx that
they first stunned and then killed it. This incident, so contrary
to lynx nature, is difficult to explain. Possibly the cat had young
ones near by. Possibly—though this seems unlikely—the dog had
cornered it and it was compelled to assume the offensive in or
der to make its way out. Be that as it may, the two boys who
killed it with their crude weapons were among the proudest
youngsters in America—almost as proud as a small friend of
mine of about their age who, some years ago, killed a bear.

In this episode of the Old Town lynx the dog which figured
in the affray was a very small one. One hears tales from time to
time of battles in which some lone hound, ranging the woods
in the night, was severely handled by a wildcat, but very few
of these stories are worthy of credence. I happened the other
day upon an instance in which the honors rested with the dog
though he deserved little credit for it.

I had gone before dawn to the cabin of a certain negro
hunter of my acquaintance to pay an early morning visit to a

flock of wild turkeys whose feeding ground we had discovered. The big, splendid birds, viewed in the first faint light of day under the great pines at the swamp's edge, would be a sight worth while; and we felt fairly confident of finding them, for the many fresh "scratches" amid the dead leaves and pine needles proved that they fed there pretty regularly. Moreover, I liked the place for other reasons also, since the trail to the turkey woods led, with many turns and windings, through a swampy country full of dark ponds and pools where otters lived, while we never failed to find along the way tracks of deer and many signs of lynxes. My dusky woodsman was ready; and as we made our way in the darkness through the woods, he explained to me why he was in such high spirits.

For a month or more a wildcat had been raiding his chickens. He had set traps, and at last, after much scheming, had outwitted the robber. The cat, however, had contrived to jerk the trap loose from its moorings and had dragged it off into the woods, and, although the hunter and his dog had worked hard on the trail they had failed to run down the quarry. All this had happened two weeks before, and the hunter had dismissed the lynx from his mind; but only two or three hours before I had arrived, the dog—a lanky black and white mongrel with some hound in him—had come upon the animal in the bed of a small stream in the woods, and had closed with it and killed it. This was no great feat, for the lynx was so emaciated that it could offer only feeble resistance. The left forefoot, by which the trap had caught it, had rotted off or had been bitten off, and the lynx, unable to kill enough food to support life, was perishing of hunger.

One day last fall I walked a lonely path which I call Lynx Lane. It was a cold, clear, autumn morning. The thought of work in a stuffy study was repugnant and by ten o'clock had become intolerable. By eleven we had left the city some fifteen miles behind us and stood in the midst of that varicolored glory—crimson and gold and coppery-bronze—which November spreads wherever young sweet gums mass themselves along the borders of small swamps. The path which would take us to

Lynx Lane led straight through such a thicket; but at the swamp's edge we paused to have a look at a certain bare space of sand which I never pass without examination.

That spot is an unfailing treasure house of thrills; mild thrills, but pleasant nevertheless. Aside from a few small finches, we are likely to see no living thing there, for cover is lacking; but always we find in the clean sand a fascinating record of wild things that passed in the night. We found trails of deer, apparently seven or eight, ranging all the way from the delicate impression of a fawn's tiny foot to the deep, bold, strong, yet graceful track of a splendid buck; and as a fitting prelude to a walk along Lynx Lane, we found amid the deer tracks the rounded print of a wildcat's paw.

It was what I was looking for and we passed on, through the gold and crimson and coppery glory of the sweet-gum thicket, across the small stream flowing through the swamp, and so with cautious, deliberate steps to the remote woodland spot where the swamp path joins Lynx Lane. It was well that we had come noiselessly. Around the corner, hidden from us until that moment by the low, dense undergrowth, three wild turkeys, at least two of which were big gobblers, stood not forty feet away in the narrow path, their burnished plumage glowing in the sun. In that wild, secluded place, in that rich setting of gorgeously painted foliage, they were a sight never to be forgotten, as we gazed for a brief instant, rapt and motionless.

The wonderful moment passed, to be succeeded by another not less memorable. As though powerful steel springs propelled them, they shot upward—up and up and up, with strong, surging strokes of their wide wings—until they topped the trees bordering the trail. Some hunters say that a turkey must run a considerable distance before rising; and I know of one hunter, who, flushing a wild turkey in a woods road closely hemmed in by trees, spurred his horse and, riding madly, actually snatched the flying bird out of the air, the turkey being unable to rise swiftly because the impetus of its start was insufficient.

But these gobblers of Lynx Lane needed no running start. Possibly they took two steps before rising. Then they simply catapulted upward. They had been facing towards us and took no time to turn; hence, if they were not to fly over us, they had to mount very sharply and wheel in the air. They flew not straight up, of course, but at so steep a grade that their ascent was almost rocket-like. I have some fine memories of wild turkeys, some spirited mind pictures of noble gobblers seen in the woods. But those rocketing turkey cocks of Lynx Lane make the finest picture of all.

A good beginning, indeed, for a walk along Lynx Lane; and in high spirits we followed that tunnel-like trail for five miles or so through wild swamp woods full of life and full of mystery. Yet, except birds of various common kinds, we saw scarcely a living thing. Again and again, in dozens or even scores of places, we found evidences of the unseen life that was all around us— tracks and sign of deer, of raccoon, of otter, and of wildcat. At least twenty times in those five miles we found wildcat sign. In one spot four or five wildcats had paused on the same log, and none of the sign was more than two nights old; but all day long we saw not a wildcat.

That is generally the way of it in lynx-haunted woods—in these woods of Lynx Lane and in all other woods that are inhabited by bay lynxes. Other good things you may see—a big buck, a raccoon, a log cock, a rare warbler, perhaps three splendid bronze wild turkeys; but ninety-nine times out of a hundred you will look in vain for *Lynx ruffus,* as the naturalists call him. At last, after long seeking, a lucky, wholly unexpected glimpse, a glimpse so brief that you can scarcely be sure of what you saw —this is the utmost you can hope for; and months may pass before this meager reward is repeated.

Yet his tracks and his sign show that he is still with us, that he walks familiarly at night where we walk in the day; and here in the Low Country the proofs of his presence are so numerous that he will surely be with us for a long while to come. Perhaps it is just as well that we see him so seldom in the woods or on the trails. The mere possibility of meeting him in some green solitary place is precious; but if we met him often, the mystery which is his principal charm would vanish.

Herbert Ravenel Sass

THE CAT OF GOD

WHEN FERGUS GILYAN came up through the virgin wilderness to the rolling country within sight of the Blue Mountains, he did not place his cabin on any of the wooded knolls that he might have chosen. Instead, he made a small clearing in a dense cane-brake bordering a creek and built his little log house there in the heart of the canes.

Some say he did this for safety's sake. The Muskogees were making war talks at the time, and a house on a height would have been a temptation to roving bands raiding the Overhills, as the mountain Cherokees called their high domain of purple peaks and ranges. But there was another reason besides this one.

Gilyan was a born hunter, and the canebrake, extending for miles along the stream, was alive with game. Around his cabin on every side the smooth straight stems towered thirty feet or more, an evergreen jungle walling in his tiny clearing, a jungle so dense that he could penetrate it only by following the wind-ing trails made by the buffalo and the deer. These trails were his highways to the outside world. From his cabin door to the creek he cut a straight wide path through the canes. There was scarcely an hour from dawn to dusk when, sitting in his door-way he could not see some wild animal moving up or down the creek bed across that path.

One May afternoon, when he was sitting there smoking, he saw a sight more strange. He saw a small Indian boy, a slim naked youngster of perhaps ten years, back slowly down the creek bed and, still walking backward, turn into the path. Gilyan's right hand reached swiftly for the loaded rifle leaning against the wall just inside the door. In the half-light under the over-arching canes there was something deeply uncanny about that backward-walking Indian; but in a moment Gilyan had the answer to the riddle.

A long, gaunt, yellow-brown beast followed the boy; a big she-puma or panther, wild-eyed with hunger. At a glance Gilyan knew all that he needed to know. The puma's lower jaw had been broken. Some strange mischance—probably a blow from a wild horse's hoof—had shattered it and twisted it awry, so that it hung useless and crooked. The beast had starved for days, perhaps for weeks, and now famine had maddened her.

Yet her madness had not wholly conquered her fear of man. Grimly she dogged the boy's footsteps, but because he kept his face turned to her, she had not yet leaped upon him. Plainly, however, she had now nerved herself for the onset. Gilyan knew that in another instant she would hurl herself upon her victim.

Gilyan did not rise from his stool. He flung the long heavy rifle to his shoulder, glanced for a fraction of a second along its steady barrel. The bullet passed not six inches from the young Indian and struck the puma midway between the eyes.

Gilyan was on his feet before she had struck ground. At top speed he raced down the path past the Indian boy and the dead puma to the point where the path met the creek. There he halted and gazed eagerly up and down the sandy bed of the stream hedged in by the tall, dense canes.

He saw nothing, but he knew that his eyes had not tricked him. He knew that at the moment when he had pulled trigger he had glimpsed along his rifle barrel another face besides the one at which he aimed—a wide, flat, tawny face in the midst of which gleamed a round white spot like a gigantic eye. For an instant this face had glared at him from the end of the path close beside the creek. Then, at the crack of the rifle, the face had vanished.

Gilyan was a clean man in those days. The raw poisonous taffai rum of the traders had not blurred his eye or his brain. The face that he had seen was no phantasm, yet he had never seen such a face before. He searched the sands of the creek margin and found certain tracks there in addition to the tracks of the she-puma which he had killed. He studied them carefully; then, sure of his woodcraft, announced his conclusions in a guttural whisper, talking to himself, as was his habit.

"Ay," he muttered, "a big he-cub, bigger than the old she and not yet full grown; a big he-cub with a white spot on his forehead. Some day I'll stretch his hide."

Then he turned and walked back along the path towards the slender, copper-colored lad awaiting him beside the she-puma's body.

This was the beginning of two things. It was the beginning of Fergus Gilyan's knowledge of Koe Ishto (as he was afterwards known), the puma of Unaka Kanoos; and it was the beginning of the long friendship, if such it could be termed, between Gilyan, the first white man to settle on Gilyan's Creek at the foot of the Blue Mountains, and Corane the Raven, a war captain of the mountain Cherokees.

The Indian boy whose life Gilyan saved was Corane's son. Corane the Raven was no friend of the whites, for long ago, at a time when trouble threatened, they had captured him by trickery and had held him as a hostage until the war drums no longer throbbed in the Overhills. But if the Raven never forgot that injury, neither could he forget what Gilyan had done. Thenceforward he was the white hunter's pledged brother.

There was one other who did not forget.

The big he-cub whose face Gilyan had glimpsed along his rifle barrel that May afternoon in the canebrake learned, that afternoon, a lesson which struck deep. Crouching behind the creek bank where the path came down to the stream, he saw his mother meet her end. He saw, too, in that same moment, a man leap from the doorway of the cabin in the clearing—a tall, stoop-shouldered man clad in buckskin and wearing a coon-skin cap. In an instant the cub was gone, a lithe yellow-brown shape speeding in long bounds up the creek bed, hidden from the man's view by the canes.

Thus at the very outset of his independent career—for until

then he had hunted with his mother and accepted her guidance
—Koe Ishto, the puma of Unaka Kanoos, learned the deadly
power of the tall buckskin-clad woodsman with whom, through
no desire of his own, he was to wage a long war of craft and
cunning. The experience amazed and terrified him. The young
puma ran half a mile, a great distance for one of his short-
winded race, before he halted; and even then his halt was only
temporary. Traveling all the rest of the day and most of the
night, he pushed steadily northward through the vast, parklike
virgin forest until, almost suddenly, the rolling hills became
mountains. The high, humped bulk of Unaka Kanoos stood
well behind the first ridges of the mountain bulwark. Not until
he was back on the peak where he had been born—the peak
which had always been his home until, in an evil moment, his
mother had led him down into the foothills—would the big cub
feel that he was safe.

Even into that lofty fastness fate followed him swiftly. Within
a month after his return to Unaka he heard for the second time
in his life the crack of a rifle. He fled from it, yet it seemed to
pursue him, for two hours later he heard it again. An hour
before sunset he ventured down to the lower slopes in search
of game. He was stalking a young buck grazing a little apart
from its fellows in a grassy flat under gigantic beech trees when
a crashing roar deafened his ears and a fierce burning pain
stabbed his right hind leg.

The wound was a slight one. It healed in less than a week.
But the terror of that moment was stamped indelibly upon his
consciousness; and even in his panic he recognized the man who
had wounded him—a tall, stoop-shouldered, buckskin-clad man
in a coonskin cap, the man who had leaped from the door of the
cabin in the canebrake.

Already in Koe Ishto's brain this man stood for Fear; but
it was in the beech wood on the lower slopes of Unaka Kanoos
that the long war between Koe Ishto and Fergus Gilyan had its
real beginning. Gilyan had come to Unaka in search of deer
hides. Corane the Raven, whose village lay close to that mountain, had told him of the droves of whitetails to be found there,

and he had come to see for himself. To his astonishment, he had chanced suddenly upon a puma which he recognized at once. It was an easy shot; yet, inexplicably, Gilyan had failed to kill.

The incident provoked him, whetted his determination. Having shot as many deer as he could skin, he spent two days searching for the puma on the rocky upper heights of Unaka, and when, early the following spring, he returned to the mountain for another deer hunt, he searched the upper heights again. His quest was fruitless, but he found puma tracks larger than any that he had ever seen before.

He was satisfied then that the big cub, now grown to adult estate and a veritable giant of his kind, lived always on Unaka Kanoos; and again Gilyan swore—despite certain things that Corane the Raven had made known to him—that soon or late he would stretch the huge cat's hide.

What the Raven had told him was this: that among certain clans or tribes of the red men the puma was held sacred and that this puma of Unaka Kanoos had become to the people of the Raven's clan more sacred than any other of his race. Klandaghi was the Cherokee name for the puma kind, an honorable name, worthy of the big lion-like cats of the forest who were the greatest of all the wild hunters. But to the puma of Unaka Kanoos an even loftier title had been given—Koe Ishto—and to all the warriors and hunters he was known as the Cat of God.

There were several reasons, Corane explained, for the bestowal of this honor. Not only did Koe Ishto make his home on one of the mountains which the Cherokees held in special reverence, that huge, humped, granite peak which was the throne and couch of the Red Spirit whose voice was the thunder. He was, too, in his own might and bulk such a puma as no living hunter of the Overhills had ever seen before.

Nor was this all. There was yet another thing which set him apart. He bore upon his flat forehead just above the eyes a round white spot as big as a wild turkey's egg. Against the dark background of his upper face, this white spot stood out so vividly that it was visible a long bowshot away. Not even the oldest hunter of the Cherokees had seen or heard of another puma bearing a mark like this upon its face. Hence none doubted the conjurers and the shamans when they said that this white spot on Koe Ishto's forehead was the mark of that Red Spirit who ranked first among the tribesmen's gods because he was the most ruthless of them all.

To all this, as Corane the Raven told it, Gilyan listened gravely. Yet there was mockery in his heart and deceit upon his lips. The very things that made Koe Ishto sacred to the Cherokee hunters rendered Gilyan all the more desirous of securing the puma's pelt.

Koe Ishto's great size and the white spot on his forehead, which Gilyan had seen for the first time on that May afternoon in the canebrake, distinguished him from all other pumas or panthers, as the early frontiersmen called the great forest cats, and would greatly enhance the value of his skin.

Moreover, Gilyan shared in full measure the typical frontier hunter's inordinate pride in his own woodcraft; and this pride had been ruffled and pricked. Outwardly he seemed to respect the Raven's wishes; but on each of his deer-hunting trips to Unaka he devoted at least two days to a search for the white-spotted puma and tried diligently to find his lair.

Season after season Gilyan searched in vain. At last, although he did not abandon his efforts altogether, he forced himself to admit that only by enlisting the Raven's aid could he succeed. This, difficult though it seemed, might not be impossible, for the Raven was bound by the traditions of his tribe to do the will of the man to whom he owed a great debt, the man whom he had made his pledged brother.

Gilyan, confident that his opportunity would come, realized that he must not force the issue. Craftily he bided his time.

Sir Alexander Twining, Special Commissioner of His Majesty King George II to the powerful Cherokee nation whose domain was the Blue Mountains, found much to interest him in Charles Town when he landed there from the high-pooped ship which had brought him from London. Yet to Sir Alexander, a sportsman before he became a diplomat, Charles Town was only a gateway to the mysterious, alluring wilderness which lay beyond.

The preparations for his journey to the Overhills were quickly made. In early spring his caravan set out—himself and his periwigged secretary; four lean, lynx-eyed hunters selected by the Governor of Carolina and headed by Fergus Gilyan of Gilyan's Creek, somewhat the worse for rum now that he was nearing fifty, but still one of the best woodsmen in the province; a half-dozen packhorse men and negro grooms; Conerton, the ex-trader, to act as interpreter; and five tall Cherokee warriors sent down by Moytoy of Tellequo, greatest of the chiefs, to make sure that no war party of the Choctaw or the Muskogee lurked beside the trail. Corane the Raven, one of Moytoy's war captains, commanded the Indian escort.

Of him the King's Commissioner saw but little as the cavalcade rode league after league along the narrow trail winding through the endless primeval forest. The Raven, as always distrustful of the Charles Town English, held himself aloof. As a rule, he rode with two of his braves well in advance of the column, his spear held in his right hand, his long bow slung across his broad, bare shoulders; and from the first Sir Alexander's keen eye marked the careless grace of his horsemanship, the feline litheness and strength of his tall, powerful form.

Twining, for all his airs and frills, a good judge of men, sought closer acquaintance with this war captain of Moytoy, the great chief, whom he was presently to meet in conference, but found the task discouraging. The Raven, always respectful, wrapped himself in frigid dignity which effectually rebuffed the Commissioner's advances and soon strained his good humor to the breaking point. At last, flushed with anger, Sir Alexander reined in his horse.

"Faith, Gilyan!" he exclaimed, as the main body of the caravan came up, "the man's a lump! There's no sense or courtesy in him. You say he understands our English speech, but if so he has forgot how to wag his tongue. I give no thanks to the

Cherokee king for sending so unmannerly a minion to escort me to his kingdom!"

Fergus Gilyan, who had watched the play with grim amusement, smiled.

"Corane the Raven is no friend to the English, Sir Alexander," he said slowly. "He is longer-headed than most of his breed and he knows what the coming of the white man means to his people. He does not favor this treaty which you will offer the Cherokee chiefs. If he could have his way, there would be war, not peace."

Twining ripped out an oath.

"I guessed as much," he said. "We had best watch him, then, lest he lead us into some ambush. D'ye think Moytoy plans treachery?"

Gilyan shook his head.

"No fear," he replied. "Gifts and flattery from Charles Town have blinded Moytoy's eyes. He has been won by your plan to make him emperor of all the Cherokee tribes. Corane will obey Moytoy's commands."

Sir Alexander pursed his lips and muttered in his curled and scented brown beard, yet quickly forgot his fears. Soon the sights and sounds of the springtime wilderness drove weightier matters from his mind. To his English eyes this trail through the teeming virgin forest was an avenue of innumerable wonders; and always, as he rode, he carried in his right hand the long rifle which he had procured in Charles Town and with which, thanks to Gilyan's teaching, he was already fairly proficient.

Again and again he tried his marksmanship. Now his target was a platoon of tall gray cranes, standing like soldiers on parade in a flower-sprinkled savannah beside the trail. Now he brought down, amid the plaudits of his comrades, a great wild turkey cock which Gilyan had pointed out to him as it perched in fancied security on a high limb of a giant pine. A half-dozen times he wasted powder and shot on flocks of green and yellow parrakeets which at frequent intervals flew screeching overhead;

and once he rode a quarter of a mile along a sun-dappled forest vista towards a herd of twenty whitetails resting under the trees and, starting a small black wolf from its bed in a bunch of broom grass, killed it with a lucky shot as it dashed towards the cover of a wild rose thicket.

"What say you now, Gilyan?" he cried in high elation as he galloped back to his companions. "What say you now to my skill? Am I good enough yet, d'ye think, to hunt your great tawny cat of the sacred mountain—that Koe Ishto of the white spotted face whose hide you have promised me when we reach the Overhills?"

It was the time of the midday halt for rest and food. Most of the party had dismounted and were standing around the fire, where the turkey cock which Sir Alexander had killed was roasting, together with several haunches of venison brought in by Gilyan's hunters. Corane the Raven still sat his wiry Chickasaw pony a little apart from the others, but he was near enough to hear Sir Alexander's words.

For a fraction of a second his brows contracted; and Gilyan, watching the Indian keenly, saw that fleeting shadow of a frown. The white hunter laughed carelessly as he answered Sir Alexander's question.

"Koe Ishto is wise," he said, "the greatest and wisest of his kind. I have promised you that we shall hunt him when we camp under the Blue Mountains because you wish a panther skin for your lady. But as for promising you his hide, there is only one man here present who could make you that promise."

King George's Commissioner had dismounted while Gilyan was speaking. He turned towards the hunter, his silver snuff box delicately balanced in his left hand.

"And that man?" he asked eagerly.

Gilyan nodded towards the tall Indian sitting erect and impassive on his claybank pony.

"Corane's town lies in the valley in the shadow of Koe Ishto's mountain. Corane knows Koe Ishto's ways and can lead us to his lair. Corane the Raven must hunt with us or we shall fail."

For a moment Twining hesitated. Then, swallowing his

pride, he turned with an engaging smile to Moytoy's war captain.

"What say you, my brother?" he asked suavely. "Wilt lead us to the den of the great cat of the mountain—this Koe Ishto of the spotted face, concerning whom Gilyan has told me many tales?"

For a long half-minute Corane the Raven, gazing straight ahead of him, his clear cut countenance as stern as that of a bronze image, remained silent. Twining's brows drew together in a frown; the blood mounted to his pale, handsome face. At last the Indian turned his head slowly and looked at Gilyan— a look which seemed at once to convey a challenge and ask a question.

The white hunter nodded; then, frowning slightly, lowered his eyes. The Raven, addressing himself to Twining, spoke gravely in his own tongue.

"Corane will lead you to Koe Ishto's cave," he said.

While Conerton, the interpreter, was whispering to Sir Alexander the meaning of the words, the Indian wheeled his horse and rode slowly forward along the trail.

A Cherokee woman, pounding corn beside the shallow rock-strewn river which flowed through the Raven's village, glanced up at the huge humped mountain towering above the Indian town.

"See," she said to the little naked girl squatting beside her, "the Thunder God sleeps. He has drawn his robe over him so that the noonday sun will not shine on his face."

A fleecy cloud hid the upper half of Unaka Kanoos. Only the heavily wooded lower slopes of the mountain were visible, their deep, lustrous green appearing almost black in contrast with the brilliant whiteness of the cloud-curtain veiling the rocky crest. Three miles to the eastward, on a ridge across the valley, Corane the Raven noted with troubled eyes the blanket of dense vapor hiding the summit and half the bulk of Unaka. To him also this meant that the Spirit was at home on his chosen mountain and was taking his ease there, having first

thrown a coverlet of cloud over his couch so that he might not
be seen by mortal eyes.

Yet the Raven spoke no word, did not slacken his pace. Fergus Gilyan, spare, wiry, endowed with sinews of steel, strode
briskly close behind the tall Indian. But King George's Commissioner, puffing and blowing as the slope grew steeper, prayed
silently for a halt, yet was too plucky to confess his plight.

It was already mid-afternoon. Sir Alexander's caravan had
encamped in the foothills the evening before. After a long ride
over the first rampart of the Blue Ridge, with but one halt by
the high falls of the Whitewater, the Raven and his two companions had left their ponies at the foot of Unaka Kanoos and
had at once begun the ascent.

Gilyan noted with silent approval the Raven's plans for the
hunt. He knew that, unlike most pumas, Koe Ishto helped his
mate kill meat for her little ones and kept watch over the cave
which was their home. Evidently the Raven would waste no
time seeking his quarry along the runways of the deer or in
the bushy meadows where the whitetails grazed. Instead, he
would go straight to the cave where the puma had his lair, the
cave for which Gilyan had so often searched in vain. The white
hunter smiled with satisfaction and his lean brown fingers tightened their grip on the butt of the long rifle cocked across his
shoulder.

None of the three, not even Corane the Raven, knew that as
they skirted a rhododendron thicket fringing a precipitous
brook, pale yellow eyes surmounted by a round white spot as
big as a wild turkey's egg had gazed upon them coldly from the
thicket's recesses. None of them knew that when they had passed
on up the slope, a long, sinuous, tawny shape emerged from the
rhododendrons and followed in their footsteps, gliding as silently as a ghost amid the massive gray trunks of the burly oaks
and the towering tulip trees.

The fear in those pale eyes was stronger than the anger which
was in them also. Koe Ishto had learned long since that the
Raven was not his foe. But now the Raven was not alone. With
him marched two white hunters; and in one of these two Koe

Ishto recognized at once his most implacable enemy, the tall, stoop-shouldered, buckskin-clad white man who had wounded him long ago and who camped from time to time on the lower slopes of Unaka Kanoos and ranged widely over the rocky heights as well as the timbered valleys. The big puma feared the tall woodsman in the buckskin shirt and coonskin cap wherever he found him; but when Gilyan ranged high on Unaka or followed some trail which would take him to the mountain's summit, the fear in Koe Ishto's eyes became an agony of terror.

This terror clutched him now. Never before had the thing which he dreaded most seemed so imminent. Early that spring torrential rains had drenched Unaka Kanoos. Through some obscure cranny water had found its way into the high cave which Koe Ishto and his mate had used for years. Hating moisture, like all the cat tribe, the mother puma had removed the cubs to another cave, dryer but in other respects much less secure, a cave situated some distance farther down the mountain.

The move had scarcely been made when disaster befell, a mischance so strange as to be almost incredible. Salali the Squirrel, the chief conjurer of the Raven's town, had climbed to the top of Unaka Kanoos to gather certain roots and herbs which grew above the clouds. At the edge of the huge precipice near the mountain's summit the conjurer stood in rapture, shaking like a man with fever, chanting the praises of the Thunder God. Then, when the frenzy had passed, an idle impulse moved him to pick up a heavy rounded stone, as big as a man's head, and hurl it into the abyss.

The stone fell into the tree-tops far below and bounded on and on down the steep slope. No trunk of oak or poplar arrested its progress. Instead, it crashed like a cannon ball into the ribs of Koe Ishto's mate lying asleep in a shady spot near the cave where soft, fernlike mosses covered the ground. Ten minutes later the life passed out of her, and Koe Ishto, returning to the cave towards evening, found her lying bloody and stiff upon the moss.

The cubs no longer needed their mother's milk. They were

old enough now to subsist entirely upon meat, and Koe Ishto
easily supplied their wants. He had been hunting deer for them
in the deep woods of the lower slopes when he chanced upon
the Raven and his companions making their way along a trail
leading to the summit, a trail which passed within a hundred
yards of the cubs' new home. At once he had forgotten the deer
and had shadowed the hunters as they pushed upward through
the forest; and now, when the cubs' den lay not half a mile distant, the fear which had gripped him the moment he recognized Fergus Gilyan had mounted and sharpened and swelled
until he was conscious of nothing else.

Sir Alexander Twining was a proud man and sound of wind
and limb. But he had never before climbed mountains and at
last his extremity got the better of his pride. He whispered to
Gilyan that he could go no farther, and when Gilyan had informed the Raven of the fact the tall Indian stood for a moment in thought. Koe Ishto's lair, he told the white hunter
presently, still lay far ahead and above, near the summit of
Unaka; but there was a spot near at hand where they might
rest and spend the night in comfort, then push on towards
their goal before dawn.

King George's Commissioner, flat on his back in the shade,
gave a great sigh of relief when this news was imparted to him.
He was too weary to move, and his heart was pounding like a
hammer. They would remain where they were, he proposed,
until the sun sank lower, then seek their sleeping place. The
view from the spot where he lay entranced him; and the crimson and gold of a mountain sunset, painting the billowy clouds
and bathing all the wooded peaks and valleys in magic light,
held him there until dusk had fallen. Hence it was black night
when the Raven, turning aside from the trail, led the way
through the deep woods around a shoulder of the mountain
to the place where they would find shelter.

A narrow ledge traversed the face of a great rock-mass at the
head of a small ravine. Presently the ledge widened, forming
a broad, level shelf; and behind this shelf a long, horizontal

cleft, ten feet high at the entrance, struck deep into the rock. Kindling a fire, they roasted two ruffed grouse which the Raven had brought down with light cane arrows on the way up the mountain. Then the King's Commissioner lay down on a bed of odorous hemlock boughs.

Already the night chill had descended. Sir Alexander placed his couch well within the cave where he would escape the dew. Gilyan chose to sleep in the open on the broad shelf directly in front of the cave's entrance, where the branches of a great chestnut oak, springing from the base of the rock, spread themselves ten feet above him like a canopy. Long before the fire flickered out these two were sleeping soundly.

Corane the Raven, stretched at full length on the bare rock five yards to Gilyan's left, knew that for him there would be no sleep that night. For an hour or more he lay motionless, his eyes closed; but all that while his brain was in turmoil—a turmoil of anger, none the less deep because it was sternly repressed, and sorrow and foreboding.

He was grateful for the respite which Sir Alexander's fatigue had brought. But for Twining's temporary collapse, they would have reached that afternoon the high cave which had been Koe Ishto's den for years. He had planned to station Twining and Gilyan in an ambush near the path which the parent pumas used in passing to and from the den; and probably before nightfall a rifle would have cracked and Koe Ishto's life would have ended. But the respite, after all, meant little. It merely postponed for a short time the sacrilege for which the Red Spirit of Unaka Kanoos would assuredly seek vengeance.

What would that vengeance be? What punishment would be visited upon him because through his connivance the Cat of God had been killed? The Raven did not know. But he was very sure that punishment would come, that it was unescapable. He had no choice, it seemed, save to do what he was doing, for such was the law—the inviolable law which commanded loyalty to a pledged brother. But his heart blazed with hatred of the man who, taking advantage of that law, had forced this course upon him. And presently, little by little, like a specter dreadful yet somehow welcome, a grim question pushed to the threshold of his brain.

Was there a way out, after all, a way which the gods might approve or at least excuse? It was true that on that May afternoon long ago in the canebrake in the foothills he had given to Gilyan the pledge of lifelong brotherhood. It was true that his debt to the man who had saved his son's life was a debt so deep that it could never be forgotten. But it was true also that Gilyan had proved himself an enemy to the people of the Overhills, the people of Corane's race.

The white traders, coming up from Charles Town, brought rum to the Blue Mountains, that strong maddening drink known as taffai, which already had all but ruined the tribes of the lower country. From his cabin in the foothills Gilyan had introduced rum to the Cherokees. For a keg of taffai many deerskins might be had. Stealing away the red hunters' brains with his liquor, Gilyan year after year had robbed them of their pelts. Nor was this the worst. In his long pursuit of Koe Ishto, the puma of Unaka Kanoos, Gilyan had flouted the Cherokees' beliefs and had insulted their gods; and now, to curry favor with this powerful white chief who had come from beyond the Great Water, he was making the Raven himself a traitor to his own faith and exposing him to the Red God's wrath.

Suddenly there leaped full-formed into the Raven's brain a new thought. What if the vengeance which would surely come were visited not upon him alone but upon all his people? What if the Red Spirit who dwelt upon Unaka Kanoos should punish Corane's nation for Corane's crime?

The question was no sooner framed in his mind than it was answered. In a flash he knew that he had made the wrong decision, that of two evils he had chosen not the lesser but the greater. Upon him alone would rest the responsibility if he broke that law which commanded loyalty to a pledged brother, that law which required him to do as Gilyan asked. But not to him alone would punishment be meted out if, through his treachery, Koe Ishto of Unaka Kanoos were killed. Always the shamans and the conjurers had pictured the Red Master of the Thunders as that most ruthless and most potent god who held all the people of the Overhills in the hollow of his hand, and who, if he were offended, might in an instant destroy them all.

Into the Raven's heart swept such fear as he had never known before: such fear as a man must feel who opens his eyes suddenly to find himself standing on the brink of a bottomless pit into which he had been about to plunge unawares. And after the fear followed horror of the thing that must now be done; and after the horror came something that was like a terrible, fierce joy.

He had loved Gilyan. Many times in years gone by they had roamed the woods together. But those years had passed, and long ago his love for Gilyan had died. Since then there was a heavy score to settle; and now the time for settling it had come.

It was Gilyan's life or Koe Ishto's. The Raven could not, by simply withdrawing from the hunt, undo what he had done. Gilyan now knew too definitely the general location of Koe Ishto's lair. He could find it without further aid, and that he would find it sooner or later was certain. The Raven knew that there was only one way in which he could atone, only one way in which he could save his people from the calamity which he had all but brought upon them. And with that long score to settle he was glad that there was only one way.

For many minutes he did not move. He lay on his back, his eyes open now, listening to Gilyan's slow, heavy breathing, planning carefully the thing that he was about to do. At last his hand groped along the rocky surface to his left and closed upon the long knife which he had placed within easy reach beside his bow and his spear.

There would be no outcry. The King's Commissioner would awake at dawn to find a dead man lying at the entrance of the cave; and by that time the Raven would be far on his way towards the unknown wilderness beyond the headwaters of Ocona Lufta, where no white man had ever trod.

Still lying on his back, he turned his head very slowly to the right.

For some moments he was not sure of what he saw. The fire had died away to nothing. Overhead a few stars glittered. A half moon shone feebly through a thin veil of cloud. In the faint light even the Indian warrior's trained vision failed to discern the outline of the puma's form. Yet something about the shape of the stout chestnut oak limb slanting above the wide ledge in front of the cave fixed his attention. Instinctively he studied it; and all at once he knew that Koe Ishto crouched on the limb ten feet above the spot where Gilyan lay.

Amazement held him motionless, but even in his amazement he understood. Instantly he realized that only one thing could have brought Koe Ishto to that place, that only one thing could have nerved him to mount the chestnut oak at the base of the cliff and take his stand on the limb above the ledge where the hunter was sleeping. Koe Ishto had changed his lair. He had abandoned the high cave near Unaka's summit and had brought his cubs to this other cave which he had never utilized before. The Raven knew that somewhere in the black recesses of that deep slit in the rock the cubs were hiding.

In an instant his plan was formed. It came to him suddenly, complete and perfect, as though some voice had whispered it in his ear. His right hand laid down the knife, groped cautiously for a moment, closed upon the slim, straight shaft of his spear. Very slowly, so slowly that the movement was almost imperceptible, he turned over and began to crawl inch by inch across the ledge towards the cave's entrance.

Always as he crawled he watched the vague bulk of Koe Ishto on the great oak limb almost directly over Gilyan's head. He saw the long body of the puma tremble and stiffen, and immediately he halted and for perhaps five minutes remained motionless. Even more slowly than before, he crept forward again, until he vanished in the obscurity of the cave.

For some minutes there was no sound except the slow breathing of the two sleeping men. Then a shrill, piercing scream split the silence; the scream of a puma cub in fear or pain; a puma cub which had felt the prick of the Raven's spear.

At once Gilyan—a light sleeper, like all wilderness hunters—awoke and sat bolt upright. And at once a long, dark shape, dim, shadowy, incredibly huge, launched itself from the oak limb above and fell full upon him, smashing him down upon the rock.

He uttered no sound. His neck was broken; probably his skull was crushed. Koe Ishto, growling savagely, crouched upon the body, his long tail twitching to and fro, his eyes shining like huge emeralds lit with yellow fire. Sir Alexander Twining, awakened by harsh, shuddering growls which seemed to shake the air within the cave, raised himself on his elbow. He saw those eyes and the vague, dreadful bulk behind them, and gave himself up for lost.

Suddenly from the blackness of the cave Corane the Raven strode forward, his spear leveled. For an interminable minute puma and Indian faced each other; and as the slow seconds passed the Raven knew that behind the emerald eyes, burning like live coals in the darkness, fury and fear were struggling for the mastery.

He could almost read in the changing glare of those eyes the progress of the struggle; and from the beginning he had little doubt as to the outcome. For one reckless moment, as the scream of his cub rang in his ears, Koe Ishto's fury had triumphed. In the madness of that moment he had hurled himself upon his nearest enemy. So much the Raven had foreseen and expected confidently; but, knowing the puma kind, he believed that this would be the end.

For as much as a minute he waited motionless, his right hand gripping the leveled spear, ready for what might happen. Then slowly he raised his left hand above his head in the gesture of peace and farewell. Next moment the burning eyes vanished and the ledge was empty except for the dead man lying twisted and limp.

It was the Indian who broke the silence. Standing at the cliff's edge, his tall, sinewy form superbly erect, his face lifted to the faint stars, he intoned in the Cherokee tongue a chant of praise to the Spirit of Unaka Kanoos, the Red God of the Thunders, Koe Ishto's master and lord, who had given the great cat courage to serve the Raven's need. Then he turned to King George's Commissioner.

"Corane the Raven has fulfilled his promise," he said in English. "He has led the white chief to Koe Ishto, the Cat of God. When it is light he will lead the white chief back to the camp of his people."

Dorothy Quick

SNOW LEOPARD

Out of unending silences of snow
Comes the snow leopard. Gleaming in his eyes
The vision generations can bestow
To make their progeny alert and wise.
His fur is pillow gentle and his feet
Stealthily padded hold the hidden claws.
His is a world where everything is meat
For appetites prehensile. His no cause,
Yet in him there is wisdom and a sense
That makes his eyes more kindly than his might.
He is attuned to landscapes so immense
That mortals must seem puny to his sight;
Within him there is majesty and power,
Courage to meet each fateful coming hour.

W. S. Chadwick

ABOUT LEOPARDS

LESS, PERHAPS, has been written about the leopard than about any other species of African fauna. This is not because he is less interesting, or less often hunted, but because he is so elusive that encounters with him are rare, and anecdotes proportionately few. This has been my experience also, but the encounters which at long intervals have come my way have not lacked interest or excitement.

It may be confidently asserted that if he weighed three times his actual weight he would be the supreme terror of the forest. As a killer pure and simple he stands unrivalled despite that disability. He kills for the sheer love of slaughter, and is only limited by physical capacity. The physical capacity of the lion is unlimited, but he kills only for food, and much less frequently than the leopard.

A troop of lions, for instance, has been observed gambolling within two hundred yards of a herd of fat zebra, their favourite food, in apparent indifference to their proximity. But let a leopard get amongst a flock of sheep or goats, or even fowls, and he will not cease killing while one remains alive, though he may not eat even a leg of one.

I first became impressed with his capacity for slaughter on the occasion when I lost a well-loved dog. A leopard looted a native's goat-kraal two miles from my camp, and in one night killed seven. At the native's request I followed the spoor in the morning, taking my red mastiff bitch on a leash. Within two miles of the kraal we found the bodies of the seven goats, each dropped a little further away than its predecessor; with tooth marks in the

153

throat but otherwise untouched. A mile further on the trail led into some kopjes, and there we found the body of a duiker which the destroyer, unsatisfied with seven victims, had drained of its life-blood and abandoned.

Soon afterwards the spoor entered a rocky cul-de-sac, and about thirty yards in front of us, and between two shrubs on a rocky ledge, a sleek dappled head peered forth, snarling malevolent challenge. I aimed at the head and fired, and a lithe form sprang from the ledge towards us. It landed midway between us and the rock-face just as I drove a second cartridge into the breech and raised my rifle again.

As the spotted fury leaped towards us I heard a yell behind me, and the next instant that rising, yellow shape was met in mid-air by a red one I knew well, which flashed past and upwards as the other rose in its spring. They fell to earth almost at my feet, the red and yellow bodies locked in so close a death-grapple that I dared not fire. So, whipping out my automatic pistol, I waited my chance, and as the yellow shape came uppermost I placed the muzzle against its head and fired. At the same instant the native who had led the dog drove his assegai through the body, and the limbs trembled in a last convulsive shudder. Then we saw the dog's head beneath it, her fangs locked in the throat of her destroyer with a grip we had to prise loose with a spear-haft.

One glance told that she was lost to me. Her stomach had been ripped open by the flensing hind-claws, and the flesh on neck and shoulders hung in strips. Yet her grip had only tightened. It was shown later that my shot had missed the small head, and that the dog had bitten the boy who held her and had leaped to my defence. But for her heroism my first meeting with leopards might have been my last. Silently and carefully we bore her torn body home, and buried it with the respect due to gallant hearts in both men or animals.

Yet, some years before this incident I had been convinced of the leopard's ferocity, and of his limitations, in the following way. I was, at the time, patrolling the arid desert areas of Na-maqualand as a member of the Cape Mounted Police, and to save my horse I did most of my travelling by night. On the occasion I speak of I was riding slowly along a dry river-bed near the seacoast, in the moonlight, when my horse suddenly shied as we passed under the shadow of an overhanging rock. I tried in vain to urge him forward, and at last dismounted to discover the reason for his obstinacy.

Directly beneath the boulder lay the brown, almost naked form of a Hottentot. He was lying face downward upon the body of a fair-sized leopard. The sand was ploughed and furrowed in all directions by what appeared to have been a death struggle; for both figures lay motionless.

The hind claws of the leopard were still embedded in the native's thighs, whilst his front claws gripped the shoulders. But the Hottentot's hands were fast-locked in a desperate grip on the supple throat, despite the fact that the flesh hung in strips from chest and shoulders where the deadly talons had scored it. The open jaws and protruding tongue also proved that his mighty effort to strangle the beast had succeeded.

Strangely enough, the native was still alive. Restoratives were applied, and a little later a kindly farmer drove him straight to the nearest hospital. To the amazement of the doctors he eventually recovered, although they asserted that a white man must certainly have succumbed.

Possibly that dictum was correct. One remembers how Trooper Eagle of the Transvaal Police put up a similar Homeric battle with a wounded lioness, and died fourteen days afterwards from blood-poisoning. It may be that the native's diet of cereals renders his blood less susceptible to septic poisoning than that of the meat-eating European.

It subsequently transpired that the silent-footed Hottentot had unexpectedly come face to face with the leopard under the shadow of the boulder just after sundown, and as each rounded it from opposite directions. The beast had sprung at him instantly, and he had then put up his great fight in difficult circumstances. This leopard weighed only about 140 lb. and in that respect only were the combatants about equal. Had the leopard possessed the lion's weight there would have been a dead Hottentot, and no story.

On another occasion, in Namaqualand, I passed under a tall rock, on a moonlight night, to be greeted with a most unfriendly snarl. Turning my head I saw a lithe form launch itself from the rock above me, and although I drove the spurs home, the leopard landed on the horse's quarters, with front feet gripping the back of the saddle. Just as the startled horse reared I drew my revolver and fired, with the muzzle against the head of the leopard, and he fell in a heap in the roadway.

Then I let my terrified horse go at his best speed, and stayed the night at the nearest farmhouse. In the morning we found that two leopards had been feasting on a stolen goat on the top of the same rock. Doubtless they considered a policeman's presence superfluous under the circumstances, and resented it as described.

A friend of mine in the Bechuanaland Protectorate was not so fortunate as the Hottentot. He had been shooting guinea-fowl with a shotgun, and, returning to camp near sundown, saw a leopard emerging from the grass about twenty paces ahead. Unwisely, he fired at it, when, like a flash, the beast turned and raced towards him. Springing under his levelled gun, as he fired again, it knocked the weapon from his hands, but unluckily one of the sharp talons penetrated the jugular vein in his neck. When he collapsed from loss of blood the beast left him. He was found an hour or two later by natives but died before morning, medical aid being too far away to reach him in time.

Though the average leopard weighs only about 130 lb., and measures less than eight feet from tip to tip, I once shot a specimen measuring nine feet one inch from nose to tail-tip, and weighing nearly two hundred pounds. The occasion supplied more humour than most encounters with leopards present. As a rule, tragedy, or at least tense moments, predominate.

I was hunting north of Broken Hill, close to the Belgian Katanga border, and arrived one evening at a ganger's hut. He was pleased at the prospect of company, and so was I, consequently I accepted his invitation to remain the night. After dinner we sat talking of everything and nothing, in the manner of lonely

men, when a sudden commotion in the small hut he used as a
hen-roost disturbed us.

This hut was about twenty yards from the kitchen, at the back
of the house, and a few minutes previously he had asked his native servant whether he had secured the corrugated iron door.
The boy had answered affirmatively, saying that he had done so
before dinner.

Hastening outside we met this native running with a scared
face towards us, calling as he came, "Master! There is a 'schelm'
in the fowl-house!"

The Dutch word "schelm" might signify anything from a black
mamba to a lion, or even a human thief, so we hastily dashed
back, grabbed our rifles and sallied forth again. Arriving at the
hut, we heard a few faint squawks, and then silence. The sheet
of corrugated iron was in position, and wedged with poles, so we
circumnavigated the hut for a sign of felonious entry. The hut
was intact, it was therefore evident that whatever was inside had
been inside before the native closed it for the night.

Approaching closer to the pole-walls, which had not been plas-
tered with mud, we began a second circuit, and were about half-
way round when something hurled itself against the poles, and
a menacing snarl sent us several hasty paces further away. Looking in the direction of the sound, we saw a pair of baleful eyes,
and on the poles near them, two most efficient sets of claws shone
in the moonlight. Either or both of these might have belonged
to lion or leopard, and we hastily levelled our rifles.

With no thought of possible injury to the feathered inmates
we fired almost together, at about five paces, and the claws and
eyes slid earthwards with a soft thump. To make assurance doubly
sure, and in violation of Queensbury rules, we inserted our rifle-
muzzles between the poles and fired again at a soft mass that
squirmed at their base. Then we called for lights and proceeded
to investigate.

Out of about thirty fowls five roosters only remained, huddled
on the topmost perch. It was, apparently, the intruder's effort to
reach these which had occasioned the commotion we had first
noticed. In a heap by the wall lay the destroyer, and on exami-

nation next morning he proved to be the remarkably fine leopard I have described.

Without doubt he was in the hut when the boy closed the door, and for reasons of his own had made no sign. Doubtless, too, he would have killed the last surviving fowl had we not disturbed him. One wonders how he would have signified his wish to depart, or how he would have greeted the startled native next morning? The said native was unmercifully chaffed for a long time after, by both natives and Europeans, about his singular notions of "trapping leopards."

One may travel hundreds of miles, and spend many years in African forests and mountains, without seeing a leopard, although they may visit one's small stock, or destroy one's fowls and dogs frequently. They are especially fond of dogs, and will often steal upon the verandah of a lonely farmhouse, or hut, and seize the sleeping canine protector before he is aware of their presence.

This predilection for dogs led to the death of a Belgian in the Katanga some years ago. He was hunting with a companion, and while sleeping one night was awakened by a yelp of pain outside his tent. On looking for the cause he found his pet terrier missing from its usual place in the tent-entrance, and beside the spot where it had lain was the spoor of a large leopard. Calling his companion he insisted on taking the spoor at once; to avenge if not to rescue.

His Dutch companion protested at the folly of such a proceeding, and urged waiting for daylight, but in vain. With a few shivering natives behind them they sallied forth on the trail, gun and acetylene lamps in hand. They had only gone about a hundred paces when a coughing snarl greeted them, and a pair of green orbs peered from a patch of brushwood ahead. Both fired, and, as it proved, only one bullet struck the leopard, cutting a furrow along his back, but inflicting no great injury.

Without hesitation the beast rushed towards them, sprang at the Belgian, and landed on his chest, biting him savagely in the face and neck. As he fell under the impact his companion pushed his rifle against the beast's head and fired, killing it instantly. But although all attention possible was given the injured man he died from blood-poisoning on the two weeks' journey to Elisabethville.

Leopards are so strictly nocturnal that most of the skins offered for sale are obtained by trapping. But even trapping is often difficult owing to the creature's cunning. I have known one to take the head of a goat tied to the muzzle of a Martini rifle, and without injury to himself.

The barrel was inserted through the bottom of a four-gallon petrol tin, the stock rested in the fork of a pole planted in the ground. After the head had been secured on the muzzle the trigger was fastened to the fork with wire, so that any pull on the head must fire the gun. When it went off, about nine o'clock at night, we imagined we had our leopard. But in the morning we found that he had stood well aside from the mouth of the tin, had seized the edge in his jaws, and had pulled the tin itself instead of the head. After the bullet had whistled past him he had taken off the head, and had decamped without even thanks!

The leopard is both cunning and courageous, and a born murderer. In stealth and silence he is marvellous, and it is doubtful whether there exists in the whole of creation so much destructive energy in so small a body as that which his spotted hide covers.

Don Marquis

THE SPOTS OF THE LEOPARD

MISS LOLA GOLIGHTLY looked at the leopard; she looked long and she looked longingly. And Tamerlane, the leopard, looked long and longingly at Miss Lola Golightly—stared as steadily as a wild animal can stare at a human being without winking.

They were both of them gorgeous creatures, the most gorgeous, each, of her and his kind—opulent, colourful, luxurious beings; feline, carnivorous-looking beauties; warm-blooded, and lithe, and prone to sudden, vigorously graceful movements; subject to quick, overwhelming impulses and whims.

One wondered how either of them had been lured into captivity. And yet both of them were, obviously, captives—Tamerlane in his cage, in the menagerie tent of Driggins's Great Show, and Miss Lola Golightly hanging upon the arm of little Freddy Hawkster, her husband.

"Peachey," said Miss Golightly, "I want that leopard!"

She had been Miss Golightly on the screen before she married Freddy Hawkster, otherwise Peachey. And no matter how many husbands she might accumulate in the course of a career that was not by any means drawing toward its sunset—that was, indeed, still in its morning hours with noon a long way off—she would always be Miss Lola Golightly. A blazing personality such as Lola Golightly's cannot be overshadowed by a mere husband, whether he be a permanency or but a transient guest within her house of life.

Peachey, who was small and rotund and pink and had a downy blond beard and downy blond hair on his head, had been asked for so many things—just like that!—in the two years since he had ceased to be Miss Golightly's manager and had become, as her husband, Miss Golightly's managed, that not one silken hair turned in surprise.

A woman who had made—or whose embattled press-agents said she made—a million dollars a year before she was married, and whose marriage had given her a reasonable interest in her husband's income without subtracting from her own, is entitled to mingle with her fancies and her notions a certain fiscal element according to Peachey's way of thinking.

If Miss Golightly had asked for the Brooklyn Bridge, and had requested that the Woolworth Building be taken down and rebuilt in the middle of it, Peachey would merely have hemmed and hawed and giggled a little and said that he would see what could be done about it, but he would not have been astonished or shocked. Peachey had done so exceedingly well in the moving-picture business himself that the only way he could tell what he was worth, at any given moment, was to ask Morty Thompson, the head of his publicity department, and then divide Morty's answer by five.

But when asked for anything unusually spectacular, Peachey sometimes demurred a bit as a mere matter of form.

It had been that way when Morty Thompson had put into one of Lola's ads—Lola was then being shot in the rôle of Cleopatra, the well-known Egyptian vamp—the fiction that Cleopatra had bathed every morning in the milk of Abyssinian zebras, and that Miss Golightly, who studied every mood of the heroines she depicted, also bathed every morning in the milk of Abyssinian zebras while the great release was being filmed. Lola, upon reading the press notices, had demanded that Peachey get her some real Abyssinian zebras; and it was only upon proving to her that there no longer were any zebras in Abyssinia that Peachey got out of that situation.

Peachey stalled a bit now.

"Whatcha want with a leopard, Honey Bun?" If there was anyone in the world who should *not* have been described by the somewhat sticky, treacly appellation of "Honey Bun," it was the richly vital Lola; but love and fatuity are occasionally blind to these incongruities.

"I don't want just any leopard, Peachey—I want *this* leopard," said Lola.

And she continued staring at the wonderful Tamerlane, who blinked and looked away, and then looked again at her with an intensity that might have frightened a wiser or less courageous person. "I want his hide! I want his fur!"

"His fur?" said Peachey stupidly.

"Uh-huh," purred Lola, with a feline vibration of her throat and chest. "I must have his fur. I *must* have his fur! It would make the most wonderful coat in the world!"

She purred, it has been said, and as if in answer to her purring the leopard, Tamerlane, couchant on the floor of his cage with his paws before him and his muzzle upon his paws, looking at her and looking away again when he could stand the human gaze no longer, began to emit a low, growling note, a kind of restrained, jarring breath that was like a 'cello accompaniment to the tones of the woman.

"I *will* have his fur!" purred the woman again, gazing as if fascinated on the terrible, animal beauty of the beast.

And the leopard, fascinated in his turn, unable permanently to withdraw his eyes, was saying so plainly that no one who understood animal talk could mistake it: "I will have that woman! I will eat that woman!"

Tamerlane he was, and a conqueror, born a ranger of the wilds and a fierce and mighty hunter, but never before had his imagination, his latent instinct for preying upon living beings, received such an awakening fillip. He did not think or reflect any more than the woman herself thought or reflected; he looked at her and yearned, in the grip of a new and strange and overwhelming desire—here was food for the kings of the wild and the gods of the wild!

And the woman, who had never denied herself anything she wanted, and the leopard, who had never wanted anything with such imperious intensity before. looked upon each other hypnotized, curiously alike in their trance of longing, and each vowed the other's death—the barbaric appetite for adornment facing the savage lust for food, life seeking to take life and add it unto itself.

Miss Golightly and her husband had left the circus early, and were lingering in the animal tent on their way to their big purple-and-gold limousine outside, when the leopard and the lady caught sight of each other. Now Peachey, on his wife's re-iteration of her wish, began to get active immediately, as was his wont.

"Would you mind," he asked a clown, off duty, who was idling near by, "asking Mr. Exeter Dallis to come here, if he is anywhere about the grounds? Tell him that Freddy Hawkster wants to see him."

Mr. Exeter Dallis is the press-agent of Driggins's Great Show. When an elephant swims down the Hudson and is rescued by a battleship, when a giraffe steps out of the parade and restores a baby to a lady who has carelessly dropped it from a second-story window, when a faithful seal sacrifices his life to save a beloved trainer from the onslaughts of a maddened ostrich whom someone has given a cigarette to eat, Mr. Exeter Dallis is the poet who has dreamed these things first and has sung them to the strafing of his wild harp in the ears of the reporters of the daily press. Mr. Dallis has the air of not expecting anyone to believe anything he says, but for all that he is one of the best fellows in the world.

"Ex," said Peachey when Mr. Dallis arrived, with his ever-genial smile, and with the gold-headed cane, made out of a bone from an elephant's tail, which once was the property of Phineas Taylor Barnum himself, and which Mr. Dallis always carries, "Ex, Lola wants that leopard."

Mr. Dallis began to say, quite by force of habit, "It's the easi-est thing, you know——" but, as the demand penetrated to his understanding, he checked himself and asked instead: "Which leopard, Lola? Not *that* leopard?"

"Yes, that leopard, Ex," said Lola. "Tamerlane."

And Tamerlane, watching her every movement, purred again: "I want that woman! I will have that woman!"

A cloud passed over the face of Mr. Dallis, usually so genial and open. He hated to deny anyone anything. Finally he said:

"Lola, I know you won't believe me, but that leopard's the only animal in this whole show that the Old Man wouldn't part with. Wouldn't some other leopard do?"

"No leopard in the world, Ex, but that leopard! I want his hide for a coat! Look how he matches me!"

Mr. Dallis looked at her vivid colouring, at her warm golden eyes with the changing lights in them, at the luxuriance and magnificence of her hair, and he looked at the wild beauty of the gorgeous, spotted Tamerlane. He spoke with a sudden enthusiasm:

"By gad, Lola! You two *are* affinities! I'll tell the world so!"

"I will have his coat!" purred the woman.

"I will have that woman to eat!" purred the leopard.

"You oughta have him!" said Dallis, "but as I said, it's the one thing the Old Man owns that he won't sell."

"Why not, Ex?" said Peachey, who was willing to buy Lola a leopard if possible, but more than willing not to see the money spent if it were really impossible.

"It's a matter of sentiment, Peachey."

"Sentiment? Is he so attached to it?" asked Lola.

"I know you won't believe me," said Mr. Dallis, "for it's a funny yarn. You've got to understand that these circus people, especially the old timers, are the most sentimental people on earth, or you won't get me.

"The old man had a daughter. Beautiful girl. Fine girl. Looked a good deal like you, Lola, only she wasn't as big. Brought her up away from the circus. Girls' college, and all that sort of thing. But circus was in the blood. Her mother had done a turn herself under the big top, twenty years ago. The Old Man himself was born with the smell of sawdust in his nostrils. What's born in you has to come out.

"The Old Man had planned a society life for that girl, but when she got out of her college, you couldn't club her away from the big top. Where she learned to ride the way she did, I don't know—in the blood, I guess. But she surprises the Old

Man one day by turning up as a lady bareback rider in his own show. Collusion amongst his underlings, he said, but he wasn't really as mad as he made out to be.

"And animals! Animal was that kid's middle name. Her and Tamerlane here struck up a special friendship. He was captured when he was almost full-grown, and he had the reputation of being a tricky beast and hard to handle. But he did follow her. For she had the nerve to let him out of his cage one day—and lead him around the tent here and you'd have thought he was a tame tom-cat.

"Well, the kid died about two years ago. It broke the Old Man all up. He hasn't got over it, and he never will get over it. But that's the reason he won't part with that leopard."

"But he's really a dangerous beast, isn't he?" said Lola.

"They're all dangerous, all these wild animals," said Mr. Dallis soberly. "Any time you are told they aren't, it's all bunk. They're never really tamed. Tamerlane, here, would eat you in a minute if he took a fancy to."

"I want that woman! I will eat that woman!" purred the great beast, in his own language, as if confirming Mr. Dallis.

"I want that fur!" said Lola, the compunction that she had felt for a moment vanishing under Mr. Dallis's information that all wild animals, no matter how seemingly docile, are dangerous.

"You're going to have a deuce of a time getting him," said Mr. Dallis, "unless you buy the circus outright, and him with it."

"Oh, Peachey, *couldn't* we?" cried the spoiled beauty.

Peachey came nearer to giving a gasp of surprise than ever before. But he choked it back. His training conquered.

"We'll see about it, Honey Bun, we'll see."

"Would it cost such an *awful* lot of money?" asked Lola, innocently, of Mr. Dallis.

"It would if you could buy it," said Mr. Dallis. "But I doubt if the Old Man would sell it at all. He likes to think it's his."

"Honey Bun, I'm afraid we're gonna have to give it up," mildly offered Peachey.

"I want that fur!" said Lola.

"I want that woman!" purred Tamerlane. "I'm going to eat that woman!"

"Exie, where is Old Man Driggins now?"

"He's at Bridgeport, Connecticut, to-day," said Mr. Dallis.

"Come on, Peachey," said Lola, "we'll get into the car and go to Bridgeport."

They were then in Brooklyn, where the circus was showing for a week after its early season engagement at the new Madison Square Garden, New York. Lola spoke of going to Bridgeport to buy the circus as casually as another person might have suggested going to the corner drug store for a chocolate sundae.

"Why not wait until to-morrow, and he'll be here?" suggested Mr. Dallis.

"Why not, Honey Bun?" pleaded Peachey.

"No," Honey Bun said with finality. "He might be considering an offer from somebody else right now, for all you men know. That's the way with men! Women have all the business sense, really. We'll go to Bridgeport right away. It's only fifty or sixty miles."

And as they started out of the tent she cast one final lingering look at Tamerlane. "I'm going to have that fur!" she murmured.

"I'm going to eat that woman!" answered Tamerlane, returning her gaze.

"Now aren't women hades on wheels!" said Mr. Exeter Dallis, not without admiration.

That night, during the show, and after the show, and well on toward morning, there was uneasiness in the animal tent, the sort of tension that the old timers know how to appraise, and which they fear. The lions gave voice from time to time, the elephants grumbled and trumpeted, and a polar bear made oration to the world. There was a feeling of hysteria in the enclosure, which communicated itself to keepers and trainers and attendants; the beasts were on edge.

There was no storm on the way, no electrical tingling and

prickling in the air, no unusual and unseasonable heat to excite the brutes, but excited they were, and the men in charge experienced little waves of unacknowledged fear.

There was a night watchman who felt that he might have cleared up the mystery of this agitation, which had in it a vague sense of menace toward man and all his works. This was old Jim Hagerty, who had been a trainer in his prime. Now his daughter was a trainer—Florence was her name, and she was billed as Fearless Flo—and he was merely a helper in the menagerie.

Old Jim had lived all his life among animals in many parts of the world, and even claimed that he could understand their talk. He used to report long conversations to his daughter, things that he heard o' nights, and they were so nearly like what the animals *might* have said that he often left Florence gaping in amazement, almost wondering if, indeed, her father really could understand animal talk. She was convinced that he at least thought he could.

Old Jim had been an eye-and-ear witness of the mutual fascination of Miss Golightly and Tamerlane; and his daughter had been indignant at the possibility of a moving-picture actress aspiring to own the great show.

"What could *she* do with animals?" said Florence contemptuously. She walked among them herself, with pistol and whip, as confidently as if they were puppies.

"Never fear, Old Man Driggins won't sell it to her," said Jim. "The animals were all worked up last night," he continued presently. "They were all talking about Tamerlane and his wanting to make a meal from that woman."

It is a version of Jim's report that is given here.

"I will have that woman! I will eat that woman!" Tamerlane told the leopard in the next cage again and again.

"What is the matter with that fool leopard that he will let nobody sleep?" complained a two-humped camel who desired nothing better than to continue in the way of placidity which had been marked out for him by his gods.

"He is a fool, indeed! A fool! A fool! A fool!" gibbered a malicious little monkey.

"If I were out of this cage," muttered Tamerlane, "that monkey would soon see whether he or I is the bigger fool! I could kill six monkeys with one blow of my paw."

"I wish you were out of your cage, then," said a polar bear. "I have undergone many indignities and discomforts in my life, and much suffering, but my chief sorrow is that I must listen all day long and sometimes all night long to the mouthings of these accursed monkeys. A monkey is neither a man nor a beast, but something between the two, and to be despised by both, for he has the faults of both."

"Oh, be silent, you!" interrupted a zebra. "You grumble eternally and you are worse than the monkeys."

"Lie down upon your ice," another monkey advised the bear.

"Silence," roared a lion. "All of you!" And he shook his bars.

The monkeys giggled and mimicked him, and then fell into discussion again.

"Why is it," said one of them, "that the foolish leopard wishes to devour this particular woman? I had rather have an orange."

A tiger, who had been listening, and who had said nothing hitherto, stirred with a recollection of an incident that had occurred in his youth in Bengal, and sniffed the air. And then there leaped into this tiger's heart a reawakening of an old desire, and he gave a sudden loud cry of such ferocity that all the men and monkeys and all the herbivorous animals shuddered with terror. And all the carnivorous beasts cried out, while the tent shook with a naked blood-lust and the fear of it.

"I will have that woman! I will eat that woman!" said Tamerlane, the leopard.

A wise old elephant then lifted up his voice and spoke solemnly and seriously.

"Listen to me," said the elephant. "I am old and I have seen many things, in many parts of the earth, and I tell you, my friend, as one animal to another, beware of women!

"Up and down the world have I travelled, upon my own legs, and in many trains and ships, and I have seen troubles here and troubles there, troubles by land and sea, troubles in the jungle and in cities, and I tell you, my friend, that the greater part of these troubles were due to women. My friend, beware of women!

"This is not my wisdom alone, although my wisdom is great, but it is also the wisdom of men, who have made themselves our masters. And they are wiser than we, because although their strength is less than our strength——"

"We obey them too much!" roared the old lion.

"Too much!" cried the tiger.

And the word went around the tent, until one of the great lethargic snakes, behind his glass plate and his bars, uncoiled and took it up, and said it over and over again.

"I will have that woman! I must eat that woman!" moaned Tamerlane, the leopard.

But when all was quiet again the elephant went on with his tale.

"I have been with white men and with brown men," said the elephant. "I have worked with them, piling logs and pulling stumps, and I have hunted with them. And I have listened to them, while they talked about their camp-fires. And the boldest hunters and the greatest workers had ever this to say to one another, as the moral and the warning of the tales they told: Beware of women!

"I have seen much, and I warn you from what I have seen. I have heard much, and I warn you from what I have heard: Beware, my friend, beware of women! Put this yearning from you, for it will lead to trouble."

"I will have that woman! That woman I will eat," said Tamerlane, fierce and sick with the intensity of his longing.

"I will have that peanut! I must eat that peanut!" mimicked a monkey, safe behind his bars, and all there who were of the simian species giggled until the lion roared them to silence again.

So passed the night in the animal tent, but toward morning the noise died down and only the old elephant and Tamerlane, the leopard, talked with one another.

"Beware," said the elephant, "of women. Let me tell you a

story of a woman who was aboard a ship on which I was brought to this country. It was because of her that the ship was very nearly lost at sea. It happened in this way." And the elephant told the leopard that story.

"I will have that woman," answered Tamerlane, at the conclusion of the tale.

But toward dawn the leopard began to listen to the elephant more quietly and, about the time of sunrise a sagacious orang-utan, who had said nothing before, joined in the discussion and supported the elephant. A toucan bird, a camel, and a sad giraffe spoke also to the leopard, labouring for his conversion through the hour before the dawn. And then a cobra allied himself with them.

"Listen," said the cobra, "listen! I once lived near the bungalow of a Christian missionary in Burma. And because I heeded his precepts, my life has become a different thing. Listen, and I will tell you a story."

"Mr. Driggins, if you were going to sell your circus, how much would you take for it?"

Mr. Driggins named a figure that might have given pause to anyone but Miss Lola Golightly. But Lola's idea of money had always been that it was something to be spent, and figures did not mean as much to her as they might have done to a woman who had not seen press-agents toss millions about.

"But what on earth do you want with a circus?" asked Mr. Driggins.

"It's Peachey, here, that wants it," said Miss Golightly, with feminine guile. She had a habit of saying that Peachey wanted things, and she had the gift of almost making Peachey believe that he wanted them.

"Yes, sir," said Peachey loyally, playing up to Lola's lead, "I've wanted a circus all my life—ever since I was a kid. And now that I've got money enough to buy one, I'm gonna do it, if the price is reasonable." Then he added vaguely: "It'll work in with my moving-picture business, you know."

Mr. Driggins was sympathetic, but not quite convinced. He

could understand a person wanting a circus very badly, but somehow it didn't seem to him that Peachey was quite spontaneous. Peachey and Lola had found him at his Bridgeport home shortly before dinner, and had dined with him there, broaching the object of their visit at once. He had been a trifle puzzled to make them out; but he knew who Peachey and Lola were, he had confidence in their financial responsibility, and they evidently meant business. He was convinced that it was Lola who really wanted the show and not Peachey, and he was piqued because he could not find out just what her sudden, overwhelming desire was due to; he felt sure that it was sudden and it seemed to be overwhelming.

He had told them at the beginning, automatically, as he told everybody, that Driggins's Great Show, which he owned outright just as he owned the hat upon his head, was not for sale to anyone at any figure. But that had not jarred Lola. She had treated it as an entirely irrelevant statement. And as he talked to them there recurred to him a feeling that he had experienced several times since his daughter's death—the feeling that it was about time for him to retire. Before dinner was over, he had made up his mind to sell. But he wished to draw the transaction out until he discovered Lola's real motive.

Lola had no intention of telling. She had been too wise to mention Tamerlane.

Finally Mr. Driggins put it to her directly. "Mrs. Hawkster, I *know* it is you who want the show. Tell me why—and maybe I'll sell."

"You'll think I'm silly, maybe," she said, not troubling to make any further denials, "but it's because—well, I love animals!"

Driggins looked at her, and believed her, and fell into a muse, thinking of his daughter. "I'll sell it to you," he said finally.

Lola also thought of his daughter—and of why she was really buying the circus—and had the grace to feel ashamed, for a moment.

But only for a moment. All the way from Bridgeport back

to New York she talked of little else than that gorgeous coat, that wonderful coat which now rested upon the back of Tamerlane and would one day clothe herself.

"Peachey," she said, reproaching him for a lack of enthusiasm, "you don't see the business possibilities in this deal!"

"Honey Bun, I don't," Peachey confessed.

"You men never do," said Lola. "It's a good thing you have me to look after you, Peachey, or your old moving-picture business would go to pieces in no time."

"Maybe you're right, Honey Bun," said Peachey submissively. But inside of him Peachey was saying, numbly and dumbly: "My Lord! A circus! I've bought a circus to get a coat for her! My Lord! A circus!"

"If I wasn't a practical business woman, Peachey," continued Lola, "there's no telling how much money you'd lose in your ventures."

"Yes, Honey Bun," said Peachey.

"You're too good-natured with people, Peachey. You let 'em do you all the time."

Peachey flushed to a deeper peach-blow pink, and was silent. He had been thinking something of the sort himself.

"Now, honest, Peachey," Lola went on, "you haven't seen where this deal is good business. 'Fess up! Have you, now?"

"I ain't," said Peachey, losing his hold on grammar completely.

"Why, Stupid," said his loving spouse, "don't you see the idea? Lola Golightly buys a circus just to get a wonderful coat! Just think what Morty Thompson can do with that for a starter! With Exie Dallis to help! Why, Peachey, the ad from that will more than pay for the old circus, and you'll have the circus besides. Now, is your little Lola clever, or isn't she?"

"She is," responded Peachey dutifully. But he added, with a sigh: "It's gonna take quite a lot of reading matter, Honey Bun, to be worth as much as that circus costs us!"

"Don't you be a spoil-sport, Peachey," said his spouse, conveying her affection in a caress.

The caress was the sort of caress that also conveys something

very like a warning. Peachey felt it so, at any rate. He made no
further feeble struggle. The die was cast so far as Peachey was
concerned. He wouldn't be a spoil-sport. He was even grateful
that Lola hadn't made it stronger, as she sometimes did. Sometimes she said, witheringly: "I *hate* a spoil-sport!"

It was a week later, after all the formalities of the purchase
had been concluded, that Lola stood before Tamerlane's cage
again; and again that strange fascination seemed to possess both
creatures. It was late in the afternoon, "between shows," as the
profession terms that particular part of the day.

"I'll have a hard time with that leopard to-night."

Lola turned and saw Fearless Flo at her elbow; she recognized
Florence, from her costume, as the woman who had put two
lions and a leopard—Tamerlane himself—through their stunts
at the afternoon performance. And she was conscious of a certain hostility in Florence's speech and manner. She looked her
interrogation.

"When you were here before," said Florence, answering the
look, "you got him so excited that it was two days before I
could get him in hand again."

"Is he so dangerous?" asked Lola.

"All the big cats are dangerous," said Florence, "unless you
keep your nerve."

Lola turned back toward the cage, and she and Tamerlane
stared at each other once more. Florence broke the silence with
a cool interrogation, which she was at no pains to render
inoffensive.

"Who is going to kill him for you?" she said. "You haven't
got the nerve to do it yourself."

Lola felt the girl's antagonism unmistakably now, and in
spite of herself she flushed. "I suppose," she said quietly, "that
you have?"

There was a brief pause, and then Florence replied: "Yes, I
could kill him. But I wouldn't kill him. I'd be ashamed of
myself to kill an animal like that just for a whim—just because
I'd got stuck on his coat."

Florence was a slender brunette, and there was fire in her eyes as the two women faced each other. The idea that Driggins's Show was now the property of someone who cared nothing for circuses—the thought that the great, beautiful beast was to be slain to satisfy the frivolity of someone who had not the slightest interest in animals—was too much for her; she was outraged, personally and in her inherited traditions. She continued, letting her honest contempt take command of her voice:

"If I wore a tiger's coat, or a leopard's, it would be because I'd killed him myself—and I'd kill him only because I had to kill him. And it would only be an animal *that had had his fair chance to kill me*. But you wouldn't give him his chance! Everybody knows you have doubles for all the dangerous stunts in your pictures."

This was a home thrust, this latter sentence—the one thing calculated to make Lola more furious than any other insult in the world. For when she had first gone into the moving pictures there had been none so daring as she. Later, when her fame and salary grew, it was her employers who had insisted that she give up risking herself personally; she was too valuable. And Lola had yielded reluctantly. But she was too proud to explain to this circus woman who so evidently hated her.

"I'll do anything that you'll do," said Lola evenly. "I'll go in the cage with you to-night and help you with your act."

"You won't be allowed," said Florence.

"I won't!" blazed Lola. "We'll see! I own this circus!"

Florence laughed: "You haven't got the nerve!"

"Get me a costume like yours," said Lola.

Florence saw she meant it; she weakened; she thought swiftly of the possible consequences of an amateur in the arena among the big beasts. She paled a little, courageous as she was. "You mustn't do it!" she cried.

"Get me a costume like yours," repeated Lola. And she clutched the girl fiercely by the shoulder. "Or shall I rip this one off of you?" she said.

Florence led her to the dressing tent.

And that night, when she faced the three great cats and watched Florence put them through their paces, she was not in the least afraid. For Lola was used to facing crowds and cameras, and this thing seemed to her, at first, no more connected with the realities and dangers of existence than just another appearance on "location." She stood quietly in a corner, observing the other woman and her marvellous handling of the animals; and once her reluctant admiration uttered itself:

"I've got to hand it to you!"

Florence gave her a quick glance and went on with her job. Presently she murmured:

"There's only a moment more of the act now. You'd better beat it." And she motioned toward the back of the steel-barred enclosure, sitting on its platform, in which the performance had taken place. The helpers were already there, with the portable steel chutes which connect the performing arena with the vans in which the animals live and travel, ready if necessary to assist in that transition from the door of the arena back to the cage, which is the really ticklish business of most animal acts.

Lola, her whip and her pistol still in her hand, stepped out of the door of the arena and stood a moment on the margin of the platform beside it, looking at the crowd.

And even as she looked, she was aware that something had happened. A single spasm went over that great mass of faces before her as if it were one face—a spasm of fear. There was a gasp, a great involuntary whisper with the wind of terror in it; and then a hush.

Turning, she faced Tamerlane.

What had gone wrong, she never knew; whether the great silent cat had bounded after her with one leap before the door could be shut, or whether the helpers with the chute had hesitated and somehow bungled—but there he was, couched, as if for a spring, motionless, except for that slight twitching of the tail which showed the blood-lust trembling through the feline nerves.

"Don't move, for the love of God, don't move!" whispered Florence, through the bars.

But the leopard moved first—as you have seen a cat move before it leaps; a movement slight as the caress of a breeze upon the water, a ripple that started at his claws and shivered through his body; an undulation that was less physical action than the shuddering expression of a fatal idea. It was neither experience nor conscious thought which bade Lola be beforehand with the animal, when she perceived this movement; it was an instinct as primal as his own.

She struck first; again and again she lashed him, with a flailing whirlwind of blows across his muzzle and his head; blows that beat down the rising hell in him just before it reached its flaming crest and leaped; slashes edged with surprise that threw the beast off his psychic balance; blows that carried consternation, for an instant, from the stricken nerves to the brute soul; and Tamerlane, the mighty, crouched and backed and snarled and tried to box with the flying whip itself, and failed to gather himself for the swift spring that meant death. Twice Lola desisted, and then, at a renewal of movement in the beast, lashed and lashed again.

And then there fell a pause, while the forces wrapped in these two savage beings struggled with each other in naked daring, without the aid of whirling whip or bared claw; a pause wherein they seemed to hang together, grappling, in a hypnotic trance. That courage which is more primal and deeper than anything that can be expressed in action glowed from the woman and seized upon and wrestled with the essential wildness of the stark brute before her.

And she was conscious of a great exultation. Here was the real thing, the woman told herself—the thing she was born for! Here was what she had been searching for, what she had been thirsty for; here was the strong drink of peril to slake the restlessness that had expressed itself in a hundred whims and escapades. All her other hunting had been for small game! She did not reason this, but in the dangerous trance that held them both she knew it.

To be conscious of peril, and not conscious of fear—that is something that is given to but few people; but her emotions were deeper than fear. They were deeper than thought; deeper than consciousness itself; they were deep as the stream of primal life that flowed through both the pagan woman and the savage cat, the stream which had shaped them both and borne them on and flung them both together. And in some strange way, which she could never express, the woman felt herself and this leopard blended together in their sources; he was she and she was he; a sensation too profound and overwhelming for fright, and which comes mystically to every handler of snakes and feline animals and is precedent to the mastery over them.

It was the woman who broke this spell. She stepped forward and raised her whip again. The great cat turned and glided into his cage, her slave. And five thousand people burst forth into a roar of applause.

"I got to hand it to *you!*" said Florence.

It was tribute from a professional which Lola knew how to value. She smiled and put her arm over the girl's shoulder for a moment. And then the smile faded. She gazed after the cage of Tamerlane, which was being wheeled from the tent, and said, almost sombrely for Lola Golightly:

"I don't think I want his coat." She struggled, but in vain, to express some slight hint of the great joy that had possessed her, and of the strange trance that had held her. "I sort of *like* that leopard," was the best she could do. And then: "I think he's going to like me."

He did. In three months he followed her like a dog. Some of his friends in the animal tent said sneeringly that he had changed his spots and become a moral leopard; but Tamerlane did not waver in his devotion. When she was filmed as Semiramis, as the Queen of Sheba, as Zenobia, Queen of the Desert, Tamerlane figured as the leading feline.

Somehow her conquest of Tamerlane got into the papers.

"You see, Peachey," said Lola, looking at the clippings, "your old circus has almost paid for itself already. Now, who's a good business woman?"

"You are, Honey Bun," said the little pink man.

W. J. Turner

THE LION

STRANGE SPIRIT with inky hair,
  Tail tufted stiff in rage,
I saw with sudden stare
  Leap on the printed page.

The stillness of its roar
  From midnight deserts torn
Clove silence to the core
  Like the blare of a great horn.

I saw the sudden sky;
  Cities in crumbling sand;
The stars fall wheeling by;
  The lion roaring stand:

The stars fall wheeling by,
  Their silent, silver stain,
Cold on his glittering eye,
  Cold on his carven mane.

The full-orbed Moon shone down,
  The silence was so loud,
From jaws wide-open thrown
  His voice hung like a cloud.

Earth shrank to blackest air;
  That spirit stiff in rage
Into some midnight lair
  Leapt from the printed page.

Courtney Ryley Cooper

MONARCH

ONE QUALITY MADE Joe Dokes distinctly different from the other lions of the Grand Amalgamated's menagerie. That was the fact that he had been born in Africa and had grown to adult strength a feline of the wild.

Such a thing among menagerie lions is somewhat unusual. One of the fables of animaldom is the story in which a lioness asserts to some lesser animal that while she may give birth to only one cub, that cub is a lion. The truth is that baby lions arrive by twos and triplets, and with sufficient frequency to label the leonine strain as prolific. The menagerie cages frequently form the sole sources of leonine supply for every need; many lions live and die with no knowledge that anything else exists but the blatter of the white tops, the roar of trains at night and the warmth of the cat house during the season at winter quarters. Certainly, there are exceptions. Joe Dokes was an outstanding one.

Joe was old now—fourteen, in fact—and he had been a part of the Grand Amalgamated circus for eleven years of his life. He was knotty at the joints, and rheumatic, and his back had a queer dip in it, like a sway-backed horse; this had become much more pronounced in the last few years. His tremendous teeth were still good, but his digestion was bad, so they fed him carefully; the old days of excitement at the sight of the meat barrow were gone. So, for that matter, were his performing days; Old Joe Dokes was a traveling pensioner. He was a pet as well; even the rush of a late arrival, the difficulties and activities of a bad lot or rotten weather did not hinder at least a few of the me-

179

nagerie men from hanging around his cage for a little while each day. Circus people get that way about animals; especially persons close to them, like the menagerie superintendent and Shorty Allerton.

"That sway's gettin' a lot worse in his back, ain't it?" Shorty asked his superior one afternoon following the matinee. " 'Spose he's got any pain there?"

"Think it's all in his joints," answered the superintendent professionally. "His back's always seemed sort o' numb; remember how it used to give out on him when he was doin' the leaps? That's how they come to get him, you know. Some hunters had shot him, and he'd crawled off. Then a Benson party came along after leopard cats and found him, half dead and almost paralyzed. So, you see, it was his back——"

"Yeah, uh-huh," said Shorty Allerton. He had heard this same story for eleven years. "His back's bound to hurt him, though, swayin' down like that. I think I'll——"

"Ain't I telling you his back don't hurt?" asked the superintendent. "If his back hadn't been numb, so he couldn't fight 'em or nothing, how would they ever have caught him? Didn't Benson tell me the story himself?"

"Uh-huh," said Shorty again, and jammed his hands in his hip pockets. "I guess oil o' wintergreen would be best. Just rub it up an' down his spine."

"Benson says they come on him all stretched out, an' some o' the fellows wanted to kill him. But Benson, he says not for nobody to shoot him, but to get him in a cage an' try to get him well. So they did and that's why he's always been so tractable. Learned human beings could be kind if they wanted to. Finally he got to be pals with everybody."

"I could use reg'lar horse liniment up there along his spine where he couldn't lick it," said Shorty Allerton.

The menagerie superintendent scowled.

"Ain't I told you a million times his back don't hurt him?"

"Yeh, and ain't I told you the same million times you don't know what you're talking about?"

"I know it's his rheumatism," said the menagerie superintendent.

"An' where's his rheumatism comin' from?" asked Shorty Allerton. "How would he walk if his spinal column was hurt? It's them big muscles up by his shoulders that got jammed up when he was shot. That's what breeds his rheumatism."

"Yeh, and he could get rheumatism from feedin' him too much meat. What he needs is a tonic. That's what I'm goin' to give him."

"What he needs is a good rub along that back," said Shorty Allerton. "He's goin' to get it too."

"Yeh, an' he'll have a tonic," said the menagerie superintendent.

For a moment after that they were silent, each with the conviction of victory. It had been this way for years whenever Old Joe Dokes was concerned; a continuous quarrel, based not so much upon what should be done for Old Joe Dokes as upon who should have the joy of doing it.

Now, they merely stood staring past the heavy bars of the cage to where Old Joe Dokes paced thumpily upon his sore, knotted legs. There was something besides concern in their glance; there was pride. For in spite of the sway of his back, which gave his hind quarters an unusual appearance of thin weakness, in spite of the heaviness of his tread and the rheum of his old eyes, Old Joe Dokes still possessed the bearing and carriage of a lion.

To and fro he weaved against the bars, his heavy, black-maned neck arched and his old head erect, at last to halt at the far end of his prison and gaze out between the fretted steel. It was as though he were looking at something of sudden interest; the dimmed eyes had centered. His lower jaw had dropped slightly from the upper lips and their heavy bristles. Shorty Allerton cocked his cap and shifted his stance to a sloping attitude of attention.

"Seems to be doin' that a lot lately," he said to the menagerie superintendent. "Like he was lookin' out at somethin', but there ain't nothin' in front o' him but the other side o' th' tent."

"He's got a right to look out if he wants to."

"Yeh, I know, but he's kind o' got an air about him. You know, like there was somethin' away off. I've seen old soldiers look like that, when they get to talkin' about their fightin' days."

"Oh, yeah?" asked the menagerie superintendent without interest, finally to turn with the shouted news that the hippopotamus den had mired down outside the kid show. "I'll send up that tonic," he said over his shoulder as he walked away. Shorty sulked.

"Suppose I'll have to give it to him," he growled. "He's a reg'lar old woman about that lion."

Outside the menagerie tent, the superintendent paused and frowned a summons to the circus doctor.

"The settin' hen in there's talking about rubbing Joe Dokes with wintergreen," he said. "Suppose stuff like that'd upset his stomach if he'd lick it?"

"Whose—Shorty's?" laughed the circus doctor. Then he reached for his prescription pad. "Going downtown anyway," he said. "I'll send up a mixture that'll be better than just the straight stuff."

For Shorty Allerton and the menagerie superintendent were not the only ones who took the ailments of Old Joe Dokes as a serious matter. The word had traveled around that a beloved lion had not much longer to live.

A successful circus is much like a great many successful men; there is a prideful memory of other days, when life was more of a struggle; the things and beings which played their part in those formative times speedily take on a value of sentimentality as the institution progresses. More than one circus lugs a decrepit band wagon or some old performer about the country—a luck piece long bereft of intrinsic value, but enhanced, nevertheless, with every passing year. So it was with Old Joe Dokes.

This ancient lion had been a bulwark in less prosperous days. One can find every sort of mentality in the cages of a menagerie; there are dullards and star gazers, mediocre mentalities, animal morons, brilliant but flighty personalities, even the criminally inclined. There are insane animals and dangerous epileptics; there are lazy animals and workers; there are playful ones and the morose. The leonine family as it exists behind bars is an especial field for all of these, owing to the opportunities for close inbreeding and its dangerous results. But there are also the finer characters—the quick-thinking types, the business brains possessed of balance and common sense, which often are as responsible for the success of an act as the work of the trainer himself. Joe Dokes had possessed this kind of mentality.

The bullet which had felled him in Africa had been fired by an unseen enemy. The succor he had received had come from beings whom he had instinctively hated, but who had proved themselves gentle and kindly. Instead of a roaring, vicious, intractable prisoner, Joe Dokes had come to the steel arena with a strange feeling of understanding—as if anything these two-legged friends desired was proper and just. His had not been training; in fact, it had been a coeducational affair, in which trainers had learned as much about animal intelligence when properly approached as a lion had gained of the things expected of him—efforts appreciated because they took the form of pleasurable exercise. He had been one of the greatest of trained lions; he had brought many dollars through the front door of the Grand Amalgamated during its transition from a wandering, ten-car aggregation to one of the largest of outdoor attractions. And now that the creeping death of old age threatened Joe Dokes, it was a matter of personal interest with everyone. But, of course, that interest rose to a pinnacle with the menagerie superintendent, and to its peak with red-haired Shorty Allerton, who had taught Old Joe to obey his first arena command.

So Shorty dosed the lion with the menagerie superintendent's tonic, and he rubbed the ancient, swayed back with the concoction which the circus doctor prescribed; he kept the cage supplied with fresh, clean straw to form a resting place for aged bones. Then, as time passed and Old Joe Dokes became slowly weaker, he adopted the habit of going into the cage and just sitting there, talking to the animal or stroking his ancient back. It was during one of these visits that the decrepit lion rose, as if in answer to a command, and, walking to the bars, stared dimly through them for a long moment. At last his heavy throat filled and a querulous, low roar sounded against the other noises of the menagerie. Shorty Allerton went beside him and squatted there.

"What do you see out there, old podner?" he asked.

Of course, Old Joe Dokes did not answer. He could not have answered, even had he possessed the power of speech. He could only stare into the distance; then, after a time, thump back to his bed of straw and ease himself to its softness. Shorty Allerton shook his head; again he had found himself thinking of feeble old soldiers dreaming of swords and youth.

The show was on the Pacific Coast now, moving down into California in quest of warm weather for a final clean-up of performances before the end of the season. One afternoon Shorty Allerton and the menagerie superintendent wrangled for half an hour in front of the cage as to whether Old Joe would be able to stick it out until they got back to winter quarters. The menagerie superintendent didn't think he'd make the grade. Shorty Allerton said he'd have to.

"It'd be a lot better if he could pass out at home," he argued.

The menagerie superintendent scowled. "What difference does it make to him?"

"Well, I don't know as if it'd make any. Only he's worryin' about somethin'. Now, look; he's gettin' up. Now you just watch him when he walks to the bars and looks out. Like it was something important."

"Any cat'll do that."

"Yeh, I know," said Shorty Allerton, with a pull at his cap. "But there's something different about Joe there—like there was somethin' that had to be done. You get what I mean, don't you?" he asked his friendly adversary. "There's something that's got to be attended to before he can kick over."

"Ash cans!" said the menagerie superintendent. But Shorty Allerton believed sufficiently in his theory to give even a little nore time to Old Joe Dokes during the day. And often at night, vhen the show was making a long run and there was nothing to lo except to play pinochle with the gang in the sleeper, he vould make the dangerous journey over the rocking flats to Old foe's cage and just sit with him awhile.

They were traveling toward the desert one night as he went back for a visit. It was warm, with the soft, clinging warmth of Southern California. There was a full moon, blending shadow and brightness into a mellow beauty. There was the perfume of final growths of luxuriant flowers, sufficiently pungent to overcome even the handicap of roadbed dust, the hot smell of steel on steel and the oil odors of the journals as the train highballed it along a stretch of straightaway track. There was beauty and the lure of far places; Shorty Allerton felt a strange, melancholy tugging as he pulled the bar of Old Joe's cage door and, going within, slumped down beside the lion. Beautiful things always made Shorty feel that way.

Far away, the ragged tops of the Sierras cut sharply back against the platinum sky. Nearer, upon a slight eminence, the black fronds of palms waved softly, as with lazy contentment. After a while there was nothing except semi-arid land, with shadowy clumps of trees in the distance, or jagged lines of blackness, denoting the course of a half-dry stream. Finally Old Joe Dokes stirred beneath the caressing hand of his master.

The old legs straightened and sent stiffened muscles into slow play. The swayed back tensed and his head jerked upward. Then, at last, he was on his feet and moving uncertainly toward the bars of his prison.

A night like this was unusual for circus animals; ordinarily, even when the warmth was sufficient to admit of the side boards being removed, there was at least the shielding of the canvas covers to prevent a view without. But tonight there was nothing; the canvas shields were furled at the tops of the dens; before Old Joe Dokes lay a shifting world of moonlight.

He pressed himself against the bars, braced on his knotty legs against the motion of the train. He peered out toward the splotches of silver and the ragged lines of black, toward the silhouettes and undulating vistas. Then, with a strange nervousness, he began to pace, awkwardly, painfully upon the uncertain footing, halting to look outward, then pacing anew before he should pause again. It seemed to Shorty Allerton, sitting back in the shadows, that there was more of the regal about Old Joe than he had seen in years. His mane appeared to be so full and black tonight in the moonlight; Shorty knew that it was because the beast's neck was arched with a strength that had been missing lately. His heavy, broad head was tilted, now upward, now to one side, as with constant attention. Unconscious strength had taken much of the dip from his injured back; time after time he posed in tremendous silhouette, and each time it was a momentary picture of the monarch he once had been. Then at last hard against the bars, he opened his great jaws and roared in rough, barking sequences; gruff roarings, like the coughing of a giant. Shorty went beside him and crouched there, his right arm over the beast's heavy mane.

"What do you see out there, old podner?" he queried. "Do you see the water hole like it used to be on a moonlight night like this?"

Shorty had read much of Africa. He had read much of animals. Once he'd thought he'd like to sit down sometime and write something about what he personally knew about 'em. He'd have done it, too, only for the punctuation and everything.

"Is that what you're giving the once-over?" he asked as the lion roared again. "Looks like th' old water hole, huh? And I guess that black lump away off there—I guess that's you, eh, old podner?" Suddenly he extended his free arm. "Sure enough it is! And look. Ain't that a zebra comin' down over that little hill— over there where them three things stick up like giraffes' heads? Ain't that a zebra? Sure it must be, kind o' mincin' along an' stickin' up his mule ears every now and then while he samples the air to see if there's a lion around."

He caught the beast tighter in self-generated excitement.

"Is that what you're lookin' at, old stager? Easy now, watch your step; keep your head down an' that spiked tail from swishin' around too much. They've got good ears, them zebras."

Don't make a move until he's just right. Wait till he pussyfoots
past a little ways before you take the run. You know—just
enough of a start to send you curvin' just right over his back,
so you'll sink them fore claws in his shoulders to hang on by
while you crack down on his neck bone. Easy now—easy now,
old podner!"

The lion roared again, and breaking from his comrade paced
anew. But he halted finally at Shorty's side again, and once more
the little man began his imageries. That could be Africa easy
enough, out there in the moonlight, Shorty told himself. And
here could be a water hole, with zebras and wildebeests and
maybe an ill-tempered, shortsighted rhinoceros hanging around
somewhere. By and by it grew late and Shorty gave his ancient
charge a good-night pat. Then he cussed the drawbar on the
cage door as he worked to close it in the darkness; it was security, however, which angered him, rather than a lack of it.
The bar fitted so tightly that all of his strength was required to
shove it home. The most intractable animal on the circus never
could work that door open.

It was just something to grouch about because he felt melancholy. Shorty forgot it almost before he had edged around the
shrouded tableau wagons of the first flat car; other things had
returned to take his attention.

"Yeh, that's it," he mused—"thinkin' about home. I guess
everybody does that when they get along toward the end."

But Shorty in his deductions was nearer a solution than the
heavily maned beast which stood still braced against the bars,
looking out at the swirling, moonlit countryside. Old Joe did
not truly understand what urged him to this; he only realized
obedience to strange cravings which did not make themselves
clear to him, restless flashes which crossed his brain, uncertain
stirrings which forced him to forget the oldness and swellings of
his joints, and the pain of movement. What it was or why it was
—that was something beyond the mentality of Old Joe Dokes.
He saw nothing specific in the distance when, as if called, he
shuffled to the bars and stared without. He recognized nothing
familiar, he looked for nothing as a particularity. He only knew

that something would suddenly surge in his brain, and that grudgingly, he would exert himself to answer its summons. Then sometimes his heart would beat faster and he would bestir himself to an old attitude of supremacy—but he did not know why.

The show traveled over the divide and down past the Salton Sea to Yuma for its last stand of the season. There was the final dinner in the cookhouse, with a specially printed menu and speeches by the bosses. Then came the last performance, and the Home, Sweet Home finale by the band. After that, a great show disintegrated, performers leaving upon regular trains for their winter work in theaters and motion-picture studios or to winter loafing, while workingmen migrated in a dozen directions. The circus trains, carrying only skeleton crews, set forth upon the long journey eastward and northward to the winter quarters of the Grand Amalgamated in St. Louis.

The home run of a circus is a tedious affair—hour after hour of jogging along or of waiting on sidings because of the priority of fast freights and passenger trains. Beside this, there is the delay of feeding and watering stops for the care of the animals. The next afternoon found Shorty's section still dragging over hot, dry, comparatively desert country. The side boards were off menagerie cages, and the canvas raised from the shady sides; cat animals panted, led stock fretted in the horse cars, elephants trumpeted in protest against the heat and swayed uncomfortably at their ring pins. At last the menagerie superintendent approached the bunk where Shorty was sprawled.

"Just talking to the manager," he said. "Got a clear rail now, so we ain't going to make a feeding stop until after sundown. We'll hit a water tank along about that time. It makes a little longer running without a stop, but it's best. It'll be cool in the twilight; and if we have to stay a little longer, there's the moon to work by."

"Yeh," said Shorty Allerton. Then with an afterthought: "Guess I'd better go back and sit a while with Joe. I ain't seen him since morning."

"All right, is he?"

"Who—Joe? Yeh, seems kind of tired, though; he was at the bars pretty near all the time I was back there. Funny how he acts, ain't it?"

The menagerie superintendent did not give an opinion; he only cursed the heat and dropped into his berth. After a time, Shorty Allerton arose and, tossing aside his magazine, went forth for the hot journey across the flat cars toward the cage of his beloved lion.

Old Joe was pacing slowly when Shorty pulled the grudging drawbar and entered the cage; the animal trainer felt that he noticed about him the evidences of a new agitation.

"Too much scenery, old kid," said Shorty Allerton. "It's got you thinkin' about things."

But Old Joe Dokes was only doing what he had done before —answering strange, confused commands within his brain. A day of travel like this was distinctly unusual—even the Sunday runs of the circus were mostly accomplished with the side boards in place. Today there had been nothing to obstruct the view. Ever since dawn, Old Joe Dokes had watched a succession of changing scenery. There had been far-away hills and trees, and winding arroyos with perhaps a trickle of water in the center of a wide depression of sand. There had been clumps of sage, rocky slopes with stunted trees upon them, or the blue-gray of tenacious vegetation. Now and then there had been life—scrawny cattle or swarthy people standing in front of 'dobe dwellings. There was the blue of the sky, the hint of far places, and the constant blow of speed-engendered breeze, bringing strange scents to age-dulled nostrils. All these things had combined to keep him constantly alert; his coughing roar had sounded more than once that day.

Shorty Allerton's presence, however, seemed to bring a calming influence. The old beast halted for his usual petting; when he continued his pacing, it was for a shorter interval. Finally, tired, the soreness of his muscles asserting itself, he hobbled to his straw pile and settled there. After a time he slept.

Two hours passed. Screeching brake shoes gave evidence that the feeding stop had been reached. Shorty Allerton rose from his

resting place on the cage floor, and as the train came to a halt
tiptoed to the cage door, working slowly at the drawbar, again
cussing the tightness of the locking device. Then someone called
him from up the line. The animal man eased himself out and
caught the drawbar, meanwhile shouting over his shoulder as
he drove it home, with extraordinary ease, he thought.

It was only momentary consideration. There was a jam up
at the horse cars and the menagerie superintendent was yelling
for him. Shorty Allerton swung from his position, and leaping
to the ground, ran to the work ahead. In the cage, Old Joe
Dokes stirred slightly, stretched his thickened legs, rolled to his
back, and like a cat before a fire, slept on.

Moonlight had come when the lion awoke. Outside, there
were still the voices of men and the nickering of horses, combined with the chirruping and grunting of the elephants as they
fussed about their hay at a temporary picket line. But these
were fading sounds; the train was moving jerkily as the engine
gave and took up slack on the way to a siding, some half mile
away. Old Joe watched the vague, passing figures beside the
track without curiosity. Then he turned and, with equal lack of
interest, regarded a noise-making device at the end of his den.
It was the door of his cage, swinging wide or clashing, steel
against steel, as it closed momentarily, only to sway outward
again with the rocking motion of the train. Shorty Allerton had
failed to notice, when that drawbar had moved so easily, that it
was moving outside its hasp. Now, with the bar protruding, the
door could not even mesh with its framework when it closed;
the steel impediment merely rattled and sent it gaping again.
It caused little concern for Old Joe Dokes. At last, as the engi-
neer widened the throttle to back the train upon the siding, the
door swung clear against the cage proper, and tangled with a
loose rope from a canvas tie-off. The noise ceased after that, for
the door now remained open. But Old Joe Dokes paid no attention to that either.

The noises of the feeding lot had traveled far away. There
was only the creaking of night insects beside the tracks, the faint
breathing of the engine far ahead, and the thumping of cat ani-

nals in a near-by cage as they paced in answer to nocturnal
instincts. Beyond that, there was quiet—quiet and moonlight,
and strange things in the distance beckoning Old Joe Dokes
once more to go to the bars and look out. Then, from far away,
over a filmy ridge of hills, came an eerie, wailing call.

It was high-pitched and weird, breaking from the crescendo
wail into a series of sharp yappings. Then there was silence.
But after a time the call came anew, this time from a different
direction. And for a third time; then slowly the cries began to
converge, signal and answer, call and command; somewhere,
out in the dusk and silver of the distant hills, a coyote pack was
assembling with the curiosity engendered by strange animal
scents. Higher and higher the cries rose, piercing the night. Old
Joe Dokes pressed his giant head against the bars and growled.
He did not know why.

An interval of quiet followed. Then a new succession of those
weirdly engrossing cries arose. The lion began to pace, a slight
rigidity making itself apparent in his heavy, spiked tail. Strange
things were struggling within his aged brain; once he went to
the open door of his prison and stood there with his head out,
peering dimly into the moonlit distance. Then he resumed his
pacing.

Fires had begun to burn in that ancient heart now. It was
beating faster, slowly faster; and there was more warmth in his
enfeebled legs. He growled anew; suddenly his big head went
upward and the roars came, bellow upon bellow. As if in answer, there sounded from a pinnacle of the silvered night the
cry of a lone coyote, signaling to the stars.

It angered the beast; a blunt anger, achieved without mental
direction. He whirled and sent a gruff challenge into the night.
Then once more he paced, and once more he paused at the
door, with his head and shoulders protruding. Now the whole
pack was screeching, as if in answer to his sonorous call; higher
and more unearthly became the screams, and again something
writhed within his brain, struggling for freedom. The swayed
back straightened. The great throat bulged again with gruff
outbursts and the spiked tail swung in stiffened ovals. Old Joe

Dokes moved out of the cage to the floor of the flat car. But once there, he only stood peering into the distance, his rough tongue running nervously about his bristling lips. After a time he moved again, this time to the ground. It was an involuntary action. He only knew that he was obsessed, to go onward, out into the moonlit night, toward those cries of the far beyond.

It was an aberration which lasted until the lion had traveled for perhaps half a mile from the track, a period in which a rushing passenger train, its whistle hard down as it passed the feeding stop, had torn onward through the night, silencing for a time the unearthly chorus from the distant hills. Then red had glared from the fire box of the circus train, whistles had signaled, and the section had backed up to receive its cargo; a task completed in comparatively short time. Soon Old Joe Dokes, hesitating upon a slight knoll, saw a shadowy string of bulky cars begin to glide away. Farther and farther it traveled into the half light, until at last it had disappeared.

The lion growled with gruff concern. A vague understanding suddenly had come to him. He did not belong out here. He was old and crippled and tired. He was lost, directionless, far from the only thing in the world he had known as home.

For a few moments he merely circled, uncertain as to his course. In his whole life there never had been such a feeling as this; at last he struck forth, moving for short spaces, then halting to try the air with fevered sniffings. But his old nostrils told him nothing.

From a distant hill those cries began anew. Then they disappeared, to sound again. This time they were closer. An hour later, a harassed, sway-backed animal, his rheumy eyes rolling and his tongue darting at short intervals to his heavy lips, paused, listened, then strove to put more speed into the movement of protesting legs. For the first time in his life, Old Joe Dokes was under the weakening influence of fear.

He did not know where he was. He did not know where to go. Cage-bound for the greater part of his life, softened by lack of exercise and by age and illness, this comparatively short journey had sapped much of his reserve. What it was that howled

ıd screamed in the distance, he did not know; but instinct told
ım that these were the cries of pursuit, and that danger trailed
ım step by step.

It was creeping danger, skulking, cowardly. Old Joe Dokes
ıd not realize that. Neither did he realize that the ten gray,
ɔglike animals of the coyote pack moved warily, hesitantly,
ıd held to the trail only because they felt sure they pursued
›mething crippled and weak, something which they need not
·ar since it fled at their approach. Only the strangeness of the
.ent held them to a distance; this quarry could not be cata-
›gued. The ammonia smell of a cat beast in his cage is vastly
ifferent from that of any animal in the wild state.

So the pursuit was one of curious caution rather than the
urried attack of confident marauders. Step by step they dogged
ım, edging constantly closer, yet holding always to a distance
ife for flight, while in the distance, plain to their sight now in
ıe moonlight, the dragging figure of Old Joe Dokes went on-
·ard, each step an action of anguish.

Exertion was taking its toll. Each time he sent those grudg-
ıg muscles into play, the pain shot from his ankle joints to his
ıoulders with the stab of a thousand burning needles. His back
ʌayed the more; it was as if he carried a load of lead. His heavy
ıil dragged at intervals; sometimes his tongue would protrude
ʌer a sagging jaw and hang there, lifeless. Behind him, stealthy,
·eeping, sharp eyes centered, nervous nostrils to the ground,
ıe pack came on.

Another hour passed, and still another following that. Fifty
:et behind him, a gray figure, less cowardly than the rest,
ıeaked forward, yapped bravely, then skulked away. Then an-
·ther ventured, and a third and fourth. Old Joe Dokes swung
is black-maned head and growled querulously; it sent the
·hole pack scampering. Midnight came and went. The pursuers
·rew brave again.

They came closer this time, one craven figure scurried for-
ʌard, his jaws clicking as he meshed them repeatedly only a few
ıches behind the tired beast. The lion growled again and
uickened his pace. This time the pack did not retreat. That

growl was apparently harmless. Now the curious brood began 1
spread, fanning out on either side, and giving less care to th
necessity for a clear road of retreat. Old Joe Dokes began to ru
in a hampered, shuffling scamper; his great head weaved and h
dim eyes rolled; his growls now were more grunts of pain tha
outbursts of anger.

But even as he groaned his discomfort a fire began to kindl
in him again, and the slightest arch made itself apparent in h
neck. Suddenly, at the sight of an arroyo, he slid down the slo
ing bank and for a time made his way along its tortuous cours
while on either side a shadowy army trailed him, growling an
yapping above him. At last he halted and stood bewildered
The arroyo had ended in serrated sandy walls, too steep for h
aged legs to climb.

He half turned, his hind legs dragging now. He slumped fo
a moment, sprawled, and rising, strove to turn back. Enduranc
was all but gone; he sprawled again, and it seemed as if thi
action were a signal.

Down the sides of the arroyo they came, from the right, fron
the left, and behind him. They leaped at him, snapping, an
darted away. He felt the sharp blades of their teeth in hi
haunches. And with that the smoldering thing which had bee
growing anew within him for the last quarter of a mile, burs
into life. Conflict!

It was what he had wanted and not known it, what he ha
longed for and not realized it, and looked for with those ol
dim eyes. It was the thing that had sent him roaring to the bar
without a knowledge of why he had gone there. It was what ha
caused his throat to fill with roarings when he had left the trair
Conflict—conflict—one more thrill of battle before he died!

His hindquarters strengthened in new life. With one forele
braced upon the ground, he sent the other out in a swift hal
circle as a coyote leaped within his range; instantly a form trav
eled high above him and crashed to the right wall of the arroyo
screaming and scrambling there an instant before death shoul
silence it. Then another form flew away; Old Joe's other grea
forepaw had swept into action now, and a second enemy lay te

feet away, bleeding out its life. The lion roared and whirled. Skulking beasts, suddenly courageous with fear, had shot behind him and were striving to pull him down from the rear.

He swung three of them about, their teeth hooked into his flesh, as he shifted for newer battle; Joe Dokes was old no longer. Again those forepaws lashed and circled, again beasts leaped and darted in their frenzied efforts to evade him; some to succeed, two more to die. All at once, in a concerted effort at flight, the remnant of the pack strove to ascend the steep slope at the end of the arroyo. They slipped and scrambled, and in the instant of delay a black-maned monster drove them down again, by sending a hurtling, disemboweled member of their pack among them. To the bottom they came, and then, their course blocked, ratlike desperation taking the place of their usual skulking natures, they swept forward in attack, five against one.

The voice of Joe Dokes rose in tremendous crescendoes, roar atop roar, and these mingled with the yowling and screaming of desperate cowards. Under him and over him, at his sides and at his rear, they tormented and struck and parried and thrust. They caught him in his tender flanks; they rolled beneath his stomach, knifelike jaws cutting with the sharpness of vicious shears. They tangled in his greasy mane and screeched their anguish as short, jabbing blows of giant claw-fringed paws lashed out with the death blow. One rolled away and was silent. Then a second was felled, and a third and fourth. Finally there was but one survivor, screaming and scrambling as he strove to climb out of reach. But the fanlike claws of Old Joe Dokes cut him down, and then there was only the roaring of a triumphant lion.

The smell of blood was in his nostrils, the fires of victory warmed a soul no longer warped by age. His stance was straight and strong now, forelegs spread, ears flat against his head, hind legs braced as he raised his head and cupped his red-streaked jaws. The moon was just above him, shining between serrated walls. He roared to it, the thunderous, booming roar of the monarch he once had been and the monarch he had again become. A dozen times, a score of times, he sent forth his reverberations of victory. Then turning, he sniffed about him, and began to strut from one gray form to another, nosing the still-warm bodies, pawing them or scraping the rough fur with his filelike tongue. And at the salt taste of vanquished veins he roared anew. A monarch!

One after another he made the rounds, but gradually his step slowed. After a time, he halted, as with surprise, and doubling swiftly, licked at a long, jagged place in his side where teeth had torn deep into his flesh. Then another wound began to burn, and others. Old Joe Dokes settled himself and licked them one by one, pausing betimes to send his rumbling roar out of the deep arroyo and across the night—the roar of victory.

Again the moon beckoned him and he pulled himself to his feet. The process was slow and painful. When at last he stood erect, the old sway had come into his back and his hindquarters weaved with a roll that all but unbalanced him. But the coughing bark was still strong; he continued the outbursts until his breath had failed, just for the sheer joy of roaring.

At last he settled again and licked once more at the deep lacerations of battle. But finally he ceased, and stretching, extended his forelegs to scratch contentedly at the sand, like a cat, sharpening its claws upon a carpet. He sighed, but it was a sigh of glorious weariness. He allowed his head to fall between extended paws, satisfied eyes gazing upon the shadowy mementoes of his victory. Slowly, however, the scene became dimmer, dimmer; at last, it was gone forever.

It was in this position that Shorty Allerton found him the next morning after an all-night search; Old Joe's absence had been discovered some five miles down the line. For a time the little menagerie man merely stood there, rubbing nervously at his throat. At last he crouched beside the still form and a hand went out to the shaggy mane of the silent Old Joe Dokes. Then the hand rose and fell in slow, soft pattings. The animal man bent closer.

"Shorty knew all the time," came quietly. "Everything's fine now, ain't it, old podner?"

Andrè Demaison

OUARA, THE LIONESS

(Translated by Guy Endore)

THE AIR WAS HOT and leaden. It was the hour of siesta. On the circular verandah slept Ouara the lioness and her master. He lay stretched out on a chaise-longue purposely placed to the garden-side, where the afternoon was freshest and which was moreover farthest away from the natives. Ouara lay near the steps on the other side. Her body barricaded half the width of the verandah.

Her master chained her there in order to nap in peace: intruders, beggars, were not likely to insist when, through the bars of the gate, they caught sight of the tawny bulk of a ten-month-old lioness who in volume and length already exceeded a full-grown Saint-Bernard. Her chops, bristling with heavy moustaches, hid white teeth as big around as your index. Her four soft and awkward-looking paws were each as large as two hands and capable of crushing a calf.

The man, a Frenchman, was a philosopher lost between two epochs: he worked both with his head and his hands. At the age of twenty he had gone to seek the meaning of life beyond the frontiers of our civilisation and for a while had thought to have found it in a territory in the bend of the Niger, at an altitude of twenty-six hundred feet, bordering on the land of the Mossis. Here dwelt the Bobos, proud men, whose entire clothing consisted of a bow and two quivers, of which one was for arrows.

His black servants who had followed him from the Coast and from the Niger held the Bobos to be no better than savages. As for the Bobos themselves, their own personal opinion was that they were the wisest sages of the universe. Did they not lie

all day with half-shut eyes and smoke without interruption the
tobacco of their little plantations, the while their women culti
vated the millet which was their chief food? If the desire for
flesh food rose strong in their mouths, it was a simple matter
for four villages to co-operate in surrounding a corner of the
forest. With their bludgeons they would beat down everything
that breathed in that area: antelopes, boars, panthers, every
thing, whether it crept or flew, down to the lowly snakes and
rats who had not had the time to retreat into their holes. That
night the game was roasted whole in fur and feathers and the
gorging of the feasters never ceased until every bit of meat had
been consumed.

It was among these simple folk whose thoughts were as
straight as the flight of their arrows, whose god was the spirit
that dwelt in their little stream, that the man had built his
home: a single-story dwelling of sun-dried bricks, surrounded
by a verandah. Here the man was accustomed to spend his hours
of leisure, protected from the sun and cooled by the mountain
breezes.

The house with its cap of heavy thatch occupied the centre of
a plain which, entirely surrounded by forest and jungle, resembled the sawdust ring of a circus, hemmed in on all sides by
tiers of seats.

The man, aside from his routine occupations, tended his
garden, watched his cabbages grow, saw to his horse and his
salad, strove to think, and was often bored.

One day, hunters killed a mother lioness and captured her
two cubs: a male and a female. The little male betrayed a
nasty temper, he clawed a chieftain, who felled the beast at once
with a single blow of his cudgel and ate it that very evening.
The female, still spotted with yellow on her flanks, was brought
to the white man who purchased her in order to amuse himself.

She was then in her fourth month, and growled a little, for
no apparent reason, with her ears flattened against her head.
She was really three months too old for sudden adoption as a
household pet. The three months during which she had prowled
in the jungle along with her father and mother, had sufficed for

Ouara—as she was called from the diminutive of the Bambara word for lion—to acquire her innate beast-of-prey character. There was then nothing in her of that infantile submission which is to be seen in new-born lion cubs who will greedily suck at a bottle or take to a goat's nipples without qualms.

It was her savage nature that attracted the lonely man. This at any rate was not just a dog with claws, such as are the whelps who open their eyes in human habitations. Ouara had already smelt raw meat, she had even tried to lick it with short stabs of her young raspy tongue, in imitation of her mother crouching before the body of an antelope or buffalo. Such tribal manners it was that had already instilled in her that fretful soul, compounded of fear and bluff, which is so fundamental of wild animals.

Ouara's education was thus a delicate task. Her mistrust was visible in every move of her body. At the very slightest approach her ears flattened or else pricked up sharply and all too suddenly and her young claws were quick to escape from their furry sheaths; the mere odor of man caused the lines in her face to tremble; it was a long time before she would permit her back to be caressed while she lapped from a bowl of milk.

It was still worse when Ouara began to taste of meat cooked with rice. Then her paws, whose padded soles could each cover a cake-dish, her heavy and apparently unwieldy paws, flashed like steel springs.

Games, however, succeeded in half taming her: fights, dashes, somersaults, pirouettes, in all of which her master participated. The whip, lightly applied, about finished what games and fixed mealtimes had begun. At the age of six months Ouara had developed into a young lioness, still rather large-pawed, with a skin a bit too loose for her bones and with teeth rocking in their sockets, and soon to be replaced by a more permanent set; her tail was thin, her coat was ragged and unkempt, but all in all she was not badly brought up. She still ran after the cats now and then, but being replete she never dreamed of worrying the antelopes or the tamed deer, she never disturbed the lone dog or the goats.

Naught could terrify her except the oxen and the gawky, naked Bobos.

Be it observed, however, that all this was but her daytime character. In the morning she was humble, she pleaded. After meals she was in turns somnolent and turbulent. She never grew so familiar as to come to the table to beg for the bones of the cutlets. But at night, when the wind passed through the forests and brought her the scent of newly opened flowers, the breath of the thickets and the sweat of beasts, then Ouara grew unquiet. She no longer purred, she went *chahah!* to the right and then to the left, as though she were still following her mother along the trails, or along a water course, or perhaps crouching in wait for a sharp-hoofed beast.

Then she would scratch at the doors of the verandah, in order to go down into the courtyard of the concession, being curious to see at close range what her senses caused her to divine.

It would have been ridiculous to have shut her up—not only ridiculous, but contrary to the laws of the jungle, for the cage is the invention of civilised barbarians;—her master had therefore accustomed her to a leash. At first a mere ornament: a braided bit of cotton fabric. A thong displaced the braid, which in its turn gave way to a real collar with an iron buckle. A bell was fastened to the collar in order to betray Ouara's every movement, and there was furthermore a free-hanging rope. The rest was a game. Truly an impetuous game, full of madness, sudden bounds, violent veerings. But still a game.

The collar was opened bit by bit, a notch a month, but never did it leave Ouara's neck. Before her master went to sleep both at night and at siesta he attached her to the balustrade of the verandah: his was the only hand that she would obey. With a single slash of her teeth she could have readily severed the cord, but she had a certain respect for leashes, even as the Negroes will demolish a wall rather than break open the ten cent padlock which defends the door.

This habit was the cause of the following event.

Ouara was sleeping in that utter peace which can come only from a beautiful new set of teeth erupted but two months ago, a clean pelt free from insects, and a satiated belly. She slept, confident in the presence of her master, though the latter was lying at the other end of the verandah, and confident too, by virtue of an ancestral sentiment, in her own supreme inviolability . . . At that moment, the household cat slunk past. Ouara, in a pleasant mood from the after effects of a good digestion, had often played with this cat. What happened then, now? Perhaps the cat had not expected to see the lioness? Perhaps he was too full of his own personal cares, too absorbed in his own private researches concerning the basement or the attic? The fact is simply this, that a rapid pass of arms took place, that the cat took up the offensive, flung out a clawed paw at Ouara's snout and with a single bound flew through the balustrade into the court below before one of the lioness' enormous paws could reach him.

The lioness, hot in pursuit, followed right upon the cat's traces, forgetting collar, rope, balustrade, thinking only of the sport.

The leash and the collar were both well made, and as a result Ouara never reached the ground. She hung in mid-air, and swung brutally against the wall. What an uproar she made! With wild harsh screeches, she gathered herself together again and again for a desperate leap, only to fall, each time, helplessly against the wall. Her enormous bounds caused the house to rock. Her fur flew in all directions. The plaster scaled off from the wall and rained down in a shower.

Shattered was the afternoon torpor that lay over the court. In the shadow of tree or wall, niggers were accustomed to sleep: baggage-bearers, rubber-venders, messengers, travellers, pedlars, beggars, of every nationality and description. At the sound of the lion's roar, they already felt the terror of the jungle clawing at their backs. With a single bound they were up and dashing, half-asleep, to safety beyond the concession.

Each one realised in a flash that if the cord broke the lioness would wreak her anger on the nearest man she could reach.

Meanwhile the cat had taken shelter in the topmost branches of a mango, where a tribe of fruit-bats were accustomed to spend the day, hanging head-downwards. These are those large flying foxes that live on fruit, disdaining the insects, which they leave to the lesser fry of bats, with whom they compare as elephants to oxen. By the hundred the fruit-bats dropped from their trapezes and swung out into the air, fluttering about awkwardly, blindly, in the unaccustomed glare of day, like sparks drawn up by the bellows of a blacksmith.

As for the yellow cur that sometimes entered into Ouara's sport, he suddenly lost his optimism in his playmate and scurried into the kitchen where the black scullery boy was in haste to close the door.

Loud terror reigned in the court. Ouara still bounded, using her ineffective claws in vain attempts to help herself up the wall. Her voice, raucous at first, had thinned to a screech, and was now muffled. There were intervals of silence, as though she were striving to catch her breath. For in truth her breath was fast leaving her. Her neck-muscles still held, and thus maintained the integrity of her spine, but they were stretched to the utmost and threatened to give way at any moment.

At last aroused by all this din, the master appeared on the verandah clad in his light pyjamas, limp with sweat. He was about to thunder forth imprecations against the most remote ancestors of the ignominiously sired men who were tormenting his Ouara, when he leaned over the balustrade and caught sight of her singular position. Ouara too saw him and with a last effort of every muscle in her body, leaped at him, only to fall back again against the stones, leaving there a tuft of hair torn from her thigh.

She remained gathered into a ball, suspended like a sack, and turned her eyes toward her master who without a moment's hesitation had begun to tug at the rope. But Ouara was too heavy. He had to leave her there in her perilous position.

A long thin sigh issued from Ouara's squeezed throat, as from a collapsing bag: her master had disappeared.

When he returned with a knife in his hand, the lioness was immobile. Her eyes were fixed on him, immense, resigned, protruding eyes. She was foaming at the mouth.

With a single slash he severed the leash and Ouara dropped like a bale.

But not for long. In a moment she was up, had disentangled herself and was loping around the house.

Her master had scarcely laid away the knife on a near-by table and called to his boy for a drink, when he felt strangled by two enormous paws laid on his shoulders. Before he could move or cry out he was bowled over and rolled along the floor. And up against his face was the large face of the young lioness, exhaling upon him a somewhat acrid breath.

The man wished to defend himself, he strove to push aside those jaws, restrain those armored paws. But the lioness was lying on him with all the crushing weight of her hundred and thirty pounds of muscle, tough as mahogany. In his anguish he was stiff and paralysed, his body was by turns light and heavy. The cries that issued from Ouara's throat were not the hard dry sounds that an enraged lion utters, but deep, soft purrings terminating in a little tassle of a whine. Her chops did not reveal fangs, but only admitted the passage of a raspy tongue, that licked and licked; licked the hands ready to ward off an attack, the elbows raised in defence, licked her master's forehead and his hair, and all of his body through the light pyjamas.

With claws sheathed, Ouara's paws firmly embraced the prey to her good-will, her love and her gratitude.

From that day on, Ouara's friendship remained steadfast and true. When her master called her, she came running up at once, dropping whatever sport she might be pursuing, even leaving her food. If he happened to tread on her tail, she leaped from his path, but far from him in order not to hurt him. At night she kept watch at the door of his chamber, and waited for the day to bring the boy with the tray of coffee, so that she could enter the room with him and lie at her master's feet. She followed him upon excursions into the jungle, whether he went by foot or by horse. During the hours of rest she attempted to sleep on his knees and as long as she remained awake she never ceased to lick him by stealth.

Ouara, as a great and generous friend of her master, allowed some of her affection to spill over and reach other white men, for she supposed them all to be provided with instruments capable of liberating a strangling lion. This did not prevent the jealous and the hypochondriacs from declaring to her master, who took his lioness along to the club, to the tennis courts, even out for a walk in the plains: "You'll see, when she grows up and becomes ripe for motherhood! . . . You'll see how foolish you've been! . . . Better be careful then, as you value your hide! . . ."

That period came. The dry season was followed by Winter with its incessant downpour, its frenzied stubborn storms, its mad tornadoes, until again a new dry season came, and Ouara was twenty months old, which for a lioness is the age of a beautiful girl of eighteen.

Except for her size, she was unchanged. At least all the eye could note was that month by month she filled more space.

Nevertheless, at that period when certain trees were sprouting new foliage—and that does not imply that it was Spring, for in Africa there is no set season at which all nature reawakes in unison—a species of restlessness took hold of Ouara. She no longer slept at night that peaceful sleep of a lioness confident of her sovereignty and of the protection of her master. Indeed if the latter had been less exhausted by the heat and by his daily labours, and had not so quickly lapsed into deep sleep each night, he might have noticed how his lioness lifted her head, and with sloping rump tugged at her leash, sniffing at the wind, which from all directions brought the sound and the odour of the jungle.

A careless observer might have deduced that the rounded stiff tawny ears of Ouara were annoyed by the nocturnal songs and dances of the Bobos. A sorcerer might have held that the genius of the river, offended by the sight of an iron or earthenware pot, as well as by many other articles, tormented Ouara out of jealousy. But the sounds which disturbed Ouara were mere murmurs to which the ear of both black and white were insensitive: low muffled sighs scarcely as much as that which two leaves make when they rub against each other, or fat plants cause when their waxing cracks their skin, or the scarcely audible noise of grasses sharpening their thin blades against each other.

Night after night, as the moon fattened, these vague noises were amplified: no doubt the wind growing fresher shook the branches in the forest more vigorously.

That did not prevent Ouara's master from sleeping, nor the naked Bobos from dancing, dancing in utter nudity, without quiver of any kind or even a bow.

Nevertheless, a Bobo shepherd, old as the rocks, noted how the noises of the bush grew in volume and steadiness and warned the young men to light fires near their flocks. He had them arm themselves with long heavy arrows, and with big javelins such as were ordinarily never used except for funereal dances.

The vacillating flare of their small fires illuminated the night, revealed the spotted calves, the heifers, the long-horned cows and the tawny-coated oxen as well as the bulls, destined for sacrifice, whose eyes went all white when their attendants pulled at the cord.

Ouara did not alter her habits, at least not during the day. She lapped from her bowl of water, slept and played. The niggers that passed through the concession took fright at the sight of her; but that was only pretence to amuse the master, for they knew that the lioness had become a slave.

One morning, however, as he was bringing up the tray of hot coffee and fresh milk, the boy saw the beast reposing far from her leash. The rope had been severed, by a slash of her teeth, as if by a blade.

Ouara's master finished his breakfast, fastened a new and stiff length of cord to the collar and administered a sharp correction with the severed end. Wild rage and final submission. The master grumbled something about the lioness wishing no doubt just to try her teeth, and it scarcely occurred to him that she might have been unconsciously imitating the servants, who daily hide the object they crave a little more, until finally the white man no longer notices its complete disappearance.

The affair was settled. Ouara no longer cut her leash.

The waxing moon poached further and further on the darkness of the night, until finally under its full light the stars disappeared. The little plain about the grey house and the Bobo village was so brightly illuminated that one might have aimed at a fly on the shoulder of an antelope standing at the edge of the bush.

But neither antelopes nor deer nor even rabbits appeared at the black border of the thickets and the forest. It was the noise that had driven them away: the grumbling noise that had grown even as Ouara throughout these weeks had added inch by inch to her height and pound by pound to her weight. The noise grew more regular and more frequent when Ouara began to sense those mysterious effluvia that cause male butterflies to gather, from miles around, about a box containing a female— that cause the pollen of the male flowers to somehow reach the pistil of female blossoms all decked out for this great event.

On this night, then, the wind came from the forest, swept through the house and along the verandah, and caressed Ouara's spine. It brought her the odour of moist undergrowth rich with humus, and of dry treetops where tender foliage sprouted, it brought her the emanation of sap exuding from cracks in the bark, it brought her the sweat of lianas and of overripe fruits, it brought her the savour of that amorous yellow powder that falls from palm-trees when bats or nightbirds ruffle the branches in passing.

Ouara's master slept, insensible to the lioness' trouble.

The faithful watchman hummed his little song of nostalgia for the great rivers and then, having whistled the melody, dropped off to tranquil sleep, confident that his fate would always aid him to escape unharmed should robbers dare to enter his master's storerooms. The bats had finished their nightly chase for mosquitoes, they had ceased their tinkling as of little bells and had gone to sleep, hanging head downwards from their favourite mango. Only the cat and the household boa, quieter even than the silence of night, remained awake and the respect that emanated from their presence spread down into the depths of the holes where rats and field-mice cowered in fear.

Then, the low noise that had been gathering itself, having announced itself and then ceased as in preparation, broke loose. Suddenly it burst the black barrier that bounded the moon-washed plain. It began with a single throat. Another followed. Then others still. It was as though the devil himself blew through a series of organ pipes stopped by barbed and tangled wire.

At the first cry the lioness was on her paws, her head erect. Her tail whipped her flanks, beat the floor of the verandah, knocked against the railing. She began to tug at her leash, to toss her head, while from out there in the darkness lions unceasingly called to her the words that, since unnumbered centuries, lions have roared to lionesses. . . .

In their blind terror, the village oxen were stupefied. The goats butted the doors of the cabins. The dogs, after having tried to reply, hid in the millet granaries. In their huts and near the pens, the men raked the fires that keep huge wild beasts away, the fires that dispel the chill of morning air and that drive away the hovering evil spirits.

Ouara stamped, snuffled, snorted, as the distant roars slowly approached to take back what man had ravished from them.

The tawny-maned lions followed only their instincts, and too far away to sense it directly, had no idea that Ouara smelt of man, that her fur bore that odour of man more biting than the odour of the jungle, which does not eat salt. They ignored that she had been brushed, washed, curried, and combed by men. And they approached her, slowly, as though they had to beware of traps.

Held by the power of the Call, Ouara forgot her sleeping master. Her throat worked in spasms. A thin stifled noise was all that issued from it at first, then came a long hard growl that split the atmosphere of the concession.

The watchman awoke. The master awoke, and dashed out on the verandah.

There he saw an unknown Ouara. In an hour she had reached maturity. She was crouching low in order to leap up suddenly to fuller height. Her hind paws pounded the floor as though they sought support for a great bound. Her heavy fore-paws were flung brusquely into the air and slowly, cautiously lowered as though on thorns. Ouara paid no attention to her master; the verandah, the leash, so readily severed by her teeth, were forgotten: with set eyes she gazed out on the plain toward the black fringe that surrounded the farms of the Bobos.

It was the Call that the lions were crying out to Ouara, as they waited for the moment when they would battle for her possession; and meanwhile they measured each other up and down, now seated quietly, now nervously slashing through the undergrowth. It was the Call to Ouara to obey the age-old duty, to do as all lionesses did and no longer transgress the law in order to please man.

The whole bush trembled with the strength of their roaring.

"Now now! What's come over you, Ouara?"

As if she were waking out of a dream, she turned suddenly and her two eyes made two glowing spots in the shadow of the verandah. She saw her master. Against the light of the court her enormous sinuous profile sank slowly. . . . She lay down, her tail stretched out, her forepaws parallel in front of her.

"Ho! Watchman!"

"Here I am!" said the Negro, issuing from the little kitchen to the right of the concession.

"What's up? Has any one entered?"

"No one, master! It is the lions who are calling Ouara. And I'll be damned, if she didn't look as though she were listening to those bad fellows. . . ."

Ouara's master ran to fetch his rifle—which as a hunter he always kept in readiness for instant use—and took aim at the source of the roars.

The bullet flashed through the night. The explosion slapped the walls of the houses, went hurtling out to the trunks in the forest and came back all alone.

The growling had ceased. But only for a moment. The

lioness had jumped and was now straining at the cord in order
to reach her master.

He bent down and scratched her about the eyes, scratched her
on the chin and there where her tail joined her body.

"Come now, Ouara," he said. "Go to sleep."

The lioness licked his naked feet and then rolled over on her
back with her four legs drawn up and presented her belly to her
master's caresses.

. . . While beyond the plain, white-washed under the moon,
dark spots retreated, eructating into the night, hurling spas-
modic oaths against the house of the man, and following these
with long majestic raucous organ peals.

Two years later. A cage: ten feet square of sloping floor, a
ceiling at arm's reach, dirty yellow walls, and bars of iron that
would suffice for a troop of savage elephants. The reason for
their thickness lies not only in the need of securing maximum
resistance to rust but also in the necessity of justifying that
adjective "wild" applied to the beasts who live behind these
bars.

It is to this that Ouara has come.

The lioness and her master have both followed the obscure
paths of destiny. Each went his appointed way. And to both was
it given to go North. The man left first. Before returning to
France he gave his beast to a friend. The latter passed her on
to some one else until finally she entered the Governor's house.
He shipped her to Paris.

Shut up in a crate, tossed by the sea, she coasted the brutal
splendours of Morocco, and listened to the nostalgic *fados* sung
by the Portuguese mountaineers, those inhabitants of land's
end, who, in preceding centuries, drank so deep from the
world's bowl that they grew intoxicated and fell asleep at the
very moment when the rest of Europe was waking up.

Now, then, there is Ouara, with a hyena, the gift of some
minor Kabyle chieftain, to her right, and a brown bear with
a wasted pelt on her left. She takes no notice of them, for they
are not of her race. She knows that there are other lions, living

further off, for she has smelled them and heard them, but never seen them.

Thus she lives, on the banks of the Seine, occupying the fourth cell in a monument that was once, that is, in the mediocre era of black furniture and paper spills in red porcelain vases, the glory of some architect. Twenty false Doric columns divide twenty-one cells: thus are platitude and emptiness repeated twenty-one times. Behind, are twenty-one corresponding cages, facing a long many-windowed hall. Here and there, on a column a notice is posted:

Please do not annoy the animals

Above one cage, one reads:

LIONESS
Felis Leo
Gift of M. Prud'homme

It is the end of Winter.

The sun shines through sleet. A young lioness with short conical teeth who, unlike Ouara, has not grown up near man, paces her cell from door to wicket and back again, leaping now and then against the wall, ever hoping some day to find there a way out to liberty and caresses.

A crowd of idlers gathers before the cages. *Felis tigris* (Royal tiger, gift of the Emperor of Annam), *Felis pardus, Felis leo.* The cheaply purchased bears are waiting for the peanuts which children are permitted to throw to them. It provides amusement for the old gentlemen with their canes and umbrellas, the old teethless shrews, children's nurses, mothers and their babies.

On other columns one reads:

VIOLATORS WILL BE PROSECUTED BY LAW

In view of accidents that have recently occurred among the animals
It is strictly forbidden to throw anything whatsoever to the carnivores

And, to explain the word carnivores, there is a further note:

Lions, panthers, pumas

A signboard, another signboard and still another, bars, hand-rails, and a snoozing guard. Is this not the snuggest sort of post for a government employé? The public has but to read its way.

Sad cages before which passes a sadder funereal cortege, reminiscent of the era of train oil and tallow candles. Can those be human beings, those creatures in their ridiculous rags that bear the colour of death and necrosis? Are those human faces that pass in a monotone file of unexpressive masks from which peer empty looks? Their countenances are lighted with one single desire: to get their money's worth. They can still hear the forlorn drop of their two francs in the gateman's till. What packages of dreariness and darkness are these bits of humanity that hide their pale flesh in dark colours as though black and obscurity were the symbols of our age!

Occasionally Ouara will cast glances of curiosity at this procession of debility. She will utter little growls of encouragement and invitation. Will not some one play with her, as once she was played with near her native forests? The crowd cannot understand, they remain on the safe side of the bars and taunt. A silly display of bravado before a caged prisoner. The mob is cowardly and admires the fashion in which the government amuses them by sheltering them from danger. It is the same pleasant feeling that they derive when they see the photograph of a condemned murderer staring at them from the front pages of the newspaper.

Ouara has never committed any crime. But she can't stand the cold. She remains indoors. Long ago she ceased her acrobatic exercises, ceased to care about the spring of her muscles, unlike the other young lioness for whom this sport has not yet cloyed. Ouara has drained all the distractions of captivity: the sight of acacias, wretched and thin in winter and weeping under the rains, the daily passage of men whom she cannot reach to sniff at—with whom she cannot play. No longer does she toy with the dream of an imaginary prey upon which she suddenly pounces.

At first Ouara did not understand. She thought this cage would be like the one on the boat, a temporary housing. Soon she would be freed, she would get back her collar and her cord and they would bring her back to her master's house, an open house, through which the wind swept freely, with wide verandahs, bathed in luminous heat. Then gradually the monotony got her: uninspired meals perpetually alike, from day-cage to night-cage and back again, dirty yellow walls, dark iron bars, an unvarying horizon.

Day by day she grew less supple, less alert. Each month left her colder, crustier and more inactive; soon boredom and the lack of necessity to move, in fact the almost inability to move in this confined space whose dimensions were laid out by some mean, small-spirited person, had sapped all the springiness from her body. And worst of all was the endless grey humidity, such as even attacks the stones of buildings, and which finally gnawed into the joints of her limbs and her spine, and there caused such ravages that she ceased to climb onto her oaken stand, meant to substitute for the rocks of her native country. When first she had reached this prison she used to seat herself there, leaping up to it with an imperceptible flick of her muscular loins.

Then, from the depths of her soul rose the desire to see her master. Her whole life revolved about that wish. She waited. She hoped one day to discover in that procession of faces the face of him who had brought her up, who had seen her grow, who had dispelled the old misunderstanding that persists between man and lion and all the other jungle-beasts. So she would slip her paws between the bars and the floor and, having thus added a little to the extent of space allotted to her by man, she would rest, her eyes half-closed, and listen to the visitors, completely filled with her desire to hear, through the medley of vulgar talk and absurd remarks, that familiar voice which she associated with the joys of sunlight.

Now she has tired of looking. She sleeps. Between the meals which her guard brings her, Ouara sleeps. He too is a young uprooted son of soil and open spaces, who abandoned his native Cévennes, because his father thought he ought to work on the farm for nothing, though two men were necessary to replace his capable arms.

Please do not annoy the animals! . . . Nothing can disturb Ouara now. She sleeps. Sodden by her fate, she has forgotten the sensation of early-morning coolness preceding the rich living light of the sun. She has forgotten those mornings noisy with the clucking of touracos and pagoda cocks mingled with the cooing of turtle-doves and green pigeons. The barking of her master's dog, the mooing of the oxen, the silly calls of the trumpeters, the bleating of the sheep, the rhythm of tom-toms and of millet being crushed in a mortar, all that is here replaced by noisily exploding trucks, by chugging motors, by the horns of autos and by the screeching of trolleys, really the most sense-less type of locomotion in the world.

Skulking in the rear of her square cave, Ouara has nothing to amuse her but the twitter of sparrows and the voice of her guard. That's not much for a beast who can recall a brilliantly illuminated house surrounded by quiet and warm spaces to which she had every right of access—though she then disdained it—a house where games and a carefree happy life had replaced the terrors of the jungle, such as fire and serpents, and other sudden desperate terrors more savage and cruel than hunger.

Ouara has tired of the struggle which took place in her be-tween her past, with its submission to the light-skinned man of blazing eyes, and the regrets of another life which came to her from her ancestors. She either crouches obstinately, stretching out her head on her paws, or else she relaxes on her side with one ear against the floor, and thus she resigns herself to sleep. Only at the regular hours appointed by the directors does the desire for food rouse her to a little motion.

. . . One day, when Ouara least expected it, the man came: he who had taught her to play with men, he who had invented, for her, savoury warm dishes that never tired her palate, he who never let her lack for water, and who cut her leash when it threatened to kill her.

Ouara's master was in France for a brief stay. He stood waiting there, before the cage, until the flood of sad visitors had diminished. It was mealtime. Ouara went back and forth, reached up to the little trap-door, returned again to the bars, with a still supple gait, with her muscles still strong enough to hide any stiffness at the joints.

Once she stopped and considered this lonely belated visitor. She did not recognise him. The man had relinquished his pyjamas and his white suit, his helmet and cloth shoes, in order to don the dull and intricate clothes that are necessary in a country where the houses touch the sky and where the trees are stunted.

"Ouara, my girl!" he murmured even as the beast resumed her random walk. "So you no longer recognise me?"

The lioness stopped in her tracks; she leaped aside and stood thus, with a tense look, with furrowed brow, while her tail whipped the air. Her dull eyes were suddenly fired with astoundment, with incredulity, with hope. Her heart, deep in her cavernous chest, raced madly. Nothing in the world could have distracted those eyes that gazed fixedly at the man, while he continued quietly, in a serious touching voice, to speak to her those words he used to tell her, when, years ago, they played on the verandah. It was those light and childish words that had made the beast forget the open jungle and the freedom of the forest—the free forest, where spirits, tangled in the branches, whisper like the wind rustling the leaves—the jungle where vagabonding souls that have left their ancestral tombs go wandering on dark nights, where the lion herds pass, on their nocturnal hunts, and grunt in order to wake up the game that they cannot see.

Oh ooooh! Gradually, as the man spoke, the lioness' hindquarters dropped. From her wrinkled throat came a very long and very, very soft roar.

The master came nearer and Ouara rolled over on her back, folded up her legs and pulled in her claws, in readiness for the caress which she had been craving for so long: little scratches all

along her ribs like she used to get when she was but a little bit
of a lioness with clumsy paws and ocellated fur.

But she could not wait. Up she rose and snuffled at the caressing hand, licked it with her raspy tongue, rubbed up against it
with rounded back and arched head and neck. The master
stretched his hand through the bars and felt the bumps on her
body, thinly covered with worn fur. He felt the knobs on her
head and on her bones where they had been rubbed unceasingly
by the bars. He felt her desiccated tail. No one had ever dared
to bathe her, so that her whole body exuded a strong acrid odor
which made her poor hide all the more wretched.

Now and then the lioness stopped pretending to chew the
hand which nearly disappeared down her enormous gullet, and
looked reproachfully at her master. There was a questioning in
her eyes, as naïve as once before, when for the fourth time in
her life she had seen the moon wax.

Her purring filled the cage, overflowed into the corridor of
the prison and penetrated into the neighbouring cubicles. Some
male lions misunderstood and replied with hoarse roars that
shook the Doric-columned edifice, drowned out the nasal
trumpeting of the auto horns, the clangor of the street cars, and
the cries of newsboys yelling through one side of their mouth as
they ran through the rain with print-blackened papers.

The man, a bit frightened, drew back his hand. Whereupon
Ouara passed her paws beneath the bars and gently tugged him
closer until she could lick him. The call of those mad lions in
the neighbouring cages left her cold; she did not even listen to
them. All she heard was her name, that name that no one ever
called to her any more: "Ouara! Ouara!"

"All out!"

It was four o'clock. The guard came up.

"Do you know that lioness?" he asked.

"I myself raised her. Two years, now, since I've laid eyes on
her. But a lion never forgets. Do you remember Androcles? . . ."

"Androcles? Who was Androcles?"

Ouara's master had ideas about the Administration. They

proved to be all false. He applied for the freeing of the beast. He offered to buy her. In reply he was shown a copy of the by-laws. The sign above the cage was pointed out to him. The lioness was the gift of some donor. And were he himself the donor, he could not reclaim his gift.

He carried his grief to the newspapers. He pleaded for a stretching of the law.

He was told that the item was not of present-day interest.

At that time Caroline Butcher was filling all the columns. . . .

And since the affection of a lioness cannot nourish a man, her master had to leave France and in another continent earn his bread, by the sweat of his brow.

In her cubical cage sleeps Ouara, or sleeps rather some dirty yellow beast whose fur matches the color of the walls, and that people here call wild. A beast that has lost her name, who is no longer any one's lioness, who has become the government's lioness. Dead leaves have replaced summer's dust. Winter has come with low coarse clouds, with an horizon blotted out with blind fogs, with disgraceful trees, and a sticky cold that has penetrated into Ouara's lungs.

From season to season, but all in vain, she has waited for a new visit of the man who, while he scratched her around the eye and crumpled her ears, called her Ouara.

Her guard, the man from Cévennes, now, occasionally attempts a clumsy caress: but he shuns the risk. (After all he's not being paid for that . . .) And then there's more than enough to do, what with the feeding and the cleaning of cages for five bears, four cubs, a royal tiger—two cages for him—panthers from God only knows where, filthy hyenas and an American puma, who all have their separate and similar cubical cages, but did not grow up in freedom in a man's house.

At this hour, Ouara, with twisted back and limp paws is lying on her side. Near by is a horse's hock which she has failed to touch. The veterinary was there. Even an assistant-director came. Ouara no longer eats. Ouara refuses to eat. Ouara refuses to move.

All evening, now, she has been lying stretched out, with her tail straight as a broomstick, her fur on end, mussed up and dirty. At this hour, when human beings have all gone to seek their pleasure, only the lights of the boulevard cast any illumination into the prison.

It is one of the last days of that season which Winter seeks to wrest from Spring. South and north winds meet in eddies. A dark combat ensues that is fought out along the deserted quays, the bare parks and the inhospitable streets. The wind tears itself to shreds against the houses, the monuments, the black trees, and goes screaming on. It shakes the old windows in the corridor. Slates, torn from the tiled roof, fall whistling to the pavement and shatter into a thousand pieces.

Ouara leans her jaw against the floor and whines. The terrible sickness that destroys the lungs of men, and even haunts these unhealthful cages, has taken advantage of her illness. From her throat issues a long and desolate hoarseness. Surely she has not appointed a rendezvous with Death in this narrow sordid prison, with its perpetual right angles. . . . It was not the custom of her clan to await cold immobility behind bars through which come the exclamations of imbeciles and the wads blown by children through their pea-shooters. . . .

A shiver passes over the ribs and flanks of Ouara. And the dolorous complaint continues. Worn out with boredom, overburdened by fate, she gives vent to a cry of despair. She is not angry—all courage has left her—but with stubborn insistence she demands the forest where grow trees of every size and every specie, trees that likewise die of sickness limb by limb, or else perish shattered by lightning or uprooted by a tornado, but they at least die in state, among their own kind, surrounded by those noisy mysterious beings that foregather in the living branches. This is the forest, where the gods feed on fruit and blood.

In the night, feebly lighted by the dying ends of rays from the gas flames, are other lions: fierce, sombre beasts, taken as adults in some Abyssinian trap. They have heard Ouara, and they quake for they have understood all that the assistant-director and the veterinary have failed to grasp. Their lips are curled, their throats quiver. Heavy impassioned roars growl through the corridor of the prison.

Ouara, already half lost in the nonentity, which is slowly swallowing her up, has recognised the calls that shake the old and ridiculous dwelling. Are these not the calls she heard one night from the verandah of the man's house, which stood in the centre of the moon-washed plains?

With a start the lioness begins to writhe, bruising her cheek-bones against the floor. A combat ensues within her between the life that once animated her muscles and the rapidly gaining death, between the call that bids her rise and struggle and the sentiment that still fills her crippled soul and which caused her to become the slave of man.

Ouara's brain and jaw no longer function in harmony. The instincts and memories that rise within her cause her by turns to first lick the floor, then to belabour it with her teeth. The smooth hard flooring remains indifferent to both her suffering and her desires.

Night, like Fate, advances. Night is the favourite time for lions to meet after an all-day sleep in the shadow of a rock or bush. In the neighbouring cages, the faintly visible beasts circle slowly, brushing bars and walls. Their heads are lowered, their necks are tensed. They walk with a careful hunting gait and their eyes are brimming with phosphorescence.

Meanwhile Ouara in her loose skin still struggles to move her limbs as though under a heavy overcoat. Her motions become slower and slower as the congealing cold goes heartwards up the limbs and freezes and stiffens them. The claws open and close no more. The ears flatten as before rising anger. With a noisy crunch of teeth, the jaws work in awkward imitation of those of other lions who, having remained out in the jungle, gather in freedom about a slain antelope and feast themselves.

Outside, the wind whines down the hours of night. The trolleys and autos grow rarer, but the falling slate still shatters in bursts of indecent laughter.

Ouara begins again to sigh. Her flanks, rising and falling in pain, heave like a pair of old bellows. And the lions, sleepless, listen to her long complaint. She regrets once more the love she sacrificed in order to remain with the light-skinned man, to whom she was bound by the tradition of her race; life-long gratitude to him who had fed her and saved her from death.

With a quivering rattle, like a distant thunderstorm, Ouara confesses to her neighbours how she transgressed the jungle law in not fleeing when she was free, in preferring the house of man to the shadowy thickets, to the couch of sprigs and grasses, to the pursuit of the naïve and powerful males.

But a year ago the muscles of Ouara's neck were as strong as her father's, and he had once carried off a calf from the Samba Si flock, holding the heavy prey in his jaws. Now suddenly her neck muscles slacken and the last link between her head and her heart has broken down.

Then all along the dark and desolate hall, unending howls reverberate. In notes of ferocious languor and of mournful rage the kingly beasts proclaim their loss of majesty. They join in one immense call for their liberty.

On his morning round the guard found her lying there, stiff and massive. The teeth exposed by the shrunken lips had half severed the protruding tongue.

Dawn, which kills the dying, had finished Ouara. A sad un-certain morning rain bathed the impassive, leafless acacias. They gathered the moisture on their boughs and spat down their boredom in fat globules on the rare passers-by, who hastened on, deformed and obstinate, with hunched backs and mouths swollen with curses.

Edgar Saltus

THE JAGUAR

BELOW THE glow of Guatemalan skies,
   In groves where undergrass grows evergreen,
   Where saffron quetzals from the branches lean,
And lilac lizards with basaltic eyes
Dart their vermilion tongues at fireflies
   That gleam, in sudden loops of light between
   The orchids and the fuschias and their sheen—
Supremely there a spangled jaguar lies.

Curled in a velvet knot, the radiant beast
   Sleeps on the vivid grass and sleeping dreams
That out beyond the brush and buds beneath,
   Crouching he springs and knows again the feast;
The startled prey, the vain escape, the screams,
   The flesh that parts and bleeds between his teeth.

Julian Duguid

THE HARDEST CHASE OF ALL

It is no light promise to show the greatest hunter of the generation at the fell stretch of his powers and still hold the sympathy of the layman; for even this orgy of adventure must pall in the long run. It is convenient, therefore, to take artist's license, to select from the memories of two vital years the story of the hardest chase of all, leaving the rest to imagination.

During the whole of this time the *Aventureira* was moored at Barranco Branco, the White Cliff. Sacha made an income out of hides, allowing the sewing-machines of the district to repair themselves. In a little hut ashore he kept rope and frames and preservatives, and he sold his wares to the Paraguayan and Argentine merchants who came up-river on business. The ranchers within fifty miles hailed him as protector, which is hardly surprising when one remembers that a full-grown tiger will eat as many as seventy cattle in a year.

The *pantanal* or marsh jaguar of Xarayes is a far more impressive animal than is ever seen in captivity. A large male weighs anything between 300 and 350 pounds, the size of a medium Bengal tiger or an African lion. Circus trainers, who play casually with almost any cat, will not trust him in the ring, because he is apt to turn sulky, repaying the whip with his teeth. Blank cartridges fired under his nose do not distress him at all.

In the course of his South American wanderings Sacha killed 119. Of these 95 were shot with a rifle, 24 with bayonet, spear, and archery. He captured 10 cubs alive, 2 of which are now in Hagenbeck's zoo near Hamburg. Yet even these hunts which ended in a bullet were of more excitement than most men acquire in their lives. He used neither howdah, *machan,* nor *zareba;* nor did he lurk beside a waterhole. Every single one of them was pursued on foot through country that was always difficult, often blind, and sometimes so pestilential that only a Conquistador could have survived. For a hunt on horseback does not mean a finish on horseback. At the moment the tiger is bayed the rider must dismount, proceeding as his thumping heart dictates, generally quite alone. And the rifle of Sacha's choice was a superior kind of toothpick, thirty-two and a half inches long, dented by the anger of his foes. Five meters was the average range of the death-shot. Moreover, unlike the majority of big-game hunters, Sacha took no pleasure in wrenching the life out of harmless animals; to these he felt paternal. Valente, the most successful dog he had ever known, gave him 64 tigers.

Dom Antonio Cardoso of Firme, in the neighborhood of Barranco Branco, groaned beneath a tiger-plague. His ranch-land which was made up equally of swamp, cattle-plain, and forest, reeked with the death of kine. Thousands of *urubú* flew in from the surrounding farms, scarcely bothering to cruise the skies when they could gorge themselves at every mile. Even the ooze of the marsh floor was less noisome than their banquets.

At the height of Cardoso's anguish (he was losing fifty cattle a week) Sacha walked into Firme. He had picked up the rumor on the *Aventureira* and had set out immediately with his hammock and mosquito-net, his spear and bayonet-pointed rifle. Valente, Vinte, and Pardo, sneering a little at less noted hounds, preceded him to the ranch-house. Dom Antonio, a square-built Portuguese, and a famous hunter in his youth, greeted him almost with tears.

"Only last night I was praying to São Antonio, my patron saint," he said warmly, "and you arrive to-day. I am too old for the game, but look! the spearmen are gathering."

He nodded toward a group of Indians who were roasting meat near a hut. Broad-faced Chamacocos, Guaranís with Mongolian slanted eyes, Guatós with pendent breasts and stooped shoulders—they represented the nomad enemies of the tiger, who

appear not more than a shade slower than the vultures themselves. Sacha beckoned to a huge Guaraní, one José Abá, who
had helped him on at least twenty occasions. He was known
throughout the river for his courage and his beard, for a bearded
Indian is a rarity; and José's curled as if his women insisted
upon tongs. He came shambling to the call.

"Will you hunt with me again?" Sacha asked. "We have been
lucky in the past."

Abá jerked his chin to the southward, across the marshes:

"Dom Antonio wants me to collect some horses at the mouth
of the Rio Branco and bring them here."

Cardoso laughed and turned to Sacha:

"That is easy, if you do not object to a little walk. The Rio
Branco runs east and west into the Paraguay, five leagues away.
Let José go in his canoe, get the horses, and ride along the north
bank. You can join him to-morrow evening. I will lend you a
bearer for your hammock."

He plucked at his mustache, considering.

"You can keep the best horse for yourself," he ended abruptly.

When the first smell of dawn began to penetrate the darkness
Sacha felt a prod against his ribs. He was already awake, but
since he intended to join Abá without hunting that day and did
not desire to blunder in the swamp, he lay still. Valente re-
proached and whined, pawing the mosquito-net until, the hammock having ceased to be a resting-place, Sacha got up. The
three hounds at once indicted him for a sluggard and declared
a private war upon all tigers. Their enthusiasm aroused the
other hunters' dogs and the din became impressive. Dom Antonio's Indian shook himself, made some coffee, and collected
Sacha's gear. With the breaking of the light they marched,
Valente leading.

The geography of Firme is peculiar. To the west a belt of
hilly woodland runs level with the Rio Paraguay; to the east
the southernmost end of Xarayes lies in pools and meres and
flats, relieved only by an occasional capão. Sacha took the middle course, skirting the marsh. The rainy season was almost
due; the mud gleamed oilily and a sticky heat-wave rolled

above the water-plants. The islands were unsteady in the haze.

Nobody hurried. Even the dogs moved casually, a hundred yards ahead. The morning freshness had died out of them and they were as bored as any one may be whose nose is a perpetual Sheherazade. Toward ten o'clock Sacha decided to lie up.

Suddenly Valente barked. Vinte lowered his head, mutely agreed with his leader, and pattered into the marsh. Pardo followed his betters. The Indian halted and grimaced. He was no hunter.

"Senhor," he said pathetically, "there is a full league between here and the Rio Branco. If the tiger turns east you may never reach the river. Blow your horn, O spearman, and call them off."

Sacha thought quickly. The dogs were galloping on a southeasterly slant, tails erect, noses down, breathing the musky odor that clung to the swamp bushes. He had no need to study the paw-marks in the shallows to realize that the track was new. The Indian shuffled impatiently. Sacha checked him.

He knew that one blast of his horn would control Valente, that such a hunt might well leave him without shelter for the night, that the swamp might beat him. He was still in two minds when he remembered Dom Antonio's words: "You can keep the best horse for yourself." Dom Antonio had trusted him to kill tigers. There had been no bargain; the horse was his as soon as he should claim it. The implied confidence drove him as no deed of transfer could have done, even were it stamped with a king's head.

"Walk you along the border," he told the Indian. "When you come to the Rio Branco, go east until you meet Abá. Please take my spear. Rifle and bayonet are better for this job; my torch, too. I may need it to-night."

He shouted encouragement to the dogs, who heard him and ran the faster. He stepped into their wake.

At the moment that the warm marsh water seeped through the eyelets of his boots Sacha forgot himself in ecstasy. The blinding sun was no more than a snuffed taper and the reeking slime as perfume before the splendor of his dream. Here, he believed, was a chance to prove that a European, properly dis-

iplined from within, could better the native at his own game.
The idea rose to his head, and he laughed confidentially to the
ink and yellow flowers on the bushes. This attitude endured
or perhaps fifty meters.

It was the thick wet mud that changed him—that and the Indian's chuckle. He was running at top speed, his rifle parallel
with the ground and his heart four hundred yards away with
he dogs, when, all at once, his legs started a rebellion. One of
hem sank gurgling to the calf; the other, after scraping a while
with the heel, nearly split him in its anxiety to proceed. A big
black bubble hiccoughed in his face as he subsided. Luckily the
ifle was unharmed, but in that instant he lost his mental eleva-
ion. He became a serious hunter with a mission—to keep his
eet until the tiger died, lest the dogs should take harm from
his absence. Nevertheless, he spared one glance for the Indian,
who had unaccountably ceased chuckling and was now offering
advice.

"Jump a little when you run," he cried, "like *Cervo* the
wamp-buck."

Sacha pulled himself from the mire . . . he could feel it cak-
ng in his beard . . . recovered his electric torch, and went off,
sliding. For a quarter of a mile he ducked and squirmed through
bushes; but once these were past, the land fell away to the hori-
on, a vast damp plain, the color of Gorgonzola and riddled with
small pools that winked facetiously.

After one quick look at the hounds, who were dipping and
bouncing in the distance, Sacha kept his eyes a few paces before
his toes. With the instinct of a trained horse he knew just when
o leap and when to plow his way through the water. He was
helped by a certain oily gleam, product of decayed vegetation,
and he made full use of it. The hunt continued.

An hour went by, two, three. The sun reached its zenith,
hung in the balance, and tilted slowly to the west. The tiger,
knowing the advantages of swamp, had long since refused to be
harried to the Rio Branco and was enjoying himself in circles.
Sacha began to tire. In all that while his relative position had
not altered by one inch. He felt as if he were tethered in a

nightmare. Mud patches which in the beginning he had sailed
over with a cry, now oozed against his shins; and for every for
ward step he slipped back a foot. The perspiration was out of
him and his skin hurt. His breath came jerkily.

Then it was that he appreciated the chemical formula of en
durance, one part brute strength to three parts nerve resilience
or courage. He had been running since ten o'clock, it was now
past two; and that during the siesta-hours in the hottest part of
the year. Physically he should have been conquered, drained of
all power; but a single mania occupied his brain and kept him
mechanically at the trot.

"I never yet lost a dog," he thought desperately.

Somehow the hours passed. He was no longer sentient. He
was a giant toy with dry lungs and wooden arms and a pin-point
of white flame in his head. He turned aside for pools that even
at noon he would have jumped. The marsh grass lapped his
feet; the mosquitoes soared in their thousands, but their deadly,
high-pitched whine was no more than a far-off dynamo. Swamp-
deer, scared by the hunt, blundered along at a great distance.
They appeared to be bounding behind a heavy curtain. The
sky was gray with heat.

Presently he arrived at a mere which cut across the foreground like a ribbon on a councilor's breast. He could see no
beginning and no end, and the realization that he would have
to cross it very nearly broke him. He paused for a moment on
the brink. The water was absolutely calm, amber on the surface, shading off into the softest of dark greens toward the bottom. The sunlight sent golden shafts piercing and flickering,
and particles of matter floated through the beams like dust-
motes in a church. He bent to drink.

All at once his eye was captured by something glistening up
the channel. He threw some water on his face and investigated.
At first he could make out nothing, but after thirty seconds of
hard gazing he discovered the skeleton of a cow half hidden by
a rotten tree stump in a patch of water-weeds. And immediately
he was afraid.

He remembered his first journey to Xarayes, when the bones

of a *piranha* were entangled in a bush. He knew that whole shoals never see the river, being stranded by the falling marsh. He had no doubt that the remains of many cattle were strewn along the mere.

As in the majority of his decisions he was influenced not by the heroic but by the trivial. He was growing stiff. If he stayed where he was he might well spend two days without food. Better join the dogs and sleep in company. He plunged in. The surface wrinkled at his touch, and he felt his shirt go cold. Then his boots slid forward and he found himself seated in mud and gazing along the level of the water. When he scrambled up, his rifle was wet to within three inches of the foresight.

Every step of that crossing was mental agony of the most humiliating type. His sentience had returned with his fear. He was conscious of his body as only those are conscious who are going to be tortured in the dark. He felt naked and vulnerable, powerless to brace himself to a pain. The water was opaque with stirred mud; he had no means of guessing the angle of an attack. The ooze clung to his soles. He wrenched and twisted and fought, knowing that his trousers had often been soaked in tiger blood and wondering if *piranha* would recognize the taste. Fortunately, there was no current.

About half-way over, something drove against his thigh. It was pointed and sudden, and he dodged instinctively. As he did so he recalled a spectacle in the Rio Paraguay. He had been watching bullocks at a ford. The leading animals had passed and were ascending the bank toward a slaughter-house when one of the rear-guard winced. It wriggled for a moment, gazed stupidly at the river, and finally lashed out, crying. A few minutes later it was just white bones and the water was not red.

The thought released Sacha from his terror. The period of waiting was past, and his salvation was with himself. He leaned forward, lifting high his feet and thrusting backward with both arms. He used his rifle for a paddle. The extra speed neutralized the suction of the mud and within a minute he was reeling on the edge. Whereat his new-found strength evaporated and he collapsed. Nor was he more than faintly interested in the discovery that a sunken branch had ripped his thigh. He was too exhausted to care.

Soon he was goaded afresh. Except for the whistling of some ibises the marsh was empty of sound. Valente, Vinte, and Pardo had disappeared. He rose stiffly and listened, though without much hope. It was characteristic of him that he could summon the energy to reproach himself. He viewed the flat horizon with a bitter, aching shame. He looked at the sun, now falling almost visibly, and judged that it was after four o'clock. Then, reflecting that since the tiger had been running in circles all day, he might return, he lay down by the margin of the water. He was very hungry.

He must have dozed; because the next time that his brain recorded an emotion the sun was directly in his eyes and the bell that was Valente was tolling near the sky-line. He touched his rifle; the barrel was real enough, so was the dog's voice when he had shaken his head a while. It was definitely approaching. The first clangor had gone from it, but it was still courageous and unrelenting. Vinte, too, was shouting in a shriller key, and Vinte never yelled unless he could see the tiger.

A few minutes later Sacha beheld the reason. On the farther side of the dike and a short half-mile away the hunt went by. Three weary dogs, the largest no bigger than an Airedale, were hopping through the swamp in pursuit of a worn-out tiger. He could see the painted shadow as it blended with the grass; and there was not fifty yards between the animals. Moreover, the tiger had sickened of the game and was heading straight for the Rio Branco, on the southern side of which lay forest where he could climb and rest. This time Sacha did not blunder in the mere. He swam, and in the glory of his second wind, fancied himself cool and sweet. The unwholesome ground bit under his feet like turf. Before an hour had gone he was speaking to Abá, who had galloped up at Valente's war-cry.

"He has crossed, senhor," he called, excitedly waving his spear. "A large male. Muddy as a bullfrog—or yourself. Shall we swim the animals or tie them here?"

Sacha looked over the Rio Branco. The sun was dying in a

crimson bar along the water. In twenty minutes it would be dark. The river was shallow . . . chest-deep, he judged . . . yet unpleasing enough to traverse with a tiger-hide at night. Already he was counting on a kill.

"Secure them here," he said. "Then follow the noise of the hounds."

He forded diagonally, allowing the current to support him. Once through, he scrambled up the bank and vanished into a curtain of low bush, sprinkled with *caraguatá* thorn. For a while he heard Abá cursing at the horses, heard also the whack of his spear-shaft, but immediately forgot all this in the musical howling of the dogs, which was stationary. The tiger was at bay.

Presently the sun went out and with it his sense of distance. The forest seemed thicker, more malicious. His face was whipped with spikes. The beam of his torch illuminated a single brilliant avenue of massed twigs. Beyond, and on each hand, was a jet wall which the stars did little to reveal. He felt inclosed and breathless. Soft fingers touched him, pulling clear with portions of his flesh so that he was grateful for his beard.

Of a sudden he halted. There was a new tone in the barking. It was frenzied and hysterical, as if the dogs were about to realize a dream. He knew what that meant and, regardless of his skin, went forward at a run. The tiger was changing his quarters. A moment afterward the noises were receding. He sighed as he tripped among the weeds. He did not know how much longer he could endure. His sense of time joined his sense of distance in eclipse. The black woods rushed by.

Then, just as his lungs had issued a warning of the end, the barking checked, redoubled, became stationary again. He forced himself to a canter and found an exhilarated pack talking rudely to a circular mound of scrub near a gigantic fallen tree. He cheered them with his voice and they wriggled appreciatively.

"Better late than never," gasped Valente over his shoulder. "Now earn your keep. I can't move the brute."

The tiger was uneasy. A sullen growl, which appeared to rattle the bush, issued from the back of his throat. He was shifting continually. Sacha was in a quandary. The beast might charge, in which event the creepers might delay his bayonet-swing for just that fraction of a second which would mean death. On the other hand he might slink away; and Sacha was close enough to exhaustion to realize the futility of another running fight. He began to experiment.

He dropped to one knee and shone his torch toward the growls, hoping to reflect against the eyes. The tiger edged away, and the light pursued him when he rustled. Again he avoided it, and again, until Sacha knew that he had power. Using the beam like a stick, he poked and prodded with the glare, huddling his enemy to a corner, directly beneath the fallen tree. It remained to persuade the beast to ascend.

The novelty of the battle absorbed Sacha's weariness like a sponge. After the physical enormity of the day it was a relief to struggle with his mind.

Obviously he must not insist. The commands of the torchlight must be veiled hints, suggesting rather than driving. He kept it scrupulously low and took care not to flash it too near. He relied on the tiger's intelligence, and was not deceived. In three minutes, accompanied by much grumbling, the gentleman snarled openly from the tree. Sacha lit him up from below.

He was a magnificent spectacle in that cruel white radiance. His spots, divorced from the background of concealing forest, stood out. He was in an evil temper and the light was making him frantic. Sacha raised his rifle to the level of his torch and fired. There was a faint click. The cap only had exploded, the cartridge came out empty, leaving the bullet in the barrel. In his extremity he called upon Abá.

"José," he yelled. "Quickly with your spear!"

He turned for a moment and, from very far away, saw a tiny point of fire. It went out.

"I come immediately," cried an equally tiny voice.

Left to himself, Sacha tried to force the bullet with a stick. Nothing moved. With the corner of his eye he saw Valente leap for the tiger's tail, saw the sweep of the great paw. His knowledge of hunting told him that it could not be more than a minute before the tiger charged. As a final resort he rammed another bullet home and felt it jar against its mate. This time there was a tremendous explosion and the animal dropped, pierced by both bullets. At that a reaction fell upon him. His nerves grew raw.

"José, you sluggard!" he shouted. "Are you a hunter or an ostrich-feather brush?"

Humbly, from the middle distance, came the reply.

"You have boots for the *caraguatá,*" it said. "My feet are bleeding and I must strike matches."

So that was the point of light! Sacha laughed.

"I am sorry, José," he called frankly. "I know you are brave. It is the fault of the wet cartridges."

Together they stooped to the carcass, removing as much fat as was needful to the dressing, also a rump steak for their dinner.

"You light my way," said Abá. "I will carry the hide."

Now, a tiger-hide is heavier than many people think. Properly taken, with head and paws and grease, it weighs almost one third of the body; that is, not far short of a hundred pounds. Yet Abá lifted it easily and, stepping delicately, bore it through the forest. He did not pause until Sacha asked him a question:

"Which direction did we come?"

"Southeast, I believe. Why?"

"Because we have been walking in a half-circle."

The hide slid to the ground with a wet bump. The Indian straightened himself.

"Stay here and blow your horn at intervals, I will shout to you."

Whereupon the brazen notes of a horn and an Indian's musical scream played hide and seek in the darkness. After a long half-hour the notes merged and the men decided to camp where they were. The remainder of Abá's matches kindled a cheerful fire. The tiger meat was indistinguishable from calf.

Toward midnight a sharp-edged cloud rolled out of the south, as a proof that the rainy season had begun. José slung his spear between two trees, folding the hide as a breakwater. The subsequent deluge did not interfere with their rest; for they curled themselves into a fold of the damp skin and slept.

They found the horses next morning by the swollen roar of the Rio Branco.

Phyllis Bottome

CAESAR'S WIFE'S EAR

SEPPEL BERGENER DID not find it altogether easy to be a good American.

He was born ten miles from Budapest; dimly in the overgrown jungle of his restless mind he could still remember that wide yellow worm, the Danube, on whose treacherous marshy banks he had spent the first three years of his life.

Sometimes when he was drunk there spluttered in his ears the dazzling fireworks of Z's and S's which comprised his native tongue.

He could not have spoken Hungarian; but had anyone spoken it to him, his blood would have answered.

As it was, Seppel spoke a clipped fumbling American; and when he listened to the strange flat language now always in his ears, he had to make those piteous efforts to hear made by the deaf in danger.

Seppel lived in the heart of a Californian desert. All day long the hot clean wind whipped his senses.

His mother was dry and bright like a flame. She was a Hungarian gypsy. Some people said she had killed her husband. Others said that the lions had killed him. Seppel's parents bred and trained lions for show.

The police had come out into the desert to investigate the sudden death of Seppel's father. His body had been savaged by the lions, but the lions evaded the third degree and the police could not persuade them to "come clean." The police had the idea that Seppel's father might have been killed first, and then thrown to the beasts. But again the lions foiled them, for they had made the evidence quite inconclusive.

Seppel was five years old at the time; he did not care very much about his father's death. He loved his mother and he loved the lions.

He did not love a young step-father, who was their showman, and who took control of the show shortly after Seppel's father died.

Seppel grew up fast, and took his education as it was forced upon him. A huge grizzly bear caught him once and hugged one shoulder out of shape. A panther clawed his chin, and left very little of it.

Seppel played with lion and tiger cubs as if they were his human contemporaries, and the marks of his little playfellows stood out all over his compact, small body.

Seppel never grew to be a tall man, but he was very vigorous and had eyes as clear as flame.

On his sixteenth birthday his mother said to him: "You lion-man now! You mak' lions like dogs! You great little son of mine! You hav' my heart an' my blood! You no mak' showman ever, you no hav' beauty. Pity! But for one maker of lions, there is plenty showmen! Aah! a—plenty!"

His mother must have known what she was talking about, because she had five showmen husbands, one after the other. The last of the five was still living when she died. But she left him nothing. She left every lion, bear, cat and cub to her son Seppel. The whole show—cages; cars; the shack and tents; the hot dog and iced beer stands—were now Seppel's.

There was no dispute about it either, for Seppel's mother had made her will in Los Angeles itself, assisted by a famous lawyer. It was deposited in the City safe and published in the newspapers. In Caterina Syblla's life there had been 'plenty showmen' but only one son.

Seppel was twenty-three when his mother died. He got rid of his showman step-father at once, and married a desert girl, with dry crinkly hair and a voice like the cracked shriek of a desert wind. Her teeth were bad; but she spoke good American.

"You faithful," Seppel explained to her, "I—kind! You once like other feller—you die! Same as my father feeded by lions.

You 'member? I must have showman—see? You better no look
at him! Pity if you look at him!" Carrie Gladys replied rasp-
ingly with a string of oaths directed at showmen. She would not
look at showmen, she averred, not if Rudolph Valentino or
Doug Fairbanks headed the list. Carrie Gladys was not an affectionate woman. She never noticed what anybody else felt about
anything, unless she was personally involved. Her real passions
were for gin and horses, and she knew that Seppel could give
her plenty of both.

For a year after their marriage Seppel tried to do without
a showman. He trained and showed his lions singlehanded; but
the Picture people told him that he was too small and unim-
pressive-looking to draw a big public and that they could not
use him for films. So Seppel set to work to find a suitable showman, without too much charm.

Bert Kimstock was no Valentino; but he was six feet tall, with
curly brown hair, the bright eyes of a native Irishman, a long
upper lip, nerve, and no money.

Seppel engaged him reluctantly after two or three hours spent
with Bert in the cages of the easier lions.

Seppel explained carefully to the new showman how he ran
his show. "This I do," he told him; "I mak' lions easy! I mak'
'em tricks! They're my baby boys! I no hav' children! I hav'
lions! You—you can hav' children! An' you can play with my
lions—once I mak' 'em easy! I show you how to be safe: you
stan' in the big cage where people come—see? I mak' tricks an'
you look good! The lions no hurt you! But the lions are mine!
You un'erstan' you just showman?—I lion man!" Bert assented
heartily. He did not want to be a lion man. He was not without
a genuine love and knowledge of animals, he even possessed an
old tame lioness called Pansy Bell, whom Seppel allowed him
to bring into the show; and with Seppel's help he half-tamed a
lioness cub called Rosamund—but Bert only half-tamed her.
Rosamund had heaps of fun wrestling with Bert in her cage—
but there were moments when it looked as if she would have
thought it still greater fun to have killed him; and with the
male lions Bert had no success whatever.

Lions, however well trained, are never so madly affectionate as lionesses; and Seppel's lions were one-man animals, and refused to extend their patronage to Bert.

Seppel's favourite lion was called Caesar. He was the best trick lion the show had ever possessed. He had a huge brown mane, sleepy yellow eyes, and when he roared, he set the desert quivering.

Seppel told Bert confidentially, "Caesar safe as houses! Houses where no fire comes. Mustn't bring fire near desert houses. No! No! Mustn't bring flame near lions either! Flame to lions, all same flame to mens. Woman—she flame! You understan'—never come between a lion an' a lioness—then lions no safe—they kill —all same men in desert!"

Bert saw this point too; and thought that it did not concern him. He had already seen Carrie Gladys and he did not look on her in the light of a flame. Bert was an honest, rather boastful young man without intensity. He soon found that he was quite unable to teach lions tricks. He had not begun young enough nor did he possess the wild hypnotic eye-language and deep creative patience with which Seppel was endowed both by birth and training. Still the audience gave Bert their chief applause, and all he had to do to win it was to stand once a day in the big arena cage and take picturesque attitudes, while Seppel kept the male lions in their proper places.

The animals, let out of their cages by slip-gates, came through a subterranean passage one by one into the big main cage. The lionesses came first; and as they came in Seppel called them each by name to take their places. Their perches were arranged in a ring round the arena, the first seven feet from the ground, the others gradually rising in height to nine feet. The lionesses took the first perch from the top of a tub; and then sprang from perch to perch. It was Bert's business to face the lionesses, after they were seated, gluing them to their seats with his eyes and flicking them with a whip, if this reminder should be necessary. Venus was the last of the ladies upon the right, Mariposa the last upon the left.

Mariposa was the wife of Caesar. She was above suspicion in

every sense of the word; and even if she had not been Caesar would have kept her so.

Venus had the worst temper of all the lionesses, but she was deeply attached to Seppel, who had helped her on one occasion to rear her cubs, when her natural milk supply had given out. Venus looked upon Seppel as a woman and a sister, and treated him accordingly. But as far as other males were concerned, including all lions, she had what is known in psychiatric circles as "a strong masculine protest" and she took every occasion of showing it. She hunched herself up, and spat at the male lions as they entered, and if one of them came within striking distance of her, Venus promptly clawed him.

After the lionesses were seated, Seppel called for the young males.

These were not powerful or excitable lions. They sat on tubs beneath the ladies' perches, looking a little bored; and the ladies looked well over their heads, towards the hatchway door.

Seppel then called to the attendants: "Bring in my baby-boys!" Seppel's "baby-boys" were full-grown; and the most powerful male lions in the show. When they opened their jaws, if it was only to yawn, their teeth looked like the worst rocks a ship ever split on. If they roared, the cage rocked. Caesar always led them in, and then took his place at the end of the line, farthest from the hatchway, under the perch of Venus. This was intentional because Seppel trusted Caesar the most, and so great was Caesar's faithfulness to Mariposa that he never increased the masculine protest of Venus, by so much as a glance.

Mariposa sat on the perch farthest from Caesar, but she always watched him with her fond lazy yellow eyes.

When the first trick was over, Bert would turn, and stand picturesquely in the centre of any pattern which Seppel had devised. Nobody noticed Seppel very much, except the big male lions whose eyes he always held.

Caesar and Mariposa shared a large cage next to that of a handsome male tiger, the only mature male tiger possessed by the show. His name was Hector and his manners were regrettably Trojan. His mate having been temporarily removed from his society to attend to her maternal duties, Hector became highly envious of the placid domesticity enjoyed by his neighbours. One morning he jumped much higher than he was supposed to be able to jump against the wooden partition, and tore off a large piece of steel netting which separated the two cages, as if it were sponge cake. He then proceeded to seize Mariposa's ear; and tore that.

Everyone thought there was an earthquake from the noise that followed; and Mariposa thought that she was the earthquake.

More and more Tiger got through the steel netting, and Caesar, shaking the desert with his voice, skilfully seized Mariposa by the haunches, and dragged her clear of the tiger; minus half an ear. He then flung himself against the wooden partition and clawed down more netting, in order to get a stronger hold on Hector. By this time Seppel, Bert, and two terrified attendants were gathered about the cages.

A glance was enough to show Seppel what had occurred. Half of Mariposa's ear was in the tiger's cage—and a good deal of Tiger was being clawed by Caesar. The partition bulged like a piece of sailcloth caught in a breeze.

It grieved Seppel to interfere with Caesar, but he could not afford the death of his only tiger. He therefore entered Hector's cage from the rear and strikingly diverted his attention. Hector turned on him in a flash; but quicker still, Seppel covered the tiger's head with an enormous sack, and with the nervous help of Bert and the attendants, transferred Hector to a distant cage.

Mariposa yelped for hours, while Caesar lay beside her licking her torn ear, and administering consolation in low throaty growls.

In the course of a few days Mariposa, except for half an ear, completely recovered. Caesar's temper, however, was desperately ruffled; nor could he ever again feel the same trust in Seppel. "That one lil' tiger!" Seppel told him persuasively, "he no more trouble any lion! He flat skin to walk on—sure enough dead! My wife she step on him in kitchen!" Caesar blinked disdainfully at this tale for cubs. Did he not know the voice of every creature in the show, and was he likely to forget the still audible roar of a tiger that had trifled with Mariposa's ear?

Seppel excused Caesar from the ring for two weeks, though it was both difficult and dangerous to get on without him. At last he said to Bert, "My big baby-boy, he come back to-day. He lead once more. There may be lil' trouble! You look lionesses hard; and if tub fall over—you pick up tub pretty quick: better tub no fall over! Better lionesses come in lil' bit slow—an' the young lions lil' bit quick!" Bert agreed, but he did not feel too comfortable. One lioness is one thing, but somehow or other ten lionesses are a good deal more than ten things.

However, the lionesses made a good entry. Venus took some time to settle; but Mariposa leapt to her usual perch like a bird. The young lions were hurried in, to get them out of the way; and then the big male lions, led by Caesar, came in very slowly, and with great dignity. Seppel's flying, intensely beseeching eyes met Caesar's. Caesar turned his heavy head away, but after a moment's perceptible pause, he obeyed Seppel's pleading will, and took his seat on his tub. The other lions all mounted theirs in turn, while Seppel's earnest, plangent voice told them what good boys they were! What handsome children! What grand lions!

The lionesses remained on their perches, bored, but quiescent. The young males, resentfully expectant, watched their fathers advance slowly, facing Seppel, one by one. Each in his turn; each taking his exact place; following Seppel's high-keyed, imploring voice, his summoning eyes, and the direction of the whiplash, that without touching them showed each his place and warned him to take it.

Unfortunately Caesar declined. He stood at the end of the row, in his accustomed place; but lie down he would not. He snarled; he raised a paw; he lashed an angry yellow tail. His massive benevolent upper lip turned hideous with menace.

Mariposa, watching him intently from her perch, grew larger while she watched.

Seppel beseeched; he coaxed; he flung his heart out at Caesar:

his boy—his baby-boy! Surely to please him Caesar *would* lie down?

The whip flickered and flapped in front of Caesar's face. Caesar put his paw on it. He bit it; and wouldn't lie down. He even jerked back a pace or two, nearer Venus's perch. Venus snarled savagely—and in her ill-natured prudery, she clawed at the flank of the lady next to her. Dolores—the lady next to her—swayed, lost her balance and fell into the arena.

Seppel glided away from his big males. He got behind Dolores, who was slinking, perchless and nervous, round the ring, and whipped her up on to a tub. Dolores leapt; missed her footing; and the tub rolled over.

Bert had an uncomfortable feeling that he ought to do something about that fallen tub; but with nine lionesses staring at him—and Mariposa swollen out of all recognition—he knew that turning his back on them, to right the tub, would be a most unpleasant posture.

Seppel gave a whimpering cry like a frightened child. "Will no one helpa me?" he cried. "Will I be all alone forever—no one to helpa—me?" But while he whined and whimpered, he deftly righted the tub; lashed Dolores on to it, and saw her successfully negotiate her perch, before turning back with a bound, to face his baby-boys.

The lions had broken up their row. They stood on the balls of their feet, tense and terrible.

Seppel ran close up to them, calling each by name, meeting their fierce yellow eyes with the quick flame of his own. "Caesar!" he called. "Pompey! Tomboy! Kaiser! Capone! Paasha! Ajax! Lindbergh! Duce! Poppa! There you go! Easy my fine boys—you lie down! You good boys! You Caesar! You my pet boy! Oh Kay! Oh Kay! O. K. lions!" One by one they sank back, down on their haunches; into their statuesque row. Only Caesar still stood upright, lashing his tail with disdainful puckered lips. Seppel's voice cajoled on. His will burned through his eyes. At last Caesar's head sank; his beautiful lithe flanks closed in. He lay down at the end of his row. Mariposa grew slowly smaller again.

The hatch door reopened, and the lions filed out in turn.

Then Seppel faced Bert in the empty cage, while the audience still applauded.

He called out in his fierce high voice: "Why you no helpa me, showman? Why you stan' there—you great ape? You fat stuck pig! You no help me put tub straight! I say one momen' more, one lil' instan' all those lions go wild! Go mad! We get feeded by lions! I no can nothing save! I hold 'em with my eyes! I turn my back they loose—they no held! They go pieces! They no more my children! You no un'erstan'! You only showman. Oh, my God! Only showman! One day all dead for nothing! And my poor baby-boys shotted up and cursed! An' all your fault! You stupid—you God-damn stupid showman!" and Seppel tore open the cage door and ran sobbing, through the astonished audience, to find his wife.

Some women would have comforted Seppel and taken the bitterness out of his heart, by their fears for his safety; but Carrie Gladys was no comforter. Her ideal was a cave man; and she did not know that courage can be fed by tears.

Behind Seppel stood Bert; tall, handsome, and cheerfully explanatory. It was all right! The Boss had had an upset! Not an animal damaged, though—and a good audience! Plenty of money!

Carrie Gladys took Bert's explanations down like gin. She said derisively to Seppel: "Go on—and get in there—cry-baby!" She said to Bert: "Have a drink!" They had a drink and Carrie Gladys laughed. She may not have laughed at her husband; but he heard her laugh. Carrie Gladys had a good deal to learn from lionesses.

Night fell. Towards morning a lion roared. His hollow, hungry voice shattered the desert stillness into harsh, dry flakes of sound.

Seppel lay awake, brooding and resentful, by his wife's side. "My boy—my baby-boy!" he whispered to himself. He knew it was Caesar roaring. Caesar was roaring because he felt defeated. Hector was still alive; and Caesar had obeyed Seppel—who was no longer to be trusted, since he kept Hector alive.

Seppel, too, felt defeated. He had cried; and Carrie Gladys had laughed at him with his showman.

The morning broke hotter than the day before. The desert wind came in long burning puffs, as if the earth had opened a secret chimney and was sighing out fire.

Mariposa and Venus, who were lying side by side on a rock in the middle of the yard, looked as if they were made of the same yellow stone that they were lying on. Nothing moved about them except their tawny eyes. The mountains hung like jagged sheets of cardboard against a brazen sky.

There was an ominous rasping quality in the day. Men's tempers were short and uncertain. The animals were inert and unresponsive. Even the tiger cubs were less playful than usual. They bit and scratched mechanically and fell asleep while doing it.

Seppel went the round of the cages muttering to himself. The polar bear lay prostrate in his pool, with only the top of his head and one irritated red eye, showing. The monkeys were beating their wives and the wives were screaming like mad.

Seppel watched them for a time, but thought there was not much harm being done, and that it would be a pity to interfere with a male prerogative.

At last he came to Caesar's cage. Caesar was in a very low frame of mind. He refused even to come forward and speak to Seppel.

Seppel pleaded for a long time with Caesar; but Caesar only sat on his haunches and blinked. Once, he even put his paw on the bars, and shook them.

Seppel took this very much to heart; but Bert, standing goodnaturedly beside him, thought the whole affair rather a joke. "You no un'erstan' lions," Seppel said bitterly. "They gotta strong feelin's, lions! They no get over things! Once you hurt a lion—you hurt a heart!"

"Well—what you goin' ter do about it?" Bert asked him; "if Caesar's so damn hurt—how you going ter manage? Goin' ter give another lion the lead? Caesar held you up yesterday! And ter-day's Sunday! We'll have a swell audience maybe! They won't want ter wait half an hour, while you baby Caesar into lying down, will they?"

Seppel shook his head gloomily. "Caesar my stunt lion," he said sadly, "I no give up my stunt lion! Not for no Sunday audience! No! Caesar *mus'* come in! Only to-day I feed him myself —*first!* I mak' him more fren'ly. I talk him alone! She very fine lioness, Caesar's wife—she better'n a woman! But half an ear— that not enough to break a show down! No sir. Caesar—he learn understan' 'bout his wife's ear!"

It was stupid of Bert to neglect Seppel's instructions. He forgot to tell the attendants not to feed Caesar with the other lions. When Seppel came from his Sunday dinner, with a handsome meal for Caesar, it was to find that he had been already fed; nor did Bert attach any very great importance to Seppel's sudden burst of maniacal rage, when he found that he was too late to feed his pet. Like Carrie Gladys, Bert was untroubled by the feelings of others. He was a good-natured fellow, accustomed to getting his own way; and winning applause for it.

Still, he went so far as to suggest that perhaps it would be better for Caesar to remain in his cage and not take the lead in the afternoon performance. Seppel, who was just about to give this order, immediately reversed it, and told the attendant to let Caesar start the line of male lions as usual.

There was a large Sunday audience. The animals came in nicely and without confusion.

The first two tricks ran as smooth as cream.

Bert had a fine easy wrestling match with his pet lioness. Pansy Bell gave him a showy struggle and never forgot herself, for a moment. When she withdrew, Bert stood every inch a lion-tamer in front of his circle of lionesses, while Seppel inconspicuously in the back of the cage engaged the attention of the male lions.

Suddenly a blanched darkness swept over the faces of the audience. It was like a cloud crossing the sun. Bert saw rows of mouths open suddenly and eyes pricked wide with horror. Something had happened behind him, which he could not see.

Caesar had suddenly decided that if he couldn't kill Hector, the nearest male lion might do instead.

With one bound he had launched himself on Poppa and tore half his flank open. All the lions grew tense and crouched for a charge. Seppel stood alone in the middle of a ring of lions—calling—calling.

Bert looked behind him. There was just one chance in a million. Anything he did might tell now. A sudden noise might hold the lions. If he jumped through the ring and stood by Seppel, there might be a chance for their lives. A moment later, nothing could stop the lions from charging. Bert stood close to the hatchways. Once inside them he would be safe. Venus chose that moment of his conflict to leap down from her perch. The chance was over. Bert jumped for the hatchway. A terrific roar crashed behind him. He ran through the smelly passage, hot and flurried, asking himself over and over again how he could have saved Seppel.

The first cage door closed safely behind him. He was free now. He reminded himself that Seppel too had a door at his back. If Seppel broke through the ring of lions—if he risked the danger to the audience by opening the cage door that faced them—if that roar had not meant the lions were already on him—then perhaps he was safe!

The whole, hot empty yard rocked with sound. Bert found a gun, and ran through the yard towards the arena cage. It would look more like a rescue than an escape if he came back with a gun.

As he came within sight of the cage, he heard high above the pulverizing roar of the lions Seppel's voice, shrill—plangent—strained but curiously without fear or anger. "My boys! My baby-boys! Caesar! Poppa! Paasha!" Seppel was calling them still. He was down under them; but they hadn't quite killed him.

The terror-stricken audience pushed each other aside, to let Bert through. He steadied his gun against the steel rims of the cage, and shot Caesar through the heart. With a roar that drowned the shrieks of the crowd and the clamour of the other

animals, Mariposa flung herself from her perch on to the body
of Caesar.

The rest of the lions drew back, crouched and growling; but
it was not Bert's shot that controlled them. It was Seppel's voice:
he lay in the centre of the ring, incredibly mauled, a mere mask
of blood.

"Back—back, my beauties!" he cried beseechingly, and then
one by one he called their names.

The attendant opened the hatchway door. The lions withdrew sullenly, but in their usual order. The lionesses left their
perches.

Mariposa never moved, nor after that one roar, did she make
a sound. She lay across the body of Caesar so still that you could
not tell which of them was dead.

Venus, too, refused to follow her sisters. She leapt from her
perch, and crouched, swaying, across the bloody floor to Seppel's side. "God! She'll finish him!" shrieked Carrie Gladys, her
white papery face pressed against the bars; but she was judging
Venus by her own standard.

"Is that Venus? Is that my darling?" Seppel called faintly.
The lioness crouched low beside him—and with a sigh Seppel
leaned his bleeding head against her flank. She licked his wounds
with low caressing growls, nor would she let anyone approach
him, until she knew that he was safely dead.

Edwin Markham

THE PANTHER

THE MOON shears up on Tahoe now;
The panther leaps to the tamarack bough.
She crouches, hugging the crooked limbs
She hears the nearing steps of him
Who sent the little puff of smoke
That stretched her mate beneath the oak.

Her eyes burn beryl, two yellow balls,
As Fate counts out his last footfalls.
A sudden spring, a demon cry,
Carnivorous laughter to the sky.
Her teeth are fastened in his throat
(The moon rides in her silver boat)
And now one scream of long delight
Across the caverns of the night!

J. Frank Dobie

BUT WAS IT AN ONZA?

As MIGHT HAVE been expected, the Barranca de las Víboras proved to be more than three days away. By the end of the third day we had, however, come into a beautifully timbered, though rough, country; the rains of late summer and early fall had set streams usually dry to running and there were camping places everywhere. We pitched against a creek known as Arroyo de los Arrastres, across from a wraith of smoke from a solitary cabin, as silent as the smoke itself, inhabited by a native into whose veins had never been injected one drop of the blood of the conquerors. At sundown I heard a turkey gobble. "We will stay here a day or two," I said to Inocencio. I was where I wanted to be. The fever in the blood and those perplexities that prevent a man from being whole were all gone.

There were no noises in that country either by day or night except earth sounds. After darkness had fallen there came to us from the low mountain across the arroyo something like the bellow made by a bull calf.

Early next morning the native from the solitary cabin appeared.

"Did you hear that tiger up on the mountain last night?" he asked.

"Yes," I replied, "he has horns about three inches long and he thinks he is a grown bull."

"A *tigre* for sure," the native gravely responded. "I heard him again before daylight. I can prove it with your dogs."

The Mexican name for the jaguar is *tigre*.

Instead of hunting turkeys I took the dogs tiger hunting. On a narrow "coyote spine," or ridge, that broke away into gulches on either side and led to the tableland of the mountain, the hound Lead let out a deep-throated bay and coursed off like a bullet. "He knows something," exclaimed the native, and I felt jubilant in the knowledge that I had a genuine hunting dog. The fierce Airedale started too, then suddenly tucked his tail and bolted for camp.

We followed the course of the hound and soon in a patch of soft moist earth saw what the dogs had scented.

"*Ca-ramba!*" Inocencio ejaculated.

"Of a truth the wind does also blow in San Juan," exclaimed the native.

All eyes were fixed on such tracks as no mountain lion or jaguar—the only large animals of the cat tribe native to North America—that I ever heard of could make. They showed as plainly as if they had been moulded in plaster of Paris. The print of each of the four feet was as big as a saucer—and each had the outside toe missing.

Meantime, although Lead had passed out of sight, he was not out of hearing. What a voice he had! Then, suddenly, he was silent.

"He was probably going so fast that he jumped the track," I explained. "Let us wait a minute and we'll hear him again."

We waited one minute, many minutes. No cañon wall could have cut off the sound of the dog's voice. We scouted out severally. Lead was not to be seen or heard. While I was up on a high point I saw in a kind of swag a considerable distance down what appeared to be a small mound of twigs and leaves; it was against a madroña bush. I was not curious enough to descend and examine it. After we had scouted and listened until the sun was halfway to its zenith, we returned to camp. Lead never did reappear.

His sudden and utter disappearance remained a mystery. The extraordinary tracks remained a mystery. Indeed we were in a land of primeval and aboriginal mysteries. Above our camp the *arrastres* after which the creek was named had century-old trees growing up through their rock-floored bottoms, and no one knew whence the ore that Spaniards once ground in them had come. In all the country between the Arroyo de los Arrastres and the Barranca de las Víboras there was no ranch, mine, or hacienda, only two or three cabins. The land was not fit for farming; it grew no grass worth a cow's grazing and only a few bushes worth a goat's browsing; the timber on it was too remote for utilization. It belonged to deer, lobo wolves, panthers, jaguars, and other things of the wild. I found that the native who knew the difference between the bellow of a bull calf and *something* else—but what was it?—knew many other things. I liked him and for a pittance he was delighted to accompany us. His name was Estanislao.

Three days after we saw the outlandish tracks we rode for four hours and camped on a stream cutting down into the Barranca de las Víboras. Here we were lucky to find a little bench of land level enough for comfortable pallets. Above it the mountain-side rose at a steep angle; below it the water went talking over rocks and breaks. Twisting along between the bench and the stream was a deeply worn trail. Vegetation and jutting boulders prevented our seeing either up or down the trail very far. Other campers had been here, and the place was called Camp of the Forty Moons. I know not why. It was over the world and under it both, and was in a solitude as primeval as creation.

After we had settled in camp, Estanislao told me about a tiger hunter who lived "towards yonder very far away." Now there is not a wild animal in the world I had not rather live close to than kill, and every hour I spent in this Barranca de las Víboras territory I was more pleased with living and less inclined to wish myself where there were women or electrical appliances. Nevertheless, I wanted to kill a jaguar. With the disappearance of the hound all chance of trailing one down was gone. Estanislao kept watching ravens and buzzards for the purpose of locating a kill by their flight, but not even a fresh kill would exactly locate the killer. I sent Estanislao to bring the tiger hunter.

He left afoot, was gone two days, and returned after dark with his man, also afoot. This *tigrero* wore a blanket, and after he had eaten and was squatted by the fire I saw that all he had on underneath his blanket was a pair of *calzones*. I saw too that one side of his nose and face were all gone, so that the teeth on that side looked out.

For a long time I sat secretly looking at him and wondering what had happened to him. He was silent. Then when he opened his blanket to get a cigarette, I noted great scars on his chest and a naked rib sticking out, the wound healed over but the bone uncovered. Curiosity prevailed over breeding.

"Excuse me," I said, "but were you burned?"

"*No, señor.*"

That was the only answer and we were silent a while longer. Then once again I tried. "What did happen to you?"

"*Un tigre.*"

That was all. Again there was silence, but I had to know.

"*Señor,*" he responded after a question that he could not evade, "you have sent for me because I am a hunter of the tiger. I call them to me with a caller made by stretching skin over the opening of half a gourd, and then sawing a stick back and forth in a hole made in the skin."

Here he showed me his drum-like *bramaderas,* one to imitate the cry of the male jaguar and one that of the female. He made the wild calls—and I was at the moment half relieved that no response came to them.

"When I go out," he went on with his explanation, "I hide myself where my back will be protected and where I can see in front and around me. Then I call. If a tiger hears, he will respond. I call again. He responds nearer. At last he may come into view and then I shoot him.

"I used to have two dogs. They would always point their ears and whine low and show terror when the tiger approached. I watched them so as to be ready to shoot, for often I could not see far on account of the growth.

"One time I went out with my dogs and my *carabina.* I planted myself in a clump of little trees under a bluff facing an open space. I made the call. At once. far down the *ramadero* a *tigre* answered. After a while I called again; he answered and this time he was not so far away. I knew exactly how he would approach, and I moved a little outward from the trees, my shoulders still to the bluff, bushes in front to obscure me. Now he was getting near but showing more caution. For a long while I must wait yet, I thought, and be very cunning with the calls.

"But my dogs suddenly grew very much excited. They whined hard. They had been taught not to bark. Their hair stood up. They were not looking towards the tiger approaching. They were looking behind me. I looked too, and there on the bluff right above me was a tiger, immense, ready to spring. I pointed my gun without time to aim. The tiger was already springing and the bullet missed him. He knocked me to the ground and one claw caught my face. He seemed to be trying to eat it as the dogs fought him. He clawed my breast. Then I do not know what happened.

"When I came back to life, I felt a great burning and my lips were like meat baking on coals. I felt something touching one hand. I moved it. I heard a whine. My dog, one of them, was licking my hand. His moist tongue came to my face. I could see out of only one eye. With that I saw my other dog dragging himself to me from a bush. All his entrails were torn out. He whined as if he were sorry for me. As he died at my hand, I had a tear for him.

"After many hours I saw a man on a horse passing on the hillside across from me. I managed to shoot my gun and attract his attention. He carried me to his house and I lived. I still hunt tigers."

The fall nights in that country, for we were camped far above the bottom of the *barranca*, are sharp. When we lay down to sleep that night, a fire of juniper and oak wood was burning into coals that would still be warm at dawn. I lay on the side of the fire next to the trail. The other men lay on the other side of it. The Airedale, as usual, bedded as near the fire as he could get.

I was not yet asleep and was craving the experiences of a jaguar hunter when I felt an extraordinary noise. I say *felt*, for I felt more acutely than I heard. The sound was first a kind of swish through the air. Then it went *we-ahh*, very much like the expiring sound made by a toad when a heavy boot or hoof mashes the air out of it. The noise was not at all loud.

"Did you hear that?" I asked, not knowing if any of the men were awake.

"*Sí, señor*," Inocencio responded.

"What was it?"

"*Quién sabe?* Perhaps a bird."

By now I had raised my head on my elbow so as to look about. I could see nothing out from the small circle of light made by the fire and, turning towards the fire itself, I saw a blurred object making off from it. I thought it might be some camper's burro that had wandered up the trail, and I called to the Airedale to "sic." The dog did not respond. I looked at the spot where he had been all night keeping himself warm. He was not there.

All this took much less time than it takes for me to tell of it. Then from the slope above our location there came to my ears the faint click of displaced stones. That slope was too steep for any but a wild burro to climb voluntarily. Besides, the sounds were not those made by hard hoofs.

"We'll look for tracks in the morning," I said. "Let nobody disturb the ashes."

When light broke, the soft ashes out from the fire revealed the prints of four feline feet. Each was as big as a saucer; from each the outside toe was missing. Only one animal in all the sierras of Mexico could have made that track. The jaguar hunter said that no *tigre* ever grew feet to such proportions; I was sure that no mere mountain lion ever made such tracks.

We worked up the steep mountain slope on which I had heard the thing displacing rocks the night before. Hardly two hundred yards from camp we found the Airedale's body covered over with leaves and twigs. The fate of the old hound Lead and the significance of the mound I had neglected to examine while I was looking for him were now clear. Both mountain lions and jaguars cover their prey in this manner. If this animal had the same habits, he would in all likelihood return the following night to finish his meal.

Inocencio had brought along two small steel traps, of the size used to catch coyotes. I had no faith in their power to hold the unknown beast even though he should step in one of them. Nevertheless, we set them with great care in a natural runway near the dead dog. At daybreak next morning we were climbing to the traps. Before we got within sight of them, we heard the rattle of chains and the growl of primordial savagery. Then we saw. The animal was caught in both traps.

In general it looked like a mountain lion, but it was far larger than any variety known to American hunters or naturalists. Its breast was enormous, its flanks lithe. It had devoured, excepting for the head and neck, the entire carcass of the Airedale—probably thirty pounds of flesh; but it did not appear to be gorged and was certainly not torpid. It was turning gray with age. It was a female. Even considering its size, its four-toed feet appeared abnormally large.

I was anxious to preserve the skin. After I had shot the animal, we three men had to exert our strength in carrying it down to camp, where the bench of level ground would make the process of skinning comfortable.

The carcass had been deposited beside the trail and I was drinking a cup of coffee when, as noiseless as a drift of smoke, four sandaled Indians trailed into sight. Close behind one another, in single file, they came on until the leader was right at the dead animal.

"*Válgame Dios!* (May God defend me!) It is an *onza!*"

Without even saluting, thus he exclaimed, and not pausing one step, passed on. In turn each of his followers echoed, "An *onza!*"

"And what is an *onza?*" I cried, but the exclaimers were already going around a shoulder of rock that jutted against the narrow path immediately above camp. They were as shy as wild turkeys and evidently averse to any kind of parley.

As they passed out of sight, I turned to the tiger hunter. Surely, I thought, he knows what an *onza* is. *Onza* means *ounce*, ut the ounce proper is no more an inhabitant of the western emisphere than is the Bengal tiger. It was occurring to me that his tiger-scarred man, through fear, through shyness, or for ome other reason was withholding something that he knew or elieved when an old, old Indian, too slow to keep pace with he others of his party, hobbled up.

He had two dried bloom-stalks of the sotol plant for walking ticks. The blanket over his shoulders was shredded and atched. His sandals were worn out. The skin of his face was as ry and weathered as the hide of a cow that has died on the ange and been left to carrion and the elements. A tuft of his ong straight hair stuck out of a hole in his squaw-thatched traw hat.

"*Caramba!*" he croaked as he halted, leaning over on his ticks and peering at our trophy. "It is the *onza. Válgame Dios!*" Ie went to poking about the paws of the *onza* with one of his walking sticks.

"*Onza,* yes. That is what the others say," I shouted, for I resumed that the old man was deaf—though he wasn't. "But or el amor de Dios tell me what an *onza* is."

"It is," the old man replied, shaking one of his sotol stalks in emphatic gesture, "the very worst animal in the world. Sometimes—sometimes I say—it is a cross between a bull tiger and a she lion. Look closely down on this old one's gray legs and see if there are not tiger spots."

I did perceive some dim markings, but they were more like freckles than the bold jaguar spots.

"An *onza,*" the old Indian went on, "always jumps on a dog or a man or anything else that it wants to kill in such a way that it knocks the air, the very life, out of it at one blow. It has power like a flood of water rushing down a cañon."

"You say," I interposed, at the same time offering a cigarette, "that the *onza* is sometimes a cross between a tiger and a lion. At other times what is it?"

The old one with much deliberation picked up a coal of fire in his gnarled hand to light the cigarette. Then he tasted the smoke.

"Mix your tobacco with this cup of coffee," I urged.

"*Caballero*," he at length replied, "you have done a good deed in killing this animal. I am going to tell you something very strange but absolutely true. Something I know. These eyes have seen what I am about to tell. Listen!

"My village is on the Arroyo de Peñasco. It is two days from here. Seventeen years ago there was a witch in that village. She lived alone a little down the arroyo, out from the other houses. She was not so old as you might think, but she was more hideous than any man can imagine. She was as strong as an ox, and big. She ate like a sow, but we never knew where she got her food. It was said that she could enchant deer like a tiger and make them walk into her trap. Maybe she ran them down. She could run very fast, and she tired no more than a coyote trotting towards a circle of buzzards. Her voice was hoarse like that of a bull. She was a *huera* (a woman of light complexion), and all over her body she was as freckled as the egg of a *golondrina*. Her hands and feet were enormous. Nobody knew how bad a witch she was, but all were afraid of her. Sometimes she would with a fresh *tortilla* or a bit of *panoche* (brown sugar moulded) entice some passing child into her house.

"In the same village there lived a man by the name of Ignacio Villagra. He had a wife and three boys. One of them was ten, one eight, and one six. There were some dead children too, but they do not count. These people lived in a house of two rooms. There was no door between the rooms, but each room had a door facing out to the east. There was a *ramada* running along in front of the house. There were no windows.

"One morning early before he got up Ignacio called to his oldest son, Pedro, to go bring in the burros. He wished to make a trip into the mountains that day to bring in two pack-loads of wood. Pedro did not answer. Ignacio called again. No answer. Then Ignacio went around to the room in which his sons slept. Pedro was gone. Pedro always slept next to the door. It was summer time and the door was open. Ignacio thought that perhaps Pedro had already gone for the burros; so he had no worry.

"But the sun got up high, and still there was no Pedro. Another man of the village who was out looking for his own burros found Ignacio's also and brought them in. No Pedro. Then Ignacio gave the cry. His woman was like one *loca*. Everybody went to hunting for Pedro. There was no sign. We hunted till dark. Then we built fires around on the crests of the mountains so that Pedro might see if he was lost somewhere. We put up crosses.

"In the morning a man said that maybe the witch knew where Pedro was. Ignacio and I and four others went to see her.

" 'Oh, my Pedrito,' she cried, 'my Pedrito! Is he lost? He was my only friend in the whole village. My poor little Pedrito!'

"We knew right away then that she had Pedrito hid out somewhere, in a cave perhaps. We tried to get her to tell where the boy was. She would not tell. We wanted to kill her, but if we killed her she could not tell. So we only tortured her. We did not torture her much, though. It took all six of us to hold her. We punched a hot wire through her nose, at the point of it, and through the flaps of her ears. Still she would not tell. She even called on the Holy Virgin to prove that she did not know.

"That night the second son of Ignacio disappeared. There was more hunting through the cañons and calling into the thickets of brush. All was useless. Who can find out the secrets of a witch?

"The next evening soon after dark those men of the village who were not out making signal fires hid ourselves in the brush around the witch's house. We were sure she would come out in the night time to go to the den where she kept the boys. Maybe we could follow her.

"We waited long hours. The stars gave light. About midnight the door of the cabin opened, and the witch stepped out. She stood there a great while, looking, looking, turning her head this way and that way and stretching out her neck like an old turkey who is listening. The coyotes were hushed. All I could hear was my own heart. Everything was still. Then, just like *that,* the witch disappeared. We did not see her go. She just was not there.

"At once we heard a sound over our heads. It was a sound o
horror. It went *sh-sh-sh-shoo-oo-oo*. At first it was sharp, swift
It seemed to circle over us. It went up, then down. Then i
died away.

"We came closer to each other and waited. I do not wish to
deceive, and I cannot tell how long we waited. Again came tha
sh-sh-sh-shoo-oo-oo cutting and swooping through the air, fa
away and dim at first, and then right over our heads. All a
once the witch stood again in front of her house, looking thi
way and that way and stretching out her neck. She seemed to
have come from nowhere. She did not come out of her cabin
She just appeared.

"Well, the next morning we visited her, the six men who
had gone before. Still she would not tell. We wanted to kil'
her, but if we killed her she could not tell. We tortured her a
plenty this time. We sawed off, one by one, the little toe of her
right foot, then the little toe of her left foot, then one little
finger, then the other. We sawed them off with the fiber of the
maguey plant, slow, slow, pulling the fiber back and forth.
She screamed. It took force to hold her. I was strong then. She
swore she had gone nowhere the night before. It did no good to
remind her of what we had seen and heard. She cried out to
Christ and his Mother and all the saints that she had no knowledge of Pedrito and the other boy.

"We did not know what to do. We were sure she would come
now for the third boy, the last one, who was only six years old.
Perhaps we could trap her. We worked all day arranging the
door to the boys' room so that instead of swinging open on
hinges, it would drop like a trap. We had to make a hole up
through the roof of the *ramada* and set a trigger. Ignacio wanted
to sleep in the bed alone and catch the witch when she came in;
Ignacio's woman cried against letting her baby sleep in the
room; but we assured them both that in order to bait the witch
the boy must be there alone. No harm could come to it, we said,
for, once inside, the witch would be trapped and could not get
away. Then she would have to confess and reveal the hiding
place of the other boys.

"At dark Ignacio got up on top of the house so as to drop the trapdoor should the witch miss the trigger. I was with him. Other men of the village were behind the stack of straw or in the bushes that grew near the house. Still others were where they could watch the witch's cabin as it had been watched the night before.

"How long we waited, Ignacio and I there on top of the house! We did not talk. We looked over the land. We looked at the sky. It seemed to me that the horned moon was going to hook a certain star. How slow it climbed! Then when one horn was not more than a foot away from the star, something came into the room beneath us. We did not see it come. Nobody saw it. We only heard a kind of swish through the air, *sh-sh-sh-shoo-o-oo*, very swift, and then noises in the room. Ignacio dropped the door. The devil thing was trapped.

"No man cared to go inside the room in the darkness. Yet Ignacio's woman wanted to go in and get her baby. We would not let her. The witch could not carry the little boy away now. It seemed best to wait until daylight before doing anything. Daylight was not far away. We heard scratches. We heard once a grinding of jaws. The witch might well be angry. No longer now could she call on God and the Holy Virgin to prove her innocence.

"When the first light of the east came, we got ready to handle the evil creature. We had ropes, butcher-knives, machetes, everything that might be necessary. Yet we had no guns. We are a poor people.

"Two men got in front of the trapdoor and raised it. By the life of my mother and the life of God and the life of Mary Most Pure and Joseph, I speak truth. Then what came out the door was not the form of a woman but the animal you have killed. The *onza!* It came out with a leap that knocked both men down. They were sick for a year afterwards. The *onza* never stopped. She ran like a ray of lightning for the cañon brakes."

I believe that old fellow wanted to knock us down with his

tale, as the *onza* had knocked his two friends down. He stopped as if he were through.

"But what about the little boy left in the room?" I asked.

"He was not there when we went in to look for him."

"And what became of the witch?"

"The witch?" he repeated, as if not understanding my lack of comprehension. "Listen! When the horn of that moon was hooked around the star that night as I have told you, the men who were keeping watch over the cabin of the witch saw her come out. She limped a little, they said. She stood there looking looking, just as she did the night I saw her. Then *sh-sh-sh-shoo oo-oo*. From that hour to this she has never returned."

There seemed no more to say but, knowing well I should not be understood, I remarked, "You must have felt pretty bad for torturing a human being so much when it turned out that an *onza* was to blame."

"*Onza,* yes," the old man growled back. "But what more proof could any Christian ask? Look at those four toes missing, the outside one of each foot, on this creature you have killed here. Look too at the holes in those ear flaps. But I must go on. May God guard you!"

"May you go well," I returned, and the explainer of *onzas* was gone.

The tiger hunter sawed on his gourds up and down the Barranca de las Víboras for a week without receiving a response. Then with Inocencio I turned back for Las Cinco Llagas. I shall never cease to regret that bugs destroyed the hide of the *onza*. I still have one of the claws of the beast.

CATS

ᵇETWEEN FANGS stronger and more cruel than rock
. striped cat cracks the shoulder of a steer;
eside a Bengal pool another of the stock
runches on the haunches of a deer.

triped muscles of what strength
)n high-pitched feline nerves are strung!
ᴬ female of Siberia licks her paw, lying full length,
Vith circular motion of the tongue.

ᵇeautiful Brazilian with a shower of spots,
aguar. Her easy motion of the hips
s like a woman walking. Limpid her thoughts.
.uxurious as her floral-spots Brazil to which her thought slips.

ᵇlack all black, created He them, male and female:
ᴹurderer, the black leopard, spots concealed.
ᶠixed eyes of hallucination stare till human eyes fail
ᵀill human blood is congealed.

)uietly, quietly, a mountain of sand in a cage.
ᵀhe lion's sides are as sand, so fine in grain. His mane
s furrowed like furrowed sand. His rage
s the rage of water beneath sandhills through blasts of rain.

Alan Devoe

THE TIGER

NOISELESSLY, ON CUSHIONED paws, he padded around the cage.
His movement was as soundless and flowing as the glide of
water; under the sleek-furred hide of his fulvous flanks and
shoulders the great muscles scarcely rippled. Around and
around and around he circled, pacing as rhythmically as a slow
and silent metronome. On the wooden floor of the cage was
stained a circular track, signature of his rhythmic pacing circuit, day upon day, month upon month, year upon year.

In one corner of the cage there was a cunningly simulated
tree, cast in iron and made fast with rivets to the floor; and in
another corner was a kind of kennel, fashioned of concrete and
reinforced with steel, to serve as lair. These were the furniture
of his world; this was the universe around which he prowled in
his unceasing circuit. The iron tree was coated, at the height of
his shoulder, with tawny hairs rubbed from him as he passed it
on his million rounds; the white concrete of the kennel showed
a smeary stain, where with unvarying ritual he voided his musky
urine.

The interruptions of his measured purposeless pacing were
only three. They were when he slept, with his great velvety
forepaws outstretched before him; and when the strange sounds
and movements from that uncomprehended world which lay
outside the bars became too insistent to be ignored; and when
there reached his silky tufted ears the faint and far-off rumble
which meant that the blood-smeared butcher-cart, piled with
the day's meat, had been trundled into the building and was
approaching him.

He slept as a kitten does, in utter relaxation. In the dark interior of his concrete kennel, warm with the heat of his flesh and pungent with his jungle smell, he could enter into the sanctuary of sleep, of refuge from an alien world and from bewilderment. As he slept his great curved claws would glide forth sometimes and retract again in their soft sheaths, and sometimes his tail would stir and twitch a little, and tiny growls and whimpers would mingle with the harsh rhythmic rattle of his snore. Such stirrings were the witness to his dreams, to those dim race-memories which would not be effaced except by death. In that dreaming skull were the vague elusive stuffs of recollection . . of the whipping of bamboo stalks against his flesh, of the feel of the Sumatran sun at noon, of the scent of deer-dung on a forest path.

Most of the time, in his waking hours, he gave no heed to that uncomprehended world, full of shuffling steps and meaningless speech-sounds and peering eyes, which existed outside the bars of his cage. He had been here three years, more than a thousand risings of the sun, until now the unintelligible procession which endlessly shuffled and stared and gibbered outside the bars had come to be hardly more than a dim blur on the rim of his awareness.

At first it had been different, when he was still trembling and disoriented by the quickness of his transition from his old life. The old life had ended very suddenly, when, on a moonless night, he had plunged through the cunning plaiting which hid a pit dug in the jungle path which led to his water-hole. He had been put in a wooden crate, bound with hoops, and had journeyed in a long darkness across an ocean, and then he had been set loose in his new world of the iron tree and the concrete kennel and the endless unmeaning faces outside the bars. During those first weeks and months here he had rushed often to the bars, and pressed his great muzzle against them, and loosed roar after roar to frighten away the peering faces and silence the shuffling steps. Once upon a time his roar had silenced the heavy-beaked hornbills in the forest, and the bands of chattering gibbons in the treetops had grown hushed at the

sound of it. But here, in this new world, the strange waxy-white
faces outside the bars only grew more numerous, and peered
more intently, when he made his sound. Now, after three years
he seldom roared; and his old bewilderments were mostly re
solved into a kind of dull uncaring.

Only rarely now—when the stridence of the uncomprehended
voices grew too shrill to be endured, or the stench of the white
bifurcated bodies too sour in his delicate cat's nostrils—did he
come padding silently to the front of the cage and stand there
staring out, a tumult of baffled fury in his heart.

II

He got his daily meat at half-past two. He had not liked it at
first, had scarcely known that it was meat, this cold juiceless
fiber with no smell and quiver of life in it. There was no spurt
of scarlet blood when he tore at it with his teeth, no hot and
salt-sweet trickle passing over his tongue as he licked and
sucked at the torn flesh. When he pinned it to the floor with a
great paw, as was his way with prey, it did not squirm or scream
But it did quiet the hurting hunger in his belly, that ache
which once had sent him gliding stealthily through the tropical
night, smelling the heavy jungle air and cocking his tawny head
and listening; and so at last he came to accept it as his food,
and to await its coming with a kind of lower-pitched rekindling
of the old ecstasy that once had possessed him as he awaited,
beside a water-hole, the coming of the little spotted deer.

By noon the fever would begin to infect him, and he would
pad around his endless circle with a quicker pace, his long tail
writhing and thrashing like a great furred snake, his claws in-
voluntarily extruded a little from their sheaths and clicking
against the floor. As the minutes passed he would move faster
and faster, and a fire of excitement would consume him, so
that often as his frenzy grew he would void a jet of urine or a
dropping of dung, and would not even heed the consequent
rumble of sound which came from outside the bars and which
he could not know was human laughter. And then suddenly

e would hear, faint and far away, the clang and clatter of he hand-truck that meant the approaching of his meat. Silently e would pad to the bars and crouch down beside the little slot-ike aperture through which, day after day, his meal was thrust o him. All his fury would have subsided now, giving place to taut quiet, and he would crouch as motionless as stone.

He was crouching thus now. Intently, with unwinking eyes, ie was watching while the truck was trundled to a halt outside iis cage, and while the chunks of cold flesh were sorted over. Most especially he watched, in absorbed fascination, the white iuman hand and arm which performed these things. He did iot know what it was, this curious five-pronged whitish thing hat each day flickered just outside the slot of his cage for just i few seconds and then whisked away. More than a thousand imes he had stared at it, rapt and uncomprehending. He watched it as a kitten watches a white butterfly, or as a sparrow studies a grub.

He watched it now as it pored over the meat, and then as it lifted a chunk and slid it through the slot. It was hovering in-side the aperture for a second longer than usual. He reached out a paw, quickly as the dart of a cobra, and pinioned the white flesh with his claws. And, as his claws hooked into it, there reached his silky ears a sound which he had not heard for more than a thousand risings of the sun. It was the sound of screaming.

He put forth all his curved claws to their full length, and raked at the white skin. As he ripped at it, scarlet blood spurted in great jets against his muzzle, and the smell of hot blood was in his nostrils and his lungs. He took the quivering meat be-tween his jaws, and the bones cracked and snapped, and on his tongue was a warm salt-sweetness. There rushed into him a flooding exultation, and in an instant the world of the iron tree and the concrete kennel and the latticed bars was dissolved and vanished away. In his skull raced dim-formed remembrances, evocations of the flower-heavy sweetness of the jungle night, of the pattern of wild hog's tracks in an oozy stream-bank, of the chatter of finches when the sun was rising. His cage did not exist now, and there were no bars around him, or stained boards under his cushioned feet.

He had gone from there. He had re-entered into his ancient kingdom.

They drove him off, at last, with pitchforks and pointed iron rods. And early in the morning, before the zoo was opened to the public for the day, they put a bullet through his brain.

Alan Devoe

LYNX

THE WILD ANIMALS with which we share the earth— (if "share" be not too ironic a word for our resolute attempt at usurpation) —have reacted to our presence in a variety of ways. Certain of the defenseless ones, of course, have simply vanished in quick extirpation at our hands. The passenger pigeon had no strength and no strategy with which to withstand our murderous acquisitiveness. Other wild things, more cunning or less shy or having in smaller degree the spirit of wild free independence, have gradually accommodated themselves to us, and let us make of them what we will: so that now the gentle sparrow of the English hedgerows survives adaptedly as a draggled soot-stained parasite upon us, in the clattering canyons of New York and Chicago, and the gray squirrels are become beggarly petitioners for peanuts. A few of the animals we have been able wholly to enslave. We have broken the wild horse, and made him serve our commerce. We have made of the cow a witless machine to feed us.

Though many a wild animal has vanished forever, in our vigorous march toward domination, and though many another survives only on the terms of a dingy mendicancy, there remain wild and incorruptible ones which have in no degree surrendered. By tactical withdrawals into deeper wilderness, by the exercise of subtle cunnings, and perhaps in a few cases by simply the power of their rebuking dignity, they have thus far outwitted or outfaced us. Foxes are subtly wiser in woods-ways than most of the hounds and hunters; and so they remain foxes, wild and free and persisting almost at the edges of our cities;

and many a naturalist, who has seen a fox watching the de
ceived hounds rushing clamorously past his ingenious hiding
place, has been prepared to swear that a fox can grin. The grea
horned owls are fathomlessly subtle in the darkness. Thei
squalling still sounds within earshot of the skyscrapers, and the
newspapers still periodically chronicle how a citizen, walking a
civilized street at night, has been suddenly and soundlessly
beset by a buffeting of smothering wings and a raking of crooked
talons . . . and has been left bleeding and terrified by an at
tacker who vanishes, still soundless and invisible, into the wil
derness of the night. The great blue herons still wade our
watercourses, even in the townships. They have survived, in a
manner of speaking, by their massive obliviousness of us. They
ignore that we are here. A heron stands motionless on its tall
stilt legs in one of our brooks, wrapped in the grace and the
withdrawn dignity of a being wholly impervious to the whole
hot fuss of the human episode in planetary history; and this
spirit is so communicated to even the least responsive of us,
with such overmastering rebuke, that rarely is the gun raised
to the shoulder.

However much of self-importance or aggressiveness or even
ruthless rapacity we may have in us, there exists a part of us—
a very old and deep part—which must feel a sympathy and admiration for those wild creatures that have kept their wildness
and kept free. We have hunted and hounded many a beast, and
often been terrible in our uncaring. But still a part of our own
hearts also belongs forever to the wilderness. We are animals
ourselves. We have sold much of our freedom, traded away in
a bad bargain much of our clean original animality. But a part
of us (in the useful Christian symbolism) can still remember
and look back to Eden. A portion of our spirit is comrade to the
deer. There can scarcely live a man who, with a primal part of
the psyche that can never be wholly lost however greatly it may
be overlayered and obscured, is not stirred poignantly to hear
a wolf-call, or to see a bounding white-tailed deer escape the
hunters, or to hear in the midnight the long-drawn screaming of
a lynx.

No cat is ever wholly tamed. None of the big cats is ever truly
tamed at all. With that region in the depths of us which is
cousinly to all feral things, we must on that account feel ever a
certain admiring responsiveness to the great cat that still roams
our own northern woods: the tuft-eared and silently padding
lynx. The lynx has dwindled, yes. It has had to withdraw ever
deeper and deeper into the lessening forests. But it has not been
sent down to extinction by us. It has not compromised with
what is alien. The lynx remains—wary, quiet-footed, cat-
immaculate, piercing the wilderness night with its tremendous
cry—as symbol of all things wild and unadaptable and filled
with savage pride.

II

The kits of the Canada lynx are most often born in May or
June, in a hidden wilderness den prepared by the mother in a
hollow log or a natural opening amongst boulders. In late winter
the male lynxes utter the caterwauling of their lust: a crescendo
of yowls and shivering squallings that makes the partridges
huddle closer in their evergreen cover and sends the rabbits
scampering to crouch motionless in their snow-forms with
flattened ears. About three months after the breeding, the kits
are born. There are one to four of them. They are not much
larger than the kittens of man's "domesticated" cat, but their
eyes are open; and they can stand on their broad cushiony paws
within a few hours after birth.

For some two or three months the young lynxes are seques-
tered in and around their secluded birthplace in the forest,
suckling on rank cat-milk, later growing adept in fastidiously
tearing to pieces the fresh-killed chipmunks and woodsmice
that their mother procures for them in her dozen daily miles of
wary, forest-prowling and stealthy tracking. The kits' ears grow
big and pointed, tipped with lynx-tufts. The faint spots and
stripings of kittenhood fade. The kit lynxes become ready to be
adult lynxes: great ripple-muscled cats that may attain to forty
pounds, and that will be wise in running a fox across crusted

snow, and will love the deep wilderness and the darkness, and hate humanity.

The young lynxes go forth into the woods with their mother (and sometimes their father), and for nearly a year they may travel as a band. There is much that a maturing lynx needs learn. No wild animal, of course, receives education in the human sense of a planned instruction, for it is the essence of animalness that action occurs by instinctions, spontaneities and intuitive impulses that lie below conscious mind; but native skills are educed and perfected by parental example. The life of such a hunter as a lynx demands sure cunnings.

How take a fox? Snow-time is the season for it; for then, as a young lynx finds, his great broad paws support him on the crust through which a fox's small feet penetrate. It is possible to take a fox by the throat and rip his life out. It is serviceable to rake at his belly with cat-cunning hind legs, and disembowel him. In the winter it is even possible to take a deer. The way of a lynx is to pad after the deer in the deep-lying snow, leap for the neck, and hang on relentlessly to the floundering animal until death comes from exhaustion and the loss of blood. A caribou can be so killed. Apart from the techniques that a lynx must learn for making his rare kills of such big beasts as this, he must grow proficient in the getting of his daily staples: grouse and particularly rabbits. The latter are his commonest food . . . the relationship of preyer and preyed-upon is so established that when the populace of rabbits is decimated by plague the lynxes commonly wander away from the territory to seek out new hunting-grounds. But they learn resources, too, for these times of famine: that frogs and snakes are edible, that grasshoppers will nourish for a time even the body of a great cat. A lynx, like all wholly feral things, takes on a competent self-sufficiency. It can swim a stream better than a dog can. It acquires the wisdom, when a big kill has been made, of caching part of the food against the future. To avoid skunks, to interpret the twitching of another lynx's tail or the snarling in another lynx's throat, to leave porcupines alone except in a time of gravest famine, and then to tackle them by the subtle insertion of a paw under their bellies so that with a quick gesture they can be flipped over and their unprotected undersides exposed . . . all these things and a hundred others become as much a part of lynx-personality, by the end of the subconscious process of education, as is the lynx's ingrained and immaculate cat-habit of scratching up leaves and earth-mould to cover voided droppings.

A lynx-band breaks up when the spring comes. By then, the kits know what they must know; and early in March the family is infected by the restlessness of the breeding fever, so that brotherly and sisterly relationships cease and the lynxes are become only individual males and females. Thenceforth each goes its own way, solitary, to live a life of prowling paddingly through the forest for as much as fifty miles between sun and sun, screaming and miaowing to express lust or fury in the lonely night, crouching and creeping and pouncing where hare or partridge or ground-squirrel relaxes its vigilance. These things, and of course (for it is true of all wild animals) a degree of playing. A solitary lynx, padding across the snow in the winter moonlight, has been known to stop and give a great frisking leap. In all wild hearts resides a certain primal gaiety.

Curious is the relationship of lynx to man. As the grouse are by instinct terrified of the lynx, fleeing the drifting scent of that enemy as they flee few other creatures, so does the lynx recognize us for what we are: a foe to the wilderness, boding no good for any wild cat whose home it is. To the lynx-heart, we mean the steel trap. We mean the noose-snare, evilly concealed. This being so, it were not strange if lynxes made attack upon us. But if they do, it is so rare a happening that there is hardly a record. There are, however, many records of a queerer happening:

A man travels a wilderness trail in the dark, and a lynx gets wind of him. With infinite stealth the great cat draws close, watching. It lopes along parallel to the man's trail, close to him, soundless, invisible, hour by hour, mile by mile. The lynx does not attack, no. Attack, as trappers and northern Indians have often said, would come as a blessed relief. It would dispel the fancy that the great cat is filled with a terrible amusement.

Martin Armstrong

IN THE JUNGLE

HERE THROUGH the sea-green twilight slinks
   The tiger with his jewelled eye,
And sleek and slim the crafty lynx,
   Prick-eared, like Satan, lurches by.
The lion, ruffed in kingly gold,
   Awakes and stretches in his lair;
Bright birds, like fiery meteors, scold
   Fluttering through the sunless air;
And through the spawning undergrowth
   The bronze-bright snake, flat-headed, keen,
Wakened from a month of sloth
   Flows on his rustling way unseen.
Here like a vast unburied root
   The river-horse sleeps in the ooze,
And poisonous flowers and fatal fruit
   Drip from above their deadly dews.
But hid behind the tiger's stealth,
   The lion's rage, the lynx's guile,
Behind the teeming poisonous wealth
   Of flower and fruit—older than Nile,
Craftier than palaces of popes
   And crueller than Spanish kings,
The Jungle Spirit grins and gropes,
   Snaring in stealthy-footed rings
The traveller, whose mazèd sight
   Shall never greet his native groves,
Nor ever find the sweet daylight,
   Nor see again the face he loves.

Jim Corbett

THE BACHELOR OF POWALGARH

THREE MILES FROM our winter home, and in the heart of the forest, there is an open glade some four hundred yards long and half as wide, grassed with emerald-green and surrounded with big trees interlaced with cane creepers. It was in this glade, which for beauty has no equal, that I first saw the tiger who was known throughout the United Provinces as 'The Bachelor of Powalgarh,' who from 1920 to 1930 was the most sought-after big-game trophy in the province.

The sun had just risen, one winter's morning, when I crested the high ground overlooking the glade. On the far side, a score of red jungle fowl were scratching among the dead leaves bordering a crystal-clear stream, and scattered over the emerald-green grass, now sparkling with dew, fifty or more chital were feeding. Sitting on a tree stump and smoking, I had been looking at this scene for some time when the hind nearest to me raised her head, turned in my direction, and called; and a moment later the Bachelor stepped into the open, from the thick bushes below me. For a long minute he stood with head held high surveying the scene, and then with slow unhurried steps started to cross the glade. In his rich winter coat, which the newly risen sun was lighting up, he was a magnificent sight as, with head turning now to the right and now to the left, he walked down the wide lane the deer had made for him. At the stream he lay down and quenched his thirst, then sprang across and, as he entered the dense tree jungle beyond, called three times in acknowledgment of the homage the jungle folk had paid him, for from the time he had entered the glade every

271

chital had called, every jungle fowl had cackled, and every one of a troupe of monkeys on the trees had chattered.

The Bachelor was far afield that morning, for his home was in a ravine six miles away. Living in an area in which the majority of tigers are bagged with the aid of elephants, he had chosen his home wisely. The ravine, running into the foot-hills, was half a mile long, with steep hills on either side rising to a height of a thousand feet. At the upper end of the ravine there was a waterfall some twenty feet high, and at the lower end, where the water had cut through red clay, it narrowed to four feet. Any sportsman, therefore, who wished to try conclusions with the Bachelor, while he was at home, would of a necessity have to do so on foot. It was this secure retreat, and the Government rules prohibiting night shooting, that had enabled the Bachelor to retain possession of his much sought-after skin.

In spite of the many and repeated attempts that had been made to bag him with the aid of buffalo bait, the Bachelor had never been fired at, though on two occasions, to my knowledge, he had only escaped death by the skin of his teeth. On the first occasion, after a perfect beat, a guy rope by which the machan was suspended interfered with the movement of Fred Anderson's rifle at the critical moment, and on the second occasion the Bachelor arrived at the machan before the beat started and found Huish Edye filling his pipe. On both these occasions he had been viewed at a range of only a few feet, and while Anderson described him as being as big as a Shetland pony, Edye said he was as big as a donkey.

The winter following these and other unsuccessful attempts, I took Wyndham, our Commissioner, who knows more about tigers than any other man in India, to a fire track skirting the upper end of the ravine in which the Bachelor lived, to show him the fresh pug marks of the tiger which I had found on the fire track that morning. Wyndham was accompanied by two of his most experienced shikaris, and after the three of them had carefully measured and examined the pug marks, Wyndham said that in his opinion the tiger was ten feet between pegs, and while one shikari said he was 10' 5" over curves, the other said he was 10' 6" or a little more. All three agreed that they had never seen the pug marks of a bigger tiger.

In 1930 the Forest Department started extensive fellings in the area surrounding the Bachelor's home and, annoyed at the disturbance, he changed his quarters; this I learnt from two sportsmen who had taken out a shooting pass with the object of hunting down the tiger. Shooting passes are only issued for fifteen days of each month, and throughout that winter, shooting party after shooting party failed to make contact with the tiger.

Towards the end of the winter an old dak runner, who passes our gate every morning and evening on his seven-mile run through the forest to a hill village, came to me one evening and reported that on his way out that morning he had seen the biggest pug marks of a tiger that he had seen during the thirty years of his service. The tiger, he said, had come from the west and, after proceeding along the road for two hundred yards, had gone east, taking a path that started from near an almond tree. This tree was about two miles from our home, and was a well-known landmark. The path the tiger had taken runs through very heavy jungle for half a mile before crossing a wide watercourse, and then joins a cattle track which skirts the foot of the hills before entering a deep and well-wooded valley; a favorite haunt of tigers.

Early next morning, with Robin at my heels, I set out to prospect, my objective being the point where the cattle track entered the valley, for at this point the tracks of all the animals entering or leaving the valley are to be found. From the time we started Robin appeared to know that we had a special job in hand and he paid not the least attention to the jungle fowl we disturbed, the kakar (barking deer) that let us get quite close to it, and the two sambur that stood and belled at us. Where the cattle track entered the valley the ground was hard and stony, and when we reached this spot Robin put down his head and very carefully smelt the stones, and on receiving a signal from me to carry on he turned and started down the track, keeping a yard ahead of me; I could tell from his behavior that he was on the scent of a tiger, and that the scent was hot. A hundred yards further down, where the track flattens out and runs along the foot of the hill, the ground is soft; here I saw the pug marks of a tiger, and a glance at them satisfied me we were on the heels of the Bachelor and that he was only a minute or two ahead of us.

Beyond the soft ground the track runs for three hundred yards over stones, before going steeply down onto an open plain. If the tiger kept to the track we should probably see him on this open ground. We had gone another fifty yards when Robin stopped and, after running his nose up and down a blade of grass on the left of the track, turned and entered the grass which was here about two feet high. On the far side of the grass there was a patch of clerodendron, about forty yards wide. This plant grows in dense patches to a height of five feet, and has widely spread leaves and a big head of flowers not unlike horse-chestnut. It is greatly fancied by tiger, sambur, and pig because of the shade it gives. When Robin reached the clerodendron he stopped and backed towards me, thus telling me that he could not see into the bushes ahead and wished to be carried. Lifting him up, I put his hind legs into my left-hand pocket, and when he had hooked his forefeet over my left arm, he was safe and secure, and I had both hands free for the rifle. On these occasions Robin was always in deadly earnest, and no matter what he saw, or how our quarry behaved before or after fired at, he never moved and spoilt my shot, or impeded my view. Proceeding very slowly, we had gone half-way through the clerodendron when I saw the bushes directly in front of us swaying. Waiting until the tiger had cleared the bushes, I went forward expecting to see him in the more or less open jungle, but he was nowhere in sight, and when I put Robin down he turned to the left and indicated that the tiger had gone into a deep and narrow ravine near by. This ravine ran to the foot of an isolated hill on which there were caves frequented by tigers, and as I was not armed to deal with a tiger at close quarters, and further, as it was time for breakfast, Robin and I turned and made for home.

After breakfast I returned alone, armed with a heavy .450

rifle, and as I approached the hill, which in the days of the long ago had been used by the local inhabitants as a rallying point against the Gurkha invaders, I heard the boom of a big buffalo bell, and a man shouting. These sounds were coming from the top of the hill, which is flat, and about half an acre in extent, so I climbed up and saw a man on a tree, striking a dead branch with the head of his axe and shouting, while at the foot of the tree a number of buffaloes were collected. When he saw me the man called out, saying I had just arrived in time to save him and his buffaloes from a *shaitan* of a tiger, the size of a camel, that had been threatening them for hours. From his story I gathered that he had arrived on the hill shortly after Robin and I had left for home, and that as he started to cut bamboo leaves for his buffaloes he saw a tiger coming towards him. He shouted to drive the tiger away, as he had done on many previous occasions with other tigers, but instead of going away this one had started to growl. He took to his heels, followed by his buffaloes, and climbed up the nearest tree. The tiger, paying no heed to his shouts, had then set to pacing round and round, while the buffaloes kept their heads towards it. Probably the tiger had heard me coming, for it had left only a moment before I had arrived. The man was an old friend, who before his quarrel with the Headman of his village had done a considerable amount of poaching in these jungles with the Headman's gun. He now begged me to conduct both himself and his cattle safely out of the jungle; so telling him to lead on, I followed behind to see that there were no stragglers. At first the buffaloes were disinclined to break up their close formation, but after a little persuasion we got them to start, and we had gone half-way across the open plain I have alluded to when the tiger called in the jungle to our right. The man quickened his pace, and I urged on the buffaloes, for a mile of very thick jungle lay between us and the wide, open watercourse beyond which lay my friend's village and safety for his buffaloes.

I have earned the reputation of being keener on photographing animals than on killing them, and before I left my friend he begged me to put aside photography for this once, and kill the tiger, which he said was big enough to eat a buffalo a day, and ruin him in twenty-five days. I promised to do my best and turned to retrace my steps to the open plain, to meet with an experience every detail of which has burnt itself deep into my memory.

On reaching the plain I sat down to wait for the tiger to disclose his whereabouts, or for the jungle folk to tell me where he was. It was then about 3 P.M., and as the sun was warm and comforting, I put my head down on my drawn-up knees and had been dozing a few minutes when I was awakened by the tiger calling; thereafter he continued to call at short intervals.

Between the plain and the hills there is a belt, some half-mile wide, of the densest scrub jungle for a hundred miles round, and I located the tiger as being on the hills on the far side of the scrub—about three-quarters of a mile from me—and from the way he was calling it was evident he was in search of a mate.

Starting from the upper left-hand corner of the plain, and close to where I was sitting, an old cart track, used some years previously for extracting timber, ran in an almost direct line to where the tiger was calling. This track would take me in the direction of the calling animal, but on the hills was high grass, and without Robin to help me there would be little chance of my seeing him. So instead of my going to look for the tiger, I decided he should come and look for me. I was too far away for him to hear me, so I sprinted up the cart track for a few hundred yards, laid down my rifle, climbed to the top of a high tree and called three times. I was immediately answered by the tiger. After climbing down, I ran back, calling as I went, and arrived on the plain without having found a suitable place in which to sit and await the tiger. Something would have to be done and done in a hurry, for the tiger was rapidly coming nearer; so, after rejecting a little hollow which I found to be full of black stinking water, I lay down flat in the open, twenty yards from where the track entered the scrub. From this point I had a clear view up the track for fifty yards, to where a bush, leaning over it, impeded my further view. If the tiger came down the track, as I expected him to, I decided to fire at him as soon as he cleared the obstruction.

After opening the rifle to make quite sure it was loaded, I threw off the safety-catch, and with elbows comfortably resting on the soft ground waited for the tiger to appear. I had not called since I came out on the plain, so to give him direction I now gave a loud call, which he immediately answered from a distance of a hundred yards. If he came on at his usual pace, I judged he would clear the obstruction in thirty seconds. I counted this number very slowly, and went on counting up to eighty, when out of the corner of my eye I saw a movement to my right front, where the bushes approached to within ten yards of me. Turning my eyes in that direction I saw a great head projecting above the bushes, which here were four feet high. The tiger was only a foot or two inside the bushes, but all I could see of him was his head. As I very slowly swung the point of the rifle round and ran my eyes along the sights I noticed that his head was not quite square on to me, and as I was firing up and he was looking down, I aimed an inch below his right eye, pressed the trigger, and for the next half-hour nearly died of fright.

Instead of dropping dead as I expected him to, the tiger went straight up into the air above the bushes for his full length, falling backwards onto a tree a foot thick which had been blown down in a storm and was still green. With unbelievable fury he attacked this tree and tore it to bits, emitting as he did so roar upon roar, and what was even worse, a dreadful blood-curdling sound as though he was savaging his worst enemy. The branches of the tree tossed about as though struck by a tornado, while the bushes on my side shook and bulged out, and every moment I expected to have him on top of me, for he had been looking at me when I fired, and knew where I was.

Too frightened even to recharge the rifle for fear the slight movement and sound should attract the attention of the tiger, I lay and sweated for half an hour with my finger on the left trigger. At last the branches of the tree and the bushes ceased waving about, and the roaring became less frequent, and eventually, to my great relief, ceased. For another half-hour I lay perfectly still, with arms cramped by the weight of the heavy rifle, and then started to pull myself backwards with my toes. After progressing for thirty yards in this manner I got to my feet, and, crouching low, made for the welcome shelter of the nearest tree. Here I remained for some minutes, and as all was now silent I turned and made for home.

II

Next morning I returned accompanied by one of my men, an expert tree-climber. I had noticed the previous evening that there was a tree growing on the edge of the open ground, and about forty yards from where the tiger had fallen. We approached this tree very cautiously, and I stood behind it while the man climbed to the top. After a long and a careful scrutiny he looked down and shook his head, and when he rejoined me on the ground he told me that the bushes over a big area had been flattened down, but that the tiger was not in sight.

I sent him back to his perch on the tree with instructions to keep a sharp lookout and warn me if he saw any movement in the bushes, and went forward to have a look at the spot where the tiger had raged. He had raged to some purpose, for, in addition to tearing branches and great strips of wood off the tree, he had torn up several bushes by the roots, and bitten down others. Blood in profusion was sprinkled everywhere, and on the ground were two congealed pools, near one of which was lying a bit of bone two inches square, which I found on examination to be part of the tiger's skull.

No blood trail led away from this spot and this, combined with the two pools of blood, was proof that the tiger was still here when I left and that the precautions I had taken the previous evening had been very necessary, for when I started on my 'get-away' I was only ten yards from the most dangerous animal in the world—a freshly wounded tiger. On circling round the spot I found a small smear of blood here and there on leaves that had brushed against his face. Noting that these indications of the tiger's passage led in a direct line to a giant semul tree * two hundred yards away, I went back and climbed the tree my man was on in order to get a bird's-eye view of the ground I should have to go over, for I had a very uneasy feeling that I should find him alive: a tiger shot in the head can live for days and can even recover from the wound. True, this tiger had a bit of his skull missing, and as I had never dealt with an animal in his condition before I did not know whether he was likely to live for a few hours or days, or live on to die of old age. For this reason I decided to treat him as an ordinary wounded tiger, and not to take any avoidable risks when following him up.

From my elevated position on the tree I saw that, a little to the left of the line to the semul tree, there were two trees, the nearer one thirty yards from where the blood was, and the other fifty yards further on. Leaving my man on the tree, I climbed down, picked up my rifle and a shot-gun and bag of a hundred cartridges, and very cautiously approached the nearer tree and climbed up it to a height of thirty feet, pulling the rifle and gun, which I had tied to one end of a strong cord, up after me. After fixing the rifle in a fork of the tree where it would be handy if needed, I started to spray the bushes with small shot, yard by yard up to the foot of the second tree. I did this with the object of locating the tiger, assuming he was alive and in that area, for a wounded tiger, on hearing a shot fired close to him, or on being struck by a pellet, will either growl or charge. Receiving no indication of the tiger's presence I went to the second tree, and sprayed the bushes to within a few yards of the semul tree, firing the last shot at the tree itself. After this last shot I thought I heard a low growl, but it was not repeated and I put it down to my imagination. My bag of cartridges was now empty, so after recovering my man I called it a day, and went home.

When I returned next morning I found my friend the buffalo man feeding his buffaloes on the plain. He appeared to be

---
* *Bombax malabaricum*, the silk cotton tree.

very much relieved to see me, and the reason for this I learnt later. The grass was still wet with dew, but we found a dry spot and there sat down to have a smoke and relate our experiences. My friend, as I have already told you, had done a lot of poaching, and having spent all his life in tiger-infested jungles tending his buffaloes, or shooting, his jungle knowledge was considerable.

After I had left him that day at the wide, open watercourse, he had crossed to the far side and had sat down to listen for sounds coming from the direction in which I had gone. He had heard two tigers calling; he had heard my shot followed by the continuous roaring of a tiger, and very naturally concluded I had wounded one of the tigers and that it had killed me. On his return next morning to the same spot, he had been greatly mystified by hearing a hundred shots fired, and this morning, not being able to contain his curiosity any longer, he had come to see what had happened. Attracted by the smell of blood, his buffaloes had shown him where the tiger had fallen, and he had seen the patches of dry blood and had found the bit of bone. No animal in his opinion could possibly live for more than a few hours after having a bit of its skull blown away, and so sure was he that the tiger was dead that he offered to take his buffaloes into the jungle and find it for me. I had heard of this method of recovering tigers with the help of buffaloes but had never tried it myself, and after my friend had agreed to accepting compensation for any damage to his cattle I accepted his offer.

Rounding up the buffaloes, twenty-five in number, and keeping to the line I had sprinkled with shot the previous day, we made for the semul tree, followed by the buffaloes. Our progress was slow, for not only had we to move the chin-high bushes with our hands to see where to put our feet, but we also had frequently to check a very natural tendency on the part of the buffaloes to stray. As we approached the semul tree, where the bushes were lighter, I saw a little hollow filled with dead leaves that had been pressed flat and on which were several patches of blood, some dry, others in process of congealing, and one quite resh; and when I put my hand to the ground I found it was warm. Incredible as it may appear, the tiger had lain in this hollow the previous day while I had expended a hundred cartridges, and had only moved off when he saw us and the buffaloes approaching. The buffaloes had now found the blood and were pawing up the ground and snorting, and, as the prospect of being caught between a charging tiger and angry buffaloes did not appeal to me, I took hold of my friend's arm, turned him round, and made for the open plain, followed by the buffaloes. When we were back on safe ground I told the man to go home, and said I would return next day and deal with the tiger alone.

The path through the jungles that I had taken each day when coming from and going home ran for some distance over soft ground, and on this soft ground, on this fourth day, I found the pug marks of a big male tiger. By following these pug marks I found the tiger had entered the dense brushwood a hundred yards to the right of the semul tree. Here was an unexpected complication, for if I now saw a tiger in this jungle I should not know—unless I got a very close look at it—whether it was the wounded or the unwounded one. However, this contingency would have to be dealt with when met, and in the meantime worrying would not help, so I entered the bushes and made for the hollow at the foot of the semul tree.

There was no blood trail to follow so I zigzagged through the bushes, into which it was impossible to see further than a few inches, for an hour or more, until I came to a ten-foot-wide dry watercourse. Before stepping down into this watercourse I looked up it, and saw the left hind leg and tail of a tiger. The tiger was standing perfectly still with its body and head hidden by a tree, and only this one leg visible. I raised the rifle to my shoulder, and then lowered it. To have broken the leg would have been easy, for the tiger was only ten yards away, and it would have been the right thing to do if its owner was the wounded animal; but there were two tigers in this area, and to have broken the leg of the wrong one would have doubled my difficulties, which were already considerable. Presently the leg was withdrawn and I heard the tiger moving away, and going to the spot where he had been standing I found a few drops of blood—too late now to regret not having broken that leg.

A quarter of a mile further on there was a little stream, and it was possible that the tiger, now recovering from his wound, was making for this stream. With the object of intercepting him, or failing that, waiting for him at the water, I took a game path which I knew went to the stream and had proceeded along it for some distance when a sambur belled to my left, and went dashing off through the jungle. It was evident now that I was abreast of the tiger, and I had only taken a few more steps when I heard the loud crack of a dry stick breaking as though some heavy animal had fallen on it; the sound had come from a distance of fifty yards and from the exact spot where the sambur had belled. The sambur had in unmistakable tones warned the jungle folk of the presence of a tiger, and the stick therefore could only have been broken by the same animal; so getting down on my hands and knees I started to crawl in the direction from which the sound had come.

The bushes here were from six to eight feet high, with dense foliage on the upper branches and very few leaves on the stems, so that I could see through them for a distance of ten to fifteen feet. I had covered thirty yards, hoping fervently that if the tiger charged he would come from in front (for in no other direction could I have fired), when I caught sight of something red on which the sun, drifting through the upper leaves, was shining; it might only be a bunch of dead leaves; on the other hand, it might be the tiger. I could get a better view of this object from two yards to the right so, lowering my head until my chin touched the ground, I crawled this distance with belly to ground, and on raising my head saw the tiger in front of me. He was crouching down looking at me, with the sun shining on his left shoulder, and on receiving my two bullets he rolled over on his side without making a sound.

As I stood over him and ran my eyes over his magnificent proportions it was not necessary to examine the pads of his feet to know that before me lay the Bachelor of Powalgarh.

The entry of the bullet fired four days previously was hidden by a wrinkle of skin, and at the back of his head was a big hole which, surprisingly, was perfectly clean and healthy.

The report of my rifle was, I knew, being listened for, so I hurried home to relieve anxiety, and while I related the last chapter of the hunt and drank a pot of tea, my men were collecting.

Accompanied by my sister and Robin and a carrying party of twenty men, I returned to where the tiger was lying, and before he was roped to a pole my sister and I measured him from nose to tip of tail, and from tip of tail to nose. At home we again measured him to make quite sure we had made no mistake the first time. These measurements are valueless, for there were no independent witnesses present to certify them; they are, however, interesting as showing the accuracy with which experienced woodsmen can judge the length of a tiger from his pug marks. Wyndham, you will remember, said the tiger was ten feet between pegs, which would give roughly 10′ 6″ over curves; and while one shikari said he was 10′ 5″ over curves, the other said he was 10′ 6″ or a little more. Shot seven years after these estimates were made, my sister and I measured the tiger as being 10′ 7″ over curves.

I have told the story at some length, as I feel sure that those who hunted the tiger between 1920 and 1930 will be interested to know how the Bachelor of Powalgarh met his end.

Edison Marshall

WATCH BY NIGHT

IN THE LATE AFTERNOON we were sitting under the mimosa trees, eating an early supper. A short distance off, our native boys huddled around their cooking fire, gnawing bones, gobbling fat, and jabbering in various tribal dialects that Cottar himself, my old guide, could not understand. Above us burned the African sky, calm and clear and beautiful, for all that it was one blue blaze of merciless heat; and about us the veldt lay silent, hardly breathing, as though in the deep coma of sunstroke.

Charles Cottar, as the people in Nairobi knew him, is only fifty-eight, but Africa was nearly finished with him, and he looked older. Reared in Texas, he is a frontiersman of a bygone generation. When our own West became too civilized, he migrated to the African wilderness. In those days he weighed over two hundred, all bone and sinew, was incredibly powerful of muscle, fearless, and so deadly a shot that he regularly killed wild guinea-fowl on the wing with a rifle.

Three times he has been mauled by leopards. In every case he fought the animal with his hands, beating it off until he or his gun-bearer could put in a fatal shot. Twice he has been under elephants—once a rogue bull had him down and was lowering upon him with its great knee when Cottar wriggled to one side and crawled away under the brute's belly; and once an old cow elephant, searching for him with vengeful persistence for over an hour in the thick brush and feeling for him with her trunk in every thicket, actually stepped over him. He has been thrown into the air and knocked down and run over by rhinos and buffaloes—when death was so close that he heard it

whistle by—and escaped only through remarkable resource,
quick shooting, and perhaps the favor of Mwenyieze M'ngu, the
jungle god. He has never been caught by lions. He has killed
fifty or more, and not one has scratched him. His luck is so good
in this regard that he is superstitious about it. If Cottar fears
anything in this world or the next—which sometimes I doubt—
he fears lions; down in his heart he believes that finally a lion
will get him. And this will be his end: to lie with the rest of his
old pals—the last of the "White Hunters" of African fame—in
the cemetery at Nairobi, under the tropic sun.

"Marshall, you are out here to find out about Africa," he said
to me over the coffee cups. "Don't you know you can't get acquainted with the old girl in the daytime? Really to know her,
you must sit up with her at night. She sleeps in the day—but at
night she steps out." *

I looked out over the low hills, between the mimosa forests,
on to the open plain. From my seat I could count eight herds of
big game, from thirty to five hundred animals in the herd. The
small gray dots occasionally catching the sunlight like many
mirrors were zebra. Near at hand were herds of topi and kongoni, the former fat-rumped and imposing looking, the latter—
although the topi's first cousins—among the silliest looking creatures on the continent. Yet Africa would not be Africa without
the kongoni. He gives a touch of comic relief in a land where
jests are few and inclined to be grim.

Even more comical were the Tommies—Thompson's gazelles,
as the animal books know them—feeding in the grass just below
camp. Tommy is not at all silly looking, like the kongoni, but
he has one trick that always makes the eyes brighten, no matter
how hot the sun or how bloody the trail. His queer little fly-
switch of a tail is always going. It whirls with the steady motion
of a dynamo, round and round: I think it revolves even when
he sleeps. When bucks are seen far off, it is never difficult to
recognize Tommy. There are many animals with similar horns,
but none with such energetic tails.

---

* Bwana Cottar said what amounted to this. He could have said it better than
this since, like so many backwoods dwellers, he possessed a native eloquence.

Yet Tommy has his tragic side. All small and middle-sized hunters, from leopards to wild cats, prey regularly on this most common of African game. Never the night falls in silence and mystery, but literally hundreds of these little gazelle fall, too, their absurd tails stilled at last, victims in the game of kill-and-be-killed which is Africa.

Just beyond the Tommies something that looked like the tops of tall desert cactus, twenty feet high, thrust up from the low shrub. But they were not cactus tops, because they moved from place to place. Giraffes—thirty of them—they looked like strange relics from some strange age, stragglers from Time's army of uncouth things that have passed on. It seemed incredible that they could share the same world with the radio and the airplane. Incidentally they were in amazing contrast with the little Tommies. Africa is a land of incredible contrasts, but none more striking than the twenty-foot giraffe and his little friend, the two-foot Tommy, reaching not halfway to his knees.

Under the trees was a herd of wildebeest, or gnus, as they are known to crossword puzzle fans. These, too, were queer folk, at a distance resembling our own glorious bison. Like the bison, they were given to unaccountable stampedes, they were heavy of head and shoulders, and their crazy, circling gallop when alarmed recalled Cottar to his childhood on the western buffalo plains. But I knew they would not stand close inspection. The bull I had shot for meat was a horse-faced, coarse-haired, ungainly affair, peaked of rump and altogether unimposing.

Like the wildebeests, most of the African animals are ill-proportioned, with horns too small to match their heads. But as I sat watching through binoculars, creatures of perfect symmetry wandered down through the grove. These were impalla; their glossy coats of the richest, creamiest brown, their forms slight and graceful, their horns long and finely curved. But only this morning we had found the half-devoured carcass of an impalla ram, and the great track of a leopard in the dust.

"I'm ready to sit up with Africa any night you say," I told Cottar. "But I can't believe that she could be any more wonderful in the dark than she is right now."

"You'll see," he answered me. "And tonight is as good a night as any. There won't be much moon, but that will make it all the more interesting."

At Cottar's command I shot a zebra stallion. I kept the skin for an automobile robe: the meat was to be used in the night's work. This may seem wanton killing, but actually there was no loss to the country's wild life. For this animal that was slain today, one of its fellows would be spared tonight.

The carcass was dragged close to a tree at the edge of the veldt and securely pegged down.

"You are to spend the night either in or under this tree," Cottar told me.

"With no fire?"

"With no fire. You wouldn't see anything if you kept a fire, except maybe a few pairs of eyes burning in the dark, and you wouldn't hear anything more than a little growling. If you'd rather be up in the tree, the boys will build a platform for you, and you can lie there in comfort. If you'd rather be on the ground, they'll make a boma for you."

A boma, I knew, was an enclosure of thorn brush. For our purpose it would be no more than four feet high, a few inches thick and just large enough to permit two men to lie down.

"Which do you advise, the treetop or the ground?" I asked Cottar.

"It depends. If you're up the tree, you'll be absolutely safe, even from a rhino. Not even a leopard will follow a man up a tree. If you are in the boma, you'll be practically safe and have a lot more excitement."

"What do you mean by 'practically' safe? How could a little brush fence stop a charging lion?"

"My friend, a charging lion could go through it like so much tissue-paper. A charging lion is bad. But there won't be any. They charge only when attacked or wounded. The brush will give you a feeling of safety and comfort you a heap. Besides, it will keep an old man-eater, provided there is one around, from actually sneaking up and making off with you for his supper. The point is that this boma will be made of thorn brush, and

Simba doesn't like thorns. If he gets one in his foot, he's lame
for weeks, and something will kill him. He might charge a
boma if he is good and mad, but not if he's just hungry. He's
too cute for that."

"And you say a man-eater never takes a man out of a boma?"

"Hardly ever. I can call to mind only two lions who did it as
a regular thing—those two old devils that got so famous during
the building of the railroad. They liked men so well that they'd
go smack through the toughest boma; anyway, there aren'
many man-eaters in Tanganika. Of course there are a few—
some of the savages don't bury their dead, but just chuck 'em
out, and a few lions as well as hyenas get a taste for 'em that
way—but I'd guarantee they won't come in and get you."

"I'll have my rifle," I said.

"Yes, if worse comes to worst. Fighting a lion in the dark
when he can see and you can't, isn't much fun, but that won't
happen. So which do you prefer, the treetop or the ground?
Some like one, some the other. But if you're looking for thrills
I advise the ground."

II

As a matter of fact, I preferred the tree, but I didn't dare say
so. And I knew well that if there was any considerable danger,
old Cottar would not let me face it.

With pangas (big swordlike knives), the boys cut light thorn
brush and made the boma. A hole was left for a window, facing
the dead zebra less than fifteen feet away. This seemed rather
close quarters, but Cottar knew what he was doing, and I did
not protest.

Into the boma we carried blankets for two—the nights were
chill, due to our elevation—a thermos bottle of hot coffee, a
flashlight with a powerful battery, and my rifle. Then I discovered, somewhat to my dismay, that Cottar did not propose to
share the boma with me: K'ninny, my gun-bearer, would have
the post.

"It would take away half the thrill to have another white

an in the boma with you," Cottar explained. "You came out ere looking for excitement, and by golly, I'm going to give it o you. Besides, I'm getting too old to stand loss of sleep. Good ight and good luck."

K'ninny, my black boy, and I crawled into the boma; the thers went back to camp. The sun was just setting.

At once a feeling of profound loneliness came over me. I ave been in many lonely places—the Arctic, the Siberian Coast, n the utterly desolate beach of the Alaskan Peninsula—but ever did I experience such solitude as in this little pen of rush in the middle of the open veldt at twilight. It was as hough K'ninny and I were the only human inhabitants of a rehistoric world. The shadows grew with startling rapidity, hen blended, deepened, and lost shape as the sun dropped be- ind the horizon. If there was the slightest echo of sound any- vhere on the veldt, I could not hear it.

The complete silence, however, was of short duration. Look- ng back on it now, I think of it as the hush that falls over a heater just before the play. However, it was no make-believe, ut the authentic drama of the Age of Mammals K'ninny and I aw that night.

Usually, at nightfall, a low wind springs up over the veldt, he result of the sun-baked earth cooling rapidly in the thin air. t searched through the thickets, rustle-rustle; it would pause or long minutes; and it chased its invisible prey over the plain: ve could see the grass stir as it passed. An instant later the ex- itement began with a rushing, beating sound in the air just be- ide the boma.

We both jumped, but it was only a vulture landing in a tree- op near by. Soaring lazily across the darkening sky for a last urvey of his domain, he had seen our zebra carcass and had lropped down to investigate it. Other vultures, miles away, had een him descend, because presently they were volplaning in rom all directions. They perched in the trees about our bait, strange silhouettes against the twilight sky.

They would not attack the meat so late. The shadows were

too heavy: they were afraid of what might be lying, waiting for darkness, in the grass. Had it been an hour earlier, they would have descended in a grizzly swarm. A trophy must not be left unguarded even five minutes in daylight. The undertakers of the air are an efficient gang: literally in fifteen minutes there is nothing left but naked bones for the hyenas to drag away in the darkness. Yet it serves a good purpose. In spite of the Death that stalks ever over the African prairies, the face of the land is clean.

The vultures stretched their ugly necks and peered hungrily at the meat. I thought of Isaiah and his ringing prophecy,

"Woe to the land shadowing with wings beyond the Rivers of Ethiopia."

Central Africa is that land—and the shadowing wings must be the wings of the vultures.

We heard a drumming of hoofs, and presently a herd of zebra galloped up, quivered, stamped, and ran on. Ordinarily I shouldn't have thought twice about this. We were always seeing zebra—the most common African game. But now their panic contributed to the sense of the growing menace of the night. I had seen the same herd two hours before, resting at ease in the shade or quietly grazing on the plains: if a lion had wandered near, they would merely have shifted out of his reach. Now their heads were up, their eyes wild, and they would stampede at a shadow.

The whole truth was that the great black god of Fear was striding over the veldt. I had glimpsed him a few times before, here and there in odd corners of the earth, but never at such close range. A monkey began to chatter in a tall mimosa tree, a nerve-racking sound. A big male ostrich, gay with plumes, went springing off to some unknown sanctuary across the plain.

The shadows deepened. A large star, milky white, popped through the gray twilight sky. Presently an old maribou stork, with a beak like a rapier, leaped from his perch in the top of a tree, croaked, and flapped off. One by one the vultures followed him to their roost in some haunted forest unknown to man. Some live thing rustled stealthily in the thickets just beside the

ɔoma, but whether it was bird or beast or serpent we could not
ell.

Suddenly it was night. The dark seemed to drift over us, as I
have seen fog drift in the North Pacific. We could hardly discern the outline of our bait: it was no more than a dim spot in
he heavier dark.

At that moment I realized that there was something here
ɔther than K'ninny and myself. Ten feet beyond the bait a
shadow hovered, more black than the other shadows. It had not
been there a few seconds before.

We never knew what that shadow was. It went away presently. Whether it returned in the wilder drama of midnight
would be no more than a guess at best.

About our boma the Wild wakened to life. Far away a zebra
stallion uttered a neighing scream. After a long pause, something that I took for a fawn bleated pitifully twice. Then, close
at hand, came the sudden insane howling of hyenas, always the
opening chorus of African night. The short hairs stirred at the
base of our skulls as the howl changed to a wailing chant, rising
and falling to break at last in demoniac laughter.

In all the world of hunting, I had heard only one voice like
this. I remembered the round hills of the Yukon and the coyotes clamoring at dusk. The hyena and the coyote are blood-
brothers: both have the strange, half-human intelligence of the
canines. Is this why their cries seem so creepy and forlorn? Most
beasts are dumb save for their own mysterious calls to one another, but these desert wolves are able to tell us, in their weird
songs, secret truths of life. They sing of the travail of existence—heat, thirst, endless conflict, fear most of all. What the
wild laugh at the end of the song may mean, we cannot guess.

Again the silence closed down. We waited perhaps half an
hour, watching and listening. It seemed to me that the shadows
about the carcass were moving and changing. Whether it was a
trick of my eyes, or whether the jungle people were already
gathering, I did not know. At last all doubt was removed.

I could hear the snip of sharp fangs on the meat. It was a

stealthy sound; evidently the visitors were trying to concea
their prize from their fellow hunters. This showed that they
were not of the jungle aristocracy, but mean, humble beasts
snatching a meal where they could. When the dim starlight
showed their movements, I could see they were of insignificant
size. They made no sound to reveal their identity. They might
be any one of half a dozen different species of the smaller cats
or canines. Yet when I asked K'ninny what they were, he answered instantly and in sure tones.

"*Mbwa wa mwitu.*" (Jackals)

"How do you know?"

"It is as always. The jackal is small, mean, and cowardly, but
Mwenhieze M'ngu (God) looks out for him. He will not go
hungry. When the lions and the elephants are all dead, the
jackal will still creep in the grass with a full belly." *

I suddenly pressed the button of our flashlight and the beam
made a golden circle against which every dark object stood in
bold relief. We saw the carcass in the yellow grass, and two silvery
creatures slinking away. And they were jackals—the lowest and
meanest of the whole mean clan of wild dogs.

I snapped off the light, and at once they came stealing back;
again we heard the hushed snip-snip of their scissor teeth. They
ate slowly, pausing often to listen, for nearly an hour. Then
they stopped eating and stood motionless, listening. One of
them climbed on to the carcass and gazed out into the shadows.

Presently both jackals bounded away, their little feet tenor-
drumming the hard dry earth. Something—a sound I could not
hear, a scent I could not catch—had put them in a panic.

But the mystery was soon explained. Absolutely without
warning the grass was alive with animals. There was a ravening
pack about the bait, growling, snarling, fighting, slashing the
meat with a curious wet sound, and breaking bones.

For the first moment I could not think what kind of animals
they might be. Their sudden appearance, even more the sudden

---

* K'ninny made a remark to this effect on a previous occasion, and Cottar
translated it. I knew only a few words of Swahili.

uproar after such breathless silence, seemed to knock me silly. It must be remembered that I was a tenderfoot as far as Africa was concerned. No doubt an old hunter would have grasped the situation instantly: I suppose K'ninny did so.

I could see that they were not large enough to be lions, but they looked too large to be any other African carnivora of my acquaintance. This, it seemed, was merely a trick of the light. "*Fisi*," K'ninny said scornfully. They were only hyenas, after all, notorious cowards, never ranked among the dangerous African animals.

I let them eat undisturbed for perhaps five minutes, then I turned on the light. Around the dead zebra, and climbing over it, were eight of the brutes, their sloping backs, ugly heads, and snarling, bone-cracker mouths making them look even worse ruffians than they really were. Their eyes were little twin moons, green as emerald.

They could not face the mysterious light and began to give ground. One bolder than the rest turned with a snarl, crouched as though to attack, and then slunk away.

When the light went out, they came slinking back. Ten minutes later they were all gorging again. In order to save some of the meat for later visitors I tried to frighten them away by flicking the light on and off. But they grew bolder as the night wore on, and retreated only to the edge of the shadow.

That night I saw a wonderful illustration of canine cunning. The moon rose about nine o'clock and occasionally shone through the ragged clouds. During one of these moonlit intervals I heard what I thought was a lion snarling in the grass a hundred feet distant. The hyenas heard the sound, too—they all stopped eating and raised their heads.

The snarl grew to a low growl, the growl to a roar of rage. Then some tawny beast came rushing down upon the bait.

The hyenas all scattered in panic. They had been taken in by the same trick that had fooled K'ninny and me. It was not a lion that roared down upon the bait, but only another hyena. Plainly he was not a member of the pack and had taken this way to secure a share of the feast. He attacked the bait savagely, tearing off a good-sized steak before the other hyenas saw the ruse and came snarling back. Although they drove him off at once, he had won his point. We heard him chewing and chuckling in the grass.

The amazing truth is that this lone hyena played the same trick twice more in the course of the next hour. Although the moon was behind clouds, savage voices told us what had occurred. Each time he was successful—making off into the grass with a piece of the precious meat. Plainly the hyena's nerves were just as taut as mine.*

About midnight the show began in earnest. There rose a queer coughing sound a hundred feet distant in the grass.

K'ninny shivered and touched my arm, "*Tui,*" he whispered. (Leopard)

The hyenas raised their heads and, growling hoarsely, gazed in the direction of the sound. Because the moon was riding free in a great rent in the clouds, I could see them plainly. I expected them to make off—it would be in accord with the night's program—but to my surprise they went doggedly back to their feast.

"Only one leopard—too many hyenas," K'ninny explained.†

This seemed reasonable enough. Cottar had told me, I now remembered, that hyenas will usually tree a leopard. But long ago I quit banking on any hard and fast rules for animal conduct. And tonight K'ninny and I were spectators of a terrific drama of the dark, in which any marvel could come to pass.

I perceived a growing uneasiness among the hyenas. They ate in quick, slashing bites, instantly raising their heads to stare into the shadows. Again they growled deep in their throats, a sound that grew and intensified to low, rattling chorus, indescribably ominous. Straining, I tried to see what they were seeing.

Presently a long, slinky shadow appeared in the short grass

---

* This sounds very much like the elder Theodore Roosevelt's favorite abomination, the nature fakers. The incident happened just as described. Cottar said it was not very unusual.

† K'ninny put this idea over all right, partly with sign language.

sixty feet from the bait. It was so large that I thought surely it
was a lioness, not a leopard.

"*Simba?*" I whispered to K'ninny.

He shook his head. "*Tui—kubwa.*" (A leopard and a big one)

And it *was* a big one. In the pale blue light of the moon I
could see that his long, sinuous form was nearly half again as
large as the average male leopard's.

He advanced with his head up, straight toward the bait, and
without a sound.

The hyenas gathered in a close group, growling hoarsely. I
slipped off the safety of my Mannlicher rifle. He was the most
determined-looking, boldest, proudest born killer I had ever
seen.

When he was fifteen feet from the bait one of the hyenas
broke and ran. He yelped as though he already felt the leopard's talons tearing out his side. This was the beginning of the
rout. One by one the hyenas broke, yelping, until the whole
pack had scattered in the grass.

III

One leopard had vanquished eight hyenas. It was either a
wonderful example of cold bluff, or else the aftermath of some
jungle drama of months or years before. Perhaps the big cat
had tired of scurrying up trees from the filthy packs and in
some splendid hour of pride had turned on them and found
out their secret cowardice. Nor did he deign to follow or even
look at them, but crouched beside the bait to begin his meal.

Just then the moon slipped behind dense clouds. I can remember few moments so charged with suspense. The leopard
was fifteen feet away, and I couldn't see him. And Cottar had
forgotten to tell me what to expect of a leopard visiting a boma
at night! *

I signaled to K'ninny to turn on our flashlight. The beam
burst out in a golden ring, in the center of which stood an abso-

---

* This was truly an amazing leopard, with an outsize and perfect skin. In
later trips I never saw any leopard in the least like it.

lutely perfect leopard, from a hunter's standpoint. He was as large as a young lioness, and every spot on his sinuous side was perfect.

His pelt would make a splendid trophy. The sight of it would always recall one of the most thrilling adventures of my life. Moreover he was fair game. Kill-and-be-killed is the order of events in Africa: he had slain bucks by the hundred, and now his own turn had come.

The quarters were somewhat close. If I failed to kill him instantly, he might be up into the boma in one bound.

The animal looked up when the light struck him, then insolently turned his head and began to eat the meat. Later I was to learn that this was unusual behavior in a leopard. As a rule the big cats are furtive and stealthy and flee from any unusual sight or sound.

I aimed as carefully as I could, and touched the trigger. Mortally wounded, the leopard snarled viciously and sank his teeth and claws into the zebra carcass. I shot again instantly to finish him off.

K'ninny switched off the light, and when our breath returned we whispered in the darkness, he in his native tongue and I in mine. It did not matter that we could not understand what each other said. We both understood that we had to get out of the boma and retrieve the dead leopard before the hyenas returned to devour him.

It was a discomforting prospect. The brush pen was all that stood between us and the creeping, sneaking shadows on the plain. There were all kinds of mental hazards too—the leopard's mate perhaps waiting in the darkness, blazing-eyed, with the sinister stealth of her kind. Maybe there was a black mamba, one of the deadliest of all snakes, coiled in the grass. It stood to reason there were lions near by too, with nerves as jumpy as mine; they might creep up the wrong minute and treat us as a trifling obstacle between them and the feast.

If I did not go, I would lose face not only with K'ninny but every native in the outfit. All alone Cottar would have run out there, thrown the 250-pound cat over his back, and run back.

He had once chased a wounded lion into a dark cave. But as bad as I wanted the trophy, I had no notion of going unless K'ninny would go with me to throw the light around. All I could do was mumble *"Twende."* It would be all right with me if he declined.

But K'ninny was a high type of native, one of the Wakamba people, and perhaps he had an unwarranted respect for white men. Certainly we had some miraculous gadgets, such as matches, *moto* cars, and "strong" guns. He was not such a fool as to regard any white man as a demigod but he had his own way of looking at things. He was paid and well-fed to go with his *bwana* no matter how foolishly. Also he was greatly enjoying the evening's entertainment and, for all I knew, wanted to be a good sport.

"Dio, bwana."

We pushed aside the thorn brush and crawled out into the thick dark. As I held the rifle ready, K'ninny flashed the light in all directions. We scurried up to the dead beast and with our free hands dragged it up to the boma. But we did not have that patch of grass entirely to ourselves. Out of the corner of my eye I saw two gray creatures, the size of young collies, slip away into the thickets. I am not sure, but I think they were the two jackals that had come to our bait earlier in the evening. Once, as the light swept round, it picked up a pair of yellow eyes in the high grass. Just what beast this was I do not know to this day, and I shall always be curious. The eyes looked as big as dollars—further than this we did not pause to determine.

We deposited the leopard at the edge of the thorn brush, where we could guard it, and scrambled, with marked haste, into our shelter.

Already we had had a fair share of excitement and had killed one of the finest leopards in Africa. But there remained five hours more of deep dark, and I knew that our adventure had scarcely begun. I remembered that an acquaintance of mine, who had hunted in this same territory only the year before, had counted nineteen lions about his boma in a single night.

For an hour the bait lay untouched. The moon cast an eerie

light over the plain. At last two little gray figures came stealing out of the grass. They were two jackals, no doubt the same animals we had seen before.

I would have let them eat their fill, but the matter was out of my hands. Presently the hyenas came skulking back, weird-looking brutes in the pale light, and promptly drove their smaller cousins from the meat. The jackals disappeared, but I knew they had not gone far and were waiting for the unguarded moment when even small and cowardly folk may triumph.

The game of fear-and-feared commenced again. The hyenas had been eating scarcely fifteen minutes, and were just getting warmed to the work, when I heard a subdued grunt beyond the thickets. The hyenas jumped as if they had been shot, then stiffened. Presently they bounded away in panic, their feet drumming on the hard earth.

For a few seconds I thought this was another false alarm, then K'ninny's fingernails sank into my arm. He was shaking with excitement, and the moon showed the whites of his eyes.

"They are coming, *bwana*," he whispered.*

"Who?"

"Simba!"

The written word can not record the emphasis, the strange dramatic inflection, which the black man put upon this name. Of all the words in the Swahili tongue, it is the most thrilling to hear. *Simba* means lion.

Why is it that the lion has always conjured the imaginations of men? Many beasts are nobler, one or two more dangerous, I believe. Still he is the main attraction at the zoo, and the prime reason why American big game hunters trek ten thousand miles to Africa. It is not surprising that one of the greatest of Egyptian Pharaohs saw fit to record in imperishable stone,

"I hunted the Lion."

We were both tired from the long watch, yet never in our lives more wide-awake. Every nerve was alert, every sense keyed to the highest pitch. There was a long moment of suspense,

---

* K'ninny gasped out something at this point. It is as good a guess as any.

eep and thrilling. Then three great figures marched silently ut of the grass.

They were three lions, a big maned male and two females.

They paused in the moonlight and looked at us. The big nale growled in sullen anger; one female marched deliberately p to the boma and peered through the window into my face. he was so close I could see the deep anxious-looking lines of er huge, tabby-cat countenance; I could have poked with my ifle barrel.

But I did not poke her, or take any liberties with her at all. only sat there, one lump of ice. To this day I do not know vhat stopped me from throwing up my gun and shooting her. t could have been a disastrous mistake—her dying leap might 1ave carried her into the boma and let her put her claws and angs in one of us—but if I thought of that it was way down 9elow my terrified consciousness. Cottar explained later that he resented our presence and wanted to say "to hell with you" in lioness fashion. In fact he had known the same thing to happen on previous boma-sittings. He should have warned me though. That big three-cornered countenance in the boma window was a severe shock to my nervous system. Perhaps the only reason I did not do anything wrong was that I was too paralyzed to do anything, period.

Worse she opened her mouth, with her fangs catching the moonlight, and gave us a wicked snarl. Then she insolently turned tail on us and joined her mates at the feast.

Under the pale moon I saw the large male lion place one paw on the shoulder of the carcass to hold it down and rip off the meat with the big fangs. He was so close I could hear the champ of his jaws. But he too appeared to resent our watching him from the cozy distance of fifteen or so feet. During the first fifteen minutes of his stay, he occasionally paid us the respect of a savage growl. Later the tough-looking gang treated us with contempt.

But this was all on one side. With popping eyes, K'ninny and I watched every move the beasts made and quaked at every sudden one. My best judgment told me we were in no real danger. Cottar would have shot all three of the devils—Martin Johnson would have waited for good poses and snapped pictures! For me it was a thrill raised to the nth power. My clothes had been full of little red ants only an hour before—sharp biting little pests off the thorn-balls—but, though they were no doubt nipping me as viciously as ever, I had forgotten all about them.

IV

Soon the lions forgot us entirely. They were eating steadily, uttering a strange running snarl never varying in pitch or volume, vaguely like a gang of stray cats around a plate of meat. When my hand was steady enough, I got my rifle ready for any emergency and flashed our light full upon them. They looked up, snarling, their big forms looming against the dark background beyond, their eyes rings of flame.

The big male was the first to slink off, one of his mates behind him. The other female began to growl as though she meant to attack, but she could not face the light. Snarling, she, too, backed off into the shadows.

Since it was only spoiling the show, I turned off the light. Growling as though they meant to scare us from our retreat, the big brutes came straight back to the bait and resumed their feast. In one way or another K'ninny and I kept our hearts from jumping out of our mouths, and watched and listened to them for almost two hours.

Until now we had been in no real danger. The nearest to it was when we ventured into the dark after the dead leopard, but even then no wounded animals were near by, and the flashlight protected us from any wild hunters that might have otherwise pounced upon us and dragged us away. This is the cold conclusion I came to when the excitement was over and the sun in the sky, nor were our visitors an unusual array.

Cats and canines—lions and leopards, hyenas and jackals—often come to a hunter's bait almost simultaneously. The drama of Fear is enacted nightly in these wilds: I watched it many

imes in the next few weeks. But tonight Africa surpassed her-
elf with a fitting climax to our adventure.

As we were watching through the window of our boma, the
ons suddenly faded away. I do not know how else to describe
heir sudden disappearance: it was like a piece of mesmerism.
)ne second, and they were all tearing at the meat, breaking
ones, chewing, and uttering the running snarl. The next, and
here was not an echo of sound on the whole moonlit plain,
nd there was nothing to be seen but the empty grass and the
roken meats of the feast. I do not yet know why I did not see
he brutes leave. Perhaps unconsciously I had closed my eyes
fter the long strain of watching.

K'ninny jumped as though he had been dozing. *"Ni mambo
ani haya?"* he whispered. (What does it mean?) *

I could not tell him, but could only watch and listen with
ny eyes almost popping out of my head. Presently I heard a
listinct rustling sound in the boma, and at first my dazed mind
ould not think what it might be. Then I discovered that it was
he shake of a man's knees against the brush—whether K'ninny's
r mine being no consideration.

The first sign of life was the reappearance of the two jackals.
They seized the opportunity to cram a morsel more into their
ver-hungry mouths. Whether they remained on the scene dur-
ng the wild excitement of the next two minutes, neither K'ninny
hor I could later declare for certain. We were too busy to keep
rack of them.

There was a sudden loud crash of brush in the thickets forty
ards away. Then some enormously heavy creature came plow-
ing toward us, smashing down the little thorn trees that grew
behind the boma, and cracking off the limbs like twigs. Plainly
he was making straight for us.

My first thought was that we were being charged by an elephant. If an old "rogue" had caught our smell and decided in
his flighty brain that we were enemies, he would smash our
boma to kindling wood with one foot. We could try to stop him

---

* I got this out of a book entitled *Swahili in Twelve Easy Lessons*. However,
K'ninny asked a frightened question of some sort.

with my light rifle, but the idea was hardly short of ludicrou
The only shot I know that will drop an elephant in his track
from any firearm that a man can shoot in his two hands, is
bullet at the base of the ear, from the side, straight into th
brain. Our only hope would be to hit him hard from the fron
and turn him.

The sound would not have seemed one-tenth so ominous ha
it come from any direction other than straight downwind. Thi
meant that the animal was not merely wandering by, but ha
caught our scent, had probably recognized us as human being
and was coming to make trouble.

Both of us sprang to our feet. Pushing through the thor
brush was a dark shape which for long, hair-raising seconds
could not recognize.

"Elephant?" I whispered.

"*Kifaru,*" K'ninny breathed. (Rhinoceros)

When I knew what to look for, the big black bulk took recog
nizable shape. In the pale gleam I could see an ungainly head
and two up-thrusting horns. A rhino looks grotesque enougl
even in broad daylight. Africa is not yet in the Age of Man, bu
still in the Age of Mammals: otherwise such things as thi
would be no more than fossils in the stone.

A rhino is less dangerous than an elephant—less cunning in
his wrath, clumsier, more easily angered but less vindictive
easier to kill. Yet his hide is more than an inch thick, and so
hard when dried that it can be carved into walking sticks resembling amber. His stupid brain is enclosed in a heavy safety-
vault of bone, and he weighs around three thousand pounds.
The simple truth was that if our visitor made up his sulky mind
to wipe us from the scene, he could trample out our boma and
our lives in one stabbing rush.

He was not charging yet, but advancing upon us in a kind
of burly trot.

He paused, just as we got to our feet, and snorted. One who
has never heard the snort of a rhino can not possibly believe
that living vocal cords could emit such a sound. It has something of the timbre, although, of course, not the volume, of the

dden explosive whistle of a steam locomotive, and it fairly
ps the air. I can not call it back now in memory, as I recall his
ntastic shape in the moonlight, but I know it terrified both
'ninny and myself, and reduced in a marked degree our
lances of keeping our heads and saving ourselves from disaster.

Stamping, he lowered his head and swung it back and forth.
saw its grotesque outline in silhouette against the moonlit
round.* With the horn thrusting straight out like a lance, he
dvanced sullenly toward us.

He paused again about five steps distant, stamping and snort-
ng. I believed then, and I believe now, that he was getting
eady to charge: his sullen, brutish anger was growing in his
ull brain like steam in a boiler. Then nothing but a lucky
ullet boring through the thick plates of his skull could pre-
ent a tragedy.

To give him this bullet was my instant intention. My rifle
vas at my shoulder, and my finger against the trigger. I had
eld my fire until now on the forlorn chance of avoiding a fight
nder such adverse conditions. The vitality of a rhinoceros is
normous. He will often run two hundred yards with an ounce
f lead through his heart. Rhinos have killed many old and ex-
erienced hunters, even in daylight when there was light to see
nd room to dodge it.

But we were spared this crisis, partly because of a trifling
ccident, mostly because of the quick thinking of a Negro gun-
earer.

I had told K'ninny to flash the light full into the brute's face.
This might blind him—at least, it would give me a better
hance to aim. In spite of the strain we were both under, and
he tremendous excitement, he managed to get hold of the light
nd press the button. But before he could direct the beam on
he target, a branch of thorn brush caught his arm and almost
nade him drop the light.

As he pulled free, the beam shone on a low bush a little to
ne side of the boma. The rhino saw the shrub light up, and

---

* A curious and most vivid memory.

for some incomprehensible reason it touched off the powder of his stupid rage. He lowered his head and rammed into the brush.

K'ninny told me later that he deflected the light on purpose, but this is too much to believe, even from the sharpest of gun bearers, and I had heard him struggling with the thorns. Anyway he does not need this extra honor.

When the rhino ran down the lighted bush, of course, it melted away under him. He stopped, snorting, unable to get it through his thick head what had happened. Casting about for his enemy, he saw K'ninny and myself—possibly he heard us or smelled us—and lowered his point toward us again. But now K'ninny was his master.

To this Wakamba Negro alone goes all the credit for our escape. Even now I did not see what he was trying to do, but was still waiting for the light to shine on my target. K'ninny had had an inspiration. With a swiftness of uptake any tried nimrod might envy, he threw the beam not on the rhino but on the stout trunk of a mimosa tree. Instantly the dim-eyed old fool rushed at it, missed it with his horn but struck it a resounding thud with his head or shoulder.

The impact must have shaken him, for he stood several seconds as though dumbfounded. The game was too deep for him. Instead of charging the next tree on which K'ninny had focused the beam, he whirled, snorted, and without rhyme or reason galloped away into the darkness. The last we heard of him he was still smashing down the shrubbery a quarter of a mile away.

K'ninny and I laughed hysterically as men do when imminent tragedy has a comic ending. Gradually we got ourselves in hand. I took a snort of corn that I had brought all the way from Georgia, and gave him a hearty swig at the bottle. We knew well that the night's adventures were over. Any other episode, no matter how thrilling, would seem an anticlimax. We watched a little longer, then lay down in our blankets.

As I was drifting off to sleep, two furtive shadows crept back to the remnants of the bait. I heard the snip-snip of their sharp teeth off and on till dawn.

AFTERMATH

K'ninny had been greatly impressed by the behavior of the leopard. He spoke of it often to Cottar and repeatedly went to look at the skin on the drying rack. He appeared to think we had been in considerable danger.

Whether this had anything to do with a mistake K'ninny made later in the hunt, I do not know.

We had flushed a leopard from his kill. It took cover in a patch of waist-high grass, perhaps two acres in extent. Cottar and I followed him in there, each with a rifle in our hands. K'ninny seemed a little reluctant to go with us, but he did so, first walking close behind Cottar, carrying an extra rifle.

Neither K'ninny or I liked the tall grass, and as it thickened, K'ninny's nerve failed him and he dropped some twenty steps behind us. He thought the leopard was still ahead of us. It was a disastrous mistake.

I heard him scream and an instant later the shockingly ferocious running snarl of the big cat. Cottar and I turned to see him kneeling on the ground, trying to protect his eyes and face with his arms, the leopard erect beside him, attacking him with fang and talon. The grass was scant at this place, the sun flooded it with white light, K'ninny looked shiny black except for the streaks of blood down his face and back, and the gay coat of the leopard appeared to blaze. The scene had a curious static quality and so was photographed on my brain. It was horribly colorful.

Neither Cottar nor I could fire for fear of hitting the boy. We sprinted to his help. The leopard saw us, and letting K'ninny fall, sprang toward us. We both shot the same instant, and the beast shattered to earth. It had been a rapidly moving target and I am sure it was Cottar's fading but still deadly eye that had guided the bullet.

Although the leopard had attacked K'ninny only a few seconds, the boy had a dozen wounds. His scalp hung by a thread of skin. We gave him first aid and rushed him to a hospital in a lorry. He lived to wear honorable scars.

Cottar told me that the story would have had a different end ing save for K'ninny's intelligent behavior during the attack The leopard had landed on his head and shoulders. If K'ninny had remained erect, trying to throw off the beast, its rear paw would have had free play at his lower body. By dropping to hi knees, he prevented the leopard from scooping with its hind claws, and took the attack on his head, shoulders, and forearm I thought that the intelligence shown was mainly instinctive

Cottar and I had passed within fifteen feet—an easy leap—o the leopard's covert. He had seen us but we had not seen him aware of that, he had not stirred. At least that was K'ninny' explanation of the beast letting us pass. When he came up, he saw the animal, and as if the meeting of his eyes with the yel low blazing eyes had touched off a set gun, the leopard sprang

Neither Cottar nor I would have had time for a second sho if both of us had missed. A little nearer than he, I would have had one hundred and fifty pounds of hellcat on my shoulder in one more second. I wouldn't have had sense enough to crouch, or Cottar's once great strength to hurl the beast off. He had once so thrown a leopard three times, it bouncing back faster than a rubber ball. He had carried a knife in his belt but never had time to draw it. His faithful bearer, Fundi, had run up, thrust a gun barrel against the spotted hide, and fired.

Cottar would have had to duplicate that feat, if the leopard had landed on me. The interval would have seemed very long. And what if K'ninny and I had been alone?

The leopard skin was very pretty as a rug, prettier now as handbags and turbans for my wife and teen-age daughter. But I look at them and see a garish scene, a painting of Africa in gold, black, and red.

7802